RARE
BIRDS
YEARBOOK
2008

First published in UK in 2007 by
MagDig Media Limited

ISBN 978-0-9552607-3-5

Editor
Erik Hirschfeld

Design & technical production
Ingvar Ronde

BirdLife International
Jez Bird, Stuart Butchart (Science Coordination),
Martin Fowlie, Adrian Long (General Coordination),
Gina Pfaff, John Sherwell

Features
Chris Harbard (Ecotourism)
Erik Hirschfeld & Nick Langley
Editing: Nick Langley

Front cover photo
Waved Albatross © Roy de Haas

Inside cover photo
Juan Fernández Firecrown © Kevin D. Mack

Maps
All maps have been prepared
using Google Earth Pro and are based on shapefiles
provided by BirdLife International

MagDig Media Limited
1 Brassey Road
Old Potts Way, Shrewsbury
Shropshire SY3 7FA
ENGLAND

E-mail: editor@rarebirdsyearbook.com
www.rarebirdsyearbook.com

CONTENTS

Her Imperial Highness Princess Takamado
Honorary President BirdLife International

FOREWORD

I have always found birds fascinating. But, I fear that all of us have taken them a little too much for granted. Bird extinctions are now happening faster than at any time in history. Without human interference, the natural rate of loss would be one bird each century. But extinctions are accelerating and running at 50 times that rate. In the past 30 years alone, 21 have gone – and the Po'o-uli, Hawaiian Crow and Spix's Macaw have all disappeared from the wild since the year 2000.

Over many years of intensive research, the BirdLife International Partnership has assessed and classified the conservation status of every bird species in the world. BirdLife's data set is the basis of the IUCN Red List. 'Critically Endangered' is the highest category of extinction risk on the IUCN 'Red List': those species on the brink of extinction. The task to save these species is urgent. The 2007 Red List includes 189 bird species classified as Critically Endangered – including six owls, three albatrosses, 16 birds of prey, 10 hummingbirds, 17 parrots, four woodpeckers, and six ducks. This is 51 more than there were just seven years ago. If no action is taken then many will go extinct within the next 10 years.

Have we thought of the fact that once these birds are lost to us, they are lost to us forever? Each living species is a work of art that nature took millions of years to create. It is a frightening thought that man, not necessarily through choice, but just through sheer carelessness, ignorance or possibly through stupidity, could destroy such creations in a fraction of the time that it took for them to come into being.

There is hope for these species facing imminent extinction. Between 1994 and 2004, sixteen bird species would have gone extinct if it were not for the intensive conservation actions targeting the threats that had pushed these species so close to extinction. Many are now well on the road to recovery. BirdLife has identified the problems each threatened bird faces and the priority conservation actions they require. This is the vital first step that will halt the forces of extinction in their tracks, and begin the long, slow process of recovery.

A carefully orchestrated and sustained global conservation effort is required to save all Critically Endangered birds. For this reason, BirdLife International has recently launched a major new initiative that aims to save these species and, in order to make this a success, we will need to raise over £19 million over the next five years.

This is a huge challenge – one we are taking very seriously and one we are totally committed to achieving. With more than 100 BirdLife Partners around the world, we have the expertise to prevent extinctions. What we need is more funding support from companies, institutions and even individuals. Becoming a BirdLife Species Champion provides an antidote to that 'sense of helplessness' and gives one the chance to make a difference.

It is my sincere hope that the publication of the Rare Birds Yearbook 2008 will not only highlight the plight of the 189 Critically Endangered species and the conservation efforts needed but will provide the inspiration for you to get involved with BirdLife and to take an active part in preventing their extinction.

HER IMPERIAL HIGHNESS
PRINCESS TAKAMADO

HONORARY PRESIDENT
BIRDLIFE INTERNATIONAL

INTRODUCTION

I saw my first rare bird in July 1975, after a few years of teenage birding and optimistic misidentifications of rare birds. It was a Steller's Eider that turned up in the middle of summer at my local birding spot on the Swedish west coast, far away from its normal summer haunts of Arctic Ocean shores. It was rare in many respects. It

Erik Hirschfeld, Editor Rare Birds Yearbook

was geographically rare, as this species was usually recorded off the Baltic coasts and not the west coast of Sweden. It was rare for the time of the year, as it is usually seen in the winter months and not in the middle of the summer. The eclipse plumage borne by it in summer was rare, as it was not even depicted in my bird book.

Back in the 1970s and 1980s, around 100 Steller's Eiders were recorded in Sweden each year. Today we are lucky to get 25 a year. Globally it is considered Near Threatened, so it does not qualify for this book, and I hope this very pretty duck will stay out of it as it is also one of my favourite birds. But it certainly fuelled my interest for rare birds.

This book is about even rarer birds, few of which I have seen myself. Together with my friend Ingvar Rönde, who also has helped with layout and technical sides of the book, I got the idea of publishing an annual global bird book two years ago, when I was helping him with another publication. In autumn 2006 we decided how it should be done. We should concentrate on the absolutely rarest birds, we should have a lot

of photos (a challenge indeed as some of these species have not been photographed at all), and we should include information which would change from year to year, so we could update and rewrite most of it on an annual basis.

It was also important to make sure that the book gave something more to conservation than "just" awareness, although the importance of this should not be underestimated. We thought that if we could publish such a book, we would also allow the sales to give a decent financial return to a bird conservation NGO, so that the birds themselves would profit.

I found BirdLife International to be the natural choice, especially as I have long been associated with them and some of their Partners. So in late 2006 we arranged a meeting at the BirdLife Secretariat in Cambridge, UK and presented our idea. What we did not know at that time was that BirdLife was planning the Preventing Extinctions ("Species' Champions" and "Species Guardians") campaign also focussing on these 189 species, which went hand in hand with our idea of a popular but authoritative book covering these birds. So we obtained a green light, and then began a period of intensive work.

Quite early on I realised that photos were going to be the crucial point. Some of these birds are so rare that they simply have not been photographed, except for those dusty specimens with cotton instead of eyes that may linger in museum drawers around the world - perhaps not the most exciting photos for this kind of book. Others are so newly discovered that there are hardly even any paintings of them. For others, like Eskimo Curlew and Ivory-billed Woodpecker, there may only exist single, well-published photos. To obtain a good number of photos to choose from, I arranged a web-based photo competition, which was clinched when I got the thumbs-up for a generous sponsorship deal for prizes from the high-quality optical company Minox.

The competition ran for two months on the the web, brought 15 000 visitors to the site, and resulted in over 1,000 entries covering 115 species, which far surpassed my most optimistic expectations. Hundreds of them were of an exceptional quality, and you can enjoy them here on the following pages. After having secured paintings of some unphotographed specie,s and digging into various photo archives for others, I finally had all species represented by at least one illustration.

In this book you will find the 189 rarest birds birds, those categorised as Critically Endangered globally (more on this classification on pp 80-81). The rarest of the rare, some indeed so rare that they haven't been seen for years, and it is uncertain if they may still be out there. Read about them and be inspired to go and find them or to do something to help their survival! Remember that the value of even small amounts of money donated to these birds can in many cases be much greater in their home countries than where you live. By buying this book, you have already donated £4 to conservation, and we are very grateful for that! Thank you!

You will also find features and statistics on the birds here, and in case you wish to travel and see them, you can find some tour operators listed in the end.

I hope you will find Rare Birds Yearbook 2008 interesting. While you read this I am in full swing planning for the 2009 edition. I will have some great features in it, and I am sure some species covered this year will leave the Critically Endangered ranking, which I shall be very grateful for. But, if I may be somewhat pessimistic, I am afraid I will have some new candidates to include next year.

I would be pleased to hear from readers. Please supply your feedback, ideas and constructive comments for to me. If you want to do something for conservation of these species, visit BirdLife's website, join a BirdLife partner, or even their Rare Bird Club, and think about becoming a Species Champion. And tell your friends about this book.

If you are a photographer, see if you have any species which are missing here, and help us make the 2009 edition a photographic masterpiece. If you take photos, please do it responsibly, taking great care not to disturb the birds.
I will be running the photo competition again at www.rarebirdsyearbook.com.

Malmö, Sweden October 2007

Erik Hirschfeld
Editor Rare Birds Yearbook
editor@rarebirdsyearbook.com
www.rarebirdsyearbook.com

ACKNOWLEDGEMENTS

IN THE EARLY STAGES, WHILE LAUNCHING THE IDEA of this book and getting the whole concept and production process together I had great support in a variety ways from Björn Andersson, Niklas Aronsson, Magnus Aurivillius, Hans Bister, Jan-Michael Breider, Pierre-André Crochet, Gunnar Engblom (www.kolibriexpeditions.com), Johan Fromholtz, Ricard Guterriez, Samuel Hansson (www.heliangelus.se), Felix Heintzenberg (www.biofokus.com), Dominic Mitchell (www.birdwatch.co.uk), Daniel Nilsson, Luciano Ruggieri, Tuomas Seimola and Anders Wirdheim.

The optical company Minox Germany (www.minox.com) kindly sponsored with prizes in the photo competition, which were much sought after judging from the number of entries. BirdLife also donated prizes. A big thank you to everyone who sent in photos even though not all entries could be included in the book. Felix Heintzenberg and Steve Young were jury members in the photo competition and I thank them for their efforts in this task which was not as simple as anticipated due to the overwhelming response.
Various websites have been supportive in marketing the photo competition:
www.birdguides.co.uk, www.birdingworld.co.uk, www.birdwatch.co.uk, www.cherrug.se, www.club300.se, www.fatbirder.com, www.fuglenet.d www.hypocolius.se, www.ornithomedia.com, www.surfbirds.com, www.tarsiger.com, www.travellingbirder.com, www.worldtwitcher.com. Please visit them!
Thanks also to Kristoffer Wittström and Magnus Wittström for their excellent job with the cover of the book and design of the website, www.rarebirdsyearbook.com.

The staff at the BirdLife Secretariat in Cambridge have been extremely helpful and much-pestered with emails and phone calls during production. Jez Bird, Stuart Butchart, Martin Fowlie, Jules Howard and Adrian Long have been patient correspondents and Gina Pfaff has kindly assisted with images, often at short notice. John Sherwell and Christine Alder have responded promptly to requests for some difficult-to-find reprints. Alison Stattersfield and Mike Rands have been very supportive. I am very grateful to Peter Johan Schei, President of BirdLife Council for his support and advice. I also thank Jim Lawrence for supportive advice and Nick Langley for commenting on large sections of the book.

Keith Betton, Bennett Henessey of Armonía and Jon King have provided enthusiastic input and advice.

It was certainly a challenge finding images for the book, especially of those birds that have never been photographed. In some cases paintings have been used and I especially thank Carl Johan Tofte, who did some especially commissioned paintings for the book. Josep del Hoyo of Lynx Edicions has kindly allowed me to use illustrations from "Handbook of Birds of the World" and "Threatened Birds of the World". Christopher Perrins assisted with contacts at Oxford University Press and H. Douglas Pratt and Oxford University Press graciously allowed me the use of paintings from their publications. Matthew Bird kindly provided some much-needed paintings, by Blake Twigden, taken from the book "The Fifty Rarest Birds of the World" www.inventas.co.nz.

Gunnar Engblom (Kolibri Expeditions), Britt-Marie Grönvall and Sven Lundberg have been helpful in those cases I have needed translations from Spanish. Karen Hallgren has also kindly assisted with checking English.

A number of people have assisted in different ways on the features of the book.
Glyn Young (Durrell Wildlife Conservation Trust), Rick Watson and Russell Thorstrom (both The Peregrine Fund) have been very helpful in supplying background information, texts and securing images for the feature on *Madagascar Pochard*.
I am grateful to Gonzalo Muñoz Arroya, Charlotte Curé, David Cuenca Espinoza, Meritxell Genovart, Maite Louzao, Daniel Oro, Magnus Ullman, Russell Wynn and Pierre Yésou for responding to my queries referring to *Balearic Shearwater*.
Chris Gaskin of Pterodroma Pelagics, Vaughan Ashby of Birdfinders, Steve Rooke of Sunbird, Martin Schmidt of rainforest Expeditions and Heinz Plenge of Chaparria Ecolodge have assisted with information for the *Ecotourism* feature.
Professor Staffan Bensch, Gabriel J. Bowen, Matthieu Guillemain, Dr. Debbie Pain, Bo Petersson and Anders Wirdheim have all been supportive in preparing the feature on *Isotopes*.
Phoebe Barnard, Birgit Fessl (Durrell Wildlife Conservation Trust), Anders Hedenström, Felix Heintzenberg, Esa Lehikonen, Matts Lindblad, Ara Monadjem, Henrik Kylin, Rob Simmons, Michelle Wilmers have assisted in various ways on the *Climate* feature.
Thanks also to Per Alström, Jonathan Eames, Frank Lambert and Paul Salaman for sharing their stories with me.

Tommy Tyrberg has patiently responded with his encyclopedical knowledge of birds and birders, past and present, when I encountered dead ends.

ACKNOWLEDGEMENTS

*I am grateful to the following persons for their kind assistance
in various ways concerning the directory section:*

Anders Arnell, Ciro Albano, Dave Anderson, Fernando Angulo (Proyecto de Conservación de la Pava Aliblanca, Asociación Cracidae Perú), Araripe Manakin Team (Aquasis), Brian Barber, Chris Bowden, Rachel Bristol, Alberto Campos, Constantino Aucca Chutas, Eberhard Curio, Robert Curry (Villanova University), Godi Dijkman, Jonathan Eames, John Ekwall, Johan Elmberg, Birgit Fessl (Durrell Wildlife Conservation Trust), Jon Fjeldså, Beth Flint, Weber Girão, Jaqueline Goerck, Jack van Hal, Dr. H. Ross Hawkins (The Hummingbird Society), Yolanda van Heezik, Magnus Hellström, Bennett Hennessey, Peter Hodum, Tommy Holmgren, Jon Hornbuckle, Kate Huyvaert, Jason Ibanez, Björn Johansson, Mery Juiña, Abolghasem Khaleghizadeh, Lloyd Kiff, Luc Lens, Pete McLelland, Mark Alexander MacDonald, Richard Maloney, Juan Martinez, Colin Miskelly, Ron Moorhouse (Dept. of Conservation, New Zealand), Lydi Morgan (Hawaii Audobon Society), Priscila Napoli, Edward Nicholl, Thieres Pinto, Advaldo Dias do Prado, David Priddel, Peter Pyle, Tristan Rawlence, Houssein Rayaleh, Michelle H. Reynolds, Miguel Rico, Martin Riesing, Paul Salaman, Helga Schulze, Paul Scofield, Gehan de Silva Wijeyeratne, Luís Fábio Silveira, Thomas Snetsinger, Michael Szabo, João Texeira da Costa, Russell Thorstrom (The Peregrine Fund), Liz Tuanui, Francisco Vilella, Henri Weimerskirch, John Williams, Edwin Winkel, Liu Yang.

*The following photographers and artists have contributed images to the book.
They are also acknowledged in the photo captions:*

Roger Ahlman, Ciro Albano, Richard Allen, Ulrica Alström, Inger Andersen, John Anderton, José Manuel Arcos, Lily Réné Arison Roland, Norman Arlott, Ashley Banwell, Dolora Batchelor, Mark Beaman, Stefan Behrens, Soner Bekir, Nancy C. Bell, Daniel Bengtsson, Callan Bentley, Per-Göran Bentz, Zhang Bin, Malinda Bitting, Nik Borrow, Chris Bowden, James H. Breeden Jr, Tom Brereton, Michael J Brown, Hilary Burn, Dante Buzetti, Pablo Caceres, Tom Callens, Iain Campbell, Tony Campbell, Alberto Campos, Håkan Carlestam, Danielle M. Cholewiak, William S. Clark, Peter Coe, Chris Collins, Claudio Contreras, Norbert J. Cordeiro, John Cox, Robert L.Curry, Andre de Luca, Arpit Deomurari, Sergey Dereliev, Zhao Donjiang, Michael Dryden, Jonathan C. Eames, Alec Earnshaw, Martin Elliott, Francisco Enriquez, John Fitzpatrick, Simon Fordham, Isabell Frank, Kim Franklin, Luiz Freire, Scott Frier, Göran Frisk, Adriano Gambarini, Chris Gomersall, Alexander Hafeman, Jack van Hal, Martin Hale, Jiang Hang-Dong, Samuel Hansson, Chris Harbard, Simon Harrap, Ruben Heleno, Marc Herremans, Charles Hesse, Ronald Hoff, Mark Hulme, Andy Hultberg, P. Jaganathan, Jack Jeffrey, Dick Jenkin, Park Jong-Gil, Mery Juiña, Àngels Jutglar, Francesc Jutglar, Kanit Khanikul, Jon King, Jörgen Peter Kjeldsen, Terje Kolaas, Frank Lambert, Greg Laskey, Andrew Lassey, Marcus Lawson, Miguel Lentino, Chen Lin, Rich Lindie, Matthew Linkie, Eric van der List, Natasha Lloyd, Stefan Luft, Mark Alexander MacDonald, Tom Malm, Dan Mangsbo, Luiz Claudio Marigo, Charles Marsh, Luis Mazariegos, Martim Melo, Ian Merrill, Allan Michaud, Fundacion Migres, Steve Mlodinow, C. W. Moelker, Rafael Rodriguez Mojica, Jonathan Morel, Michael J. Morel, James Morgan, Pete Morris, Devki Nanda, David Nurney, Ian Oakes, Janos Olah, Atle Ivar Olsen, Tun Pin Ong, Ronald Orenstein, Lee Pettet, Karen Phillips, Heinz Plenge, Richard Porter, Laxman Poudyal, H. Douglas Pratt, Georges Olioso, Alonso Quevedo, Don Radovich, P. Raust, Martin J. Rauzon, Tristan Rawlence, Houssein Rayaleh, Morley Read, Martin Riethmüller, Jon Riley, Don Roberson, Pauline Roberts, Jonathan Roussow, Bonnie Rusk, David Caro Sabogal, Amano Samarpan, Otto Samwald, Lluis Sanz, Fabrice Schmitt, Helmut Schuman, Roy Seadog, Tuomas Seimola, Ganesh H. Shankar, Chris Shields, Dr. José Maria Cardoso da Silva, Paras B. Singh, F. G.Smith, Per Smitterberg, Toon Spanhove, Claire Spottiswoode, Brent Stephenson, Andrea K. Suardo, Christer Sundström, Andy & Gill Swash, Alejandro Tabini, Vikash Tatayah, Alan Tate, Graeme Taylor, Alejandro Tello, Glen Tepke, Paul Thompson, Russel Thorstrom, Matt Tilghman, Jean Paul Tilly, Robert L. Tizard, Joe Tobias, Carl Johan Tofte, Andrew "Jack" Tordoff, Guy Tudor, Chris Tzaros, Magnus Ullman, Michael Utech, Juan Varela, Merlijn van Weerd, Dick Watling, Friedhelm Weick, Lyn Wells, Staffan Widstrand, Etel Vilaró, Jan Wilczur, John Williams, Edwin Winkel, Bruce Winslade, Nigel Voaden, Martin Woodcock, Tim Worfolk, Glyn Young, Hao Zhang.

Finally, to my wife Catarina and our sons Samuel, Alfred and Elias; without whose patience when urgent book matters have invaded our daily family life this book would not have been possible, I thank you from my heart.

ERIK HIRSCHFELD
EDITOR

Bengal Florican gets a second chance, thanks to Species Champions and Guardians

THE RARE BIRDS YEAR BOOK DESCRIBES THE SITUATION of the world's 189 Critically Endangered species, and the circumstances that have driven them to the edge of extinction. But the book also documents the projects which have arrested the decline in some of these species, and in some cases, set them on the road to recovery.

Preventing Extinctions: Saving the world's most threatened birds

Up to now, Birdlife International and its national Partners have been forced by lack of funding and resources to concentrate their recovery projects on "priority" species. But while we have been trying to save the world's birds one species at a time, the pressures that lead to extinction have been building relentlessly.

Despite the massive increase in conservation effort and awareness over the last half century, we have lost 21 species in the last thirty years alone. Po'o-uli, Hawaiian Crow and Spix's Macaw have all disappeared from the wild since the year 2000.

With some species, reduced to single figures, or confined to a patch of a few hectares of habitat, a small-scale event is all that is needed to push them into oblivion: the arrival of a pregnant black rat from a boat, the escape of a disease-bearing mosquito from a plane, or a few days work by a couple of chainsaws and a bulldozer.

Other species with wider distributions are the victims of larger scale changes in fishing, forestry and agriculture, and the spread of infrastructure such as roads and electricity networks.

But while they are extreme, none of these situations is completely hopeless. Alien species can be controlled or eradicated. Communities living adjacent to remnants of habitat come to value "their" rare birds, once they learn how unique and precious they are. At the national scale, raising awareness of Critically Endangered species can lead to adjustments in practices such as the use of weighted fishing lines or bird scarers to prevent albatrosses and petrels becoming hooked, or the revival of extensive grassland farming which leaves room for birds, or the creation of parks and protected areas. The birds benefit, and with the establishment of more sustainable livelihoods and new sources of revenue from eco-tourism, so do people.

Over many years of intensive research, BirdLife scientists have identified the problems each Critically Endangered bird species faces and the priority conservation actions they require. The plans are ready; and now we want put them into action – no longer for a handful of species where opportunity and funding permit, but tackling all Critically Endangered species together.

We have already begun to identify the people and organisations best placed to carry out the conservation work necessary to prevent the extinction of every Critically Endangered species. We call them 'Species Guardians'.

What we don't yet have is the funding – and we are turning to companies, institutions and individuals in our search for a new kind of active conservationist to provide it. We call them 'Species Champions'.

At its launch, BirdLife's Preventing Extinctions initiative was described in the press as the biggest and most wide-ranging bird conservation programme the world has ever seen. Over the next five years, we will need to raise £19,000,000 ($39,000,000).

The average cost of starting to turn around the fortunes of a Critically Endangered species is more than £20,000 ($40,000) per year and requires sustained investment, so Species Champions are being asked to make a minimum three-year commitment.

The Preventing Extinctions initiative was formally announced at the British Birdwatching Fair in August 2007, but well before then, potential Champions were expressing their interest. The first Species Champion to be announced publicly was the "BirdFair" itself, and the first Critically Endangered species to benefit will be the Bengal Florican *Houbaropsis bengalensis*.

With less than 1,000 individuals remaining, Bengal Florican had been given five years before disappearing forever from its stronghold, the flood-plain of the Tonle Sap lake in Cambodia. BirdFair will contribute to the conservation work being undertaken by the BirdLife Species Guardian, which is helping to implement the government-approved 'Integrated Farming and Biodiversity Areas' programme in Cambodia, encouraging communities to favour low-impact traditional farming techniques over intensive and unsustainable dry-season rice production.

Species Guardians carry out the work of preventing extinctions on the ground

Other species selected
for support by Species Champions

Apart from Bengal Florican, BirdFair is also the Champion for three other Critically Endangered species:

- Belding's Yellowthroat *Geothlypis beldingi* (Mexico)
- Djibouti Francolin *Francolinus ochropectus* (Djibouti)
- Restinga Antwren *Formicivora littoralis* (Brazil)

These four species are part of a suite of 20 Critically Endangered species BirdLife has chosen to start the Preventing Extinctions initiative. The others are:

Africa

- Long-billed Apalis *Apalis moreaui*
- Dwarf Olive Ibis *Bostrychia bocagei*
- Taita Thrush *Turdus helleri*

The Americas

- Royal Cinclodes *Cinclodes aricomae*
- Puerto Rican Nightjar *Caprimulgus noctitherus*
- Junin Grebe *Podiceps taczanowskii*

Asia

- Mindoro Bleeding-heart *Gallicolumba platenae*
- White-shouldered Ibis *Pseudibis davisoni*
- Negros Bleeding-heart *Gallicolumba keayi*
- Indian Vulture *Gyps Indicus*
- Slender-billed Vulture *Gyps tenuirostris*
- White-rumped Vulture *Gyps bengalensis*

Middle East

- Northern Bald Ibis *Geronticus eremita*

These birds have been chosen because:

- of the extreme urgency of their situation.
- there are clear and well-defined actions that are likely to make a significant difference in the near future.
- there are suitable organisations or individuals in place who are well qualified to coordinate and implement conservation action.

Many other Critically Endangered species will shortly be available for support by Species Champions.

Photo: © Jean Paul Tilly

Children campaigning to save the Endangered Indian Great Bustard

Photo: © Asad Rahmani / BNHS

Strategy meeting at Bengal Florican headquarters

Photo: © J C Eames / BirdLife

Isabel Gomez is working on conservation plans for Royal Cinclodes in Bolivia

Asociacion Armonia (BirdLife in Bolivia) has appointed Isabel Gomez, of the the Sección de Ornitologia at the Museo Nacional de Historia Natural Species in La Paz, Species Guardian for Royal Cinclodes. This bird is entirely dependent on semi-humid Polylepis woodlands, a habitat unique to Bolivia and Peru which is disappearing fast (97 percent has already gone) because of fuel wood collecting, uncontrolled burning and over-grazing.

"The species was known at only six localities, four in south-eastern Peru and two in the western Bolivia," Isabel explained. "No information on its breeding biology, demography, diet and social behaviour is available. In recent studies, we mapped the distribution of Polylepis forests in two mountain ranges and recorded Royal Cinclodes at six more localities previously unknown. This indicates that even basic information such as distribution and population status is poorly known."

Once the Species Champions come forward with the funding, Isabel and Armonia will begin a programme of work that includes completion of the distribution map and the study of population status in Bolivia. "There are still two unvisited mountain ranges where Royal Cinclodes may be found. We will search these mountain ranges for unknown populations. We will also study the basic ecology related to conservation such as habitat preference, territory size, dispersion, diet and demography. We will focus our studies on some biological aspects important for its conservation."

Human impacts such as habitat loss and modification are possibly the reason why the species is Critically Endangered. "The quantitative evaluation of human influence on the species and its habitat is extremely important if we are to devise an effective conservation strategy."

Once all this is in place, Isabel will be able to complete conservation plans for the species, and begin to implement them. "Environmental education, reforestation, alternative fuel sources and tree nurseries will be introduced to encourage local people to implement conservation actions. We have already carried out some of the conservation actions, such as environmental education at local primary schools, meeting with several local communities, providing some economic help to one community and establishing an experimental nursery at another."

"The accumulation of biological information, however, shifted our focus and priority areas from La Paz mountain range to Apolobamba mountain range. Additional biological information will help us to improve our conservation efforts," says Isabel.

One of the unique aspects of the Species Guardians approach is that it draws on the experience of the entire BirdLife network, while also making full use of the local knowledge and relationships of the Guardian. In this instance, Isabel and Armonia came to an agreement with local communities, whereby Armonia provided help with the roadside stalls which are the main source of cash income, while the community built walls around the Polylepis forest to keep cattle out.

By becoming a BirdLife Species Champion, you or your company, or institution could help Isabel and other Species Guardians get such practical programmes of work under way. You will be making a measurable contribution to the future of some of the world's most charismatic birds.

"Critically Endangered birds can be saved from extinction through this innovative approach," says Dr Mike Rands, Chief Executive of BirdLife International. "We know the priority conservation actions needed for each species – what we need now is the support of companies, organisations or even individuals – Species Champions."

Do you want to become a Species Champion?

BirdLife urgently need your donations towards our work on preventing extinctions if we are to save the 189 Critically Endangered species most at risk of global extinction. Many of these birds could become extinct within the next ten years. If you would like to know more about how you, your company or institution, could become part of the Preventing Extinctions initiative - supporting the conservation of a species that otherwise faces certain extinction - we want to hear from you.

Email: species.champions@birdlife.org

Telephone: +44 (0) 1223 277 318, ask for Species Champions desk.

Or write to us, at: BirdLife Species Champions, BirdLife International, Welbrook Court, Girton Road, Cambridge, CB3 0NA United Kingdom.

Over the coming months you will be able to witness live on our website the changes made by the BirdLife Partnership, Species Guardians and our new friends the BirdLife Species Champions. We hope you will visit regularly to see how your contribution is making a real difference.

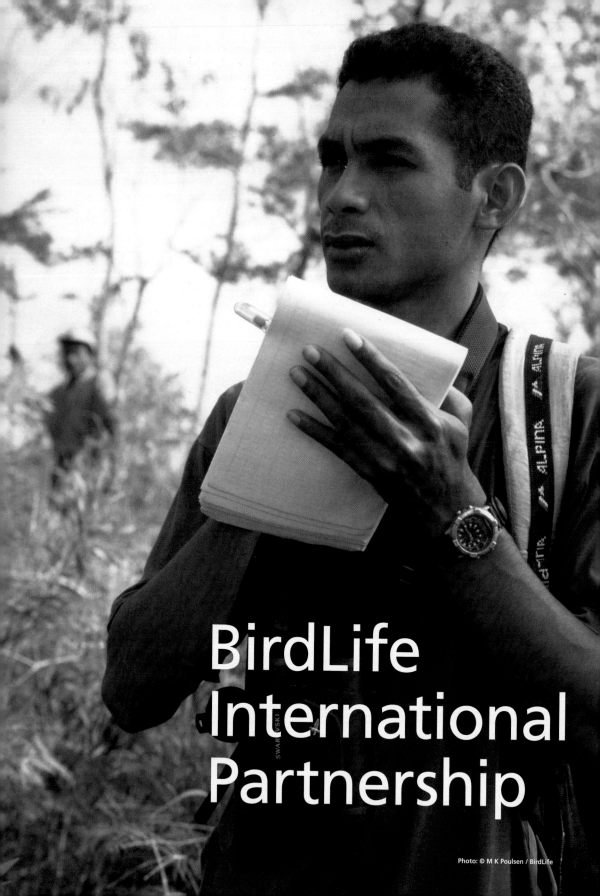

BirdLife
International
Partnership

Andorra
Associació per a la Defensa de la Natura
Apartado de Correus Espanyols No 96
Andorra La Vella, Principat d'Andorra
Tel: +376-84-3248
Fax: +376-84-3868
E-mail: adn@andorra.ad
www.adn-andorra.org

Argentina
Aves Argentinas/AOP
25 de Mayo 749
2° piso, oficina 6
1002ABO Buenos Aires
Tel: +54 (11) 4312-1015
Fax: +54 (11) 4312-2284
E-mail: info@avesargentinas.org.ar
www.avesargentinas.org.ar

Armenia
Armenian Society for the Protection
of Birds
Garegin Njdeh 27/, 10
Yerevan 0026
Tel: +374 (10) 22 65 41
Fax: +374 (10) 22 65 41
E-mail: armbirds@yahoo.com
www.aspbirds.org

Australia
Birds Australia
Suite 2-05
60 Leicester Street
Carlton VIC 3053
Tel: +61 (3) 9347-0757
Fax: +61 (3) 9347-9323
E-mail: mail@birdsaustralia.com.au
www.birdsaustralia.com.au

Austria
BirdLife Austria
Museumsplatz 1/10/8
A-1070 Wien
Tel: +43 (1) 523-46-51
Fax: +43 (1) 524-46-50
E-mail: office@birdlife.at
www.birdlife.at

Azerbaijan
Azerbaijan Ornithological Society
Mirza Ibrahimov St.56
AZ 1009 BAKU
Tel: +994 (12) 494 3630
Fax: +994 (12) 499 1588
E-mail: info@aos.az
www.aos.az

Bahamas
Bahamas National Trust
PO Box N 4105
Nassau
Tel: +242 393-1317
Fax: +242 393-4978
E-mail: bnt@batelnet.bs
www.bahamasnationaltrust.com

Bahrain
Dr Saeed A. M. Khuzai/Bahrain Natural
History Society
PO Box 40266
Tel: +973 640-055
Fax: +973 640-814
E-mail: saeed@alreem.com

Belarus
Akhova Ptushak Belarusi
PO Box 306
Minsk, 220050
Tel: +375 (17) 263-0130
Fax: +375 (17) 263-0613
E-mail: apb@tut.by
www.apb.iatp

Belgium
BirdLife Belgium
Coxiestraat 11
2800 Mechelen
Tel: +32 (-15) -29-72-49
Fax: +32 (-15) -42-49-21
www.rnob.be (French)
www.natuurpunt.be (Dutch)

Belize
Belize Audubon Society
PO Box 1001
12 Fort Street
Belize City
Tel: +501 (223) 5004
Fax: +501 (223) 4985
www.belizeaudubon.org

Bolivia
Armonía/BirdLife
400 Avenida Lomas de Arena
Casilla 3566
Santa Cruz
Tel: +591 (3) 356-8808
Fax: +591 (3) 356-8808
E-mail: armonia@armonia-bo.org

Botswana
BirdLife Botswana
Private Bag 003
Suite 348
Mogoditshane
Gaborone
Tel: +267 (371) 0050
Fax: +267 (371) 0058 (Attn: BirdLife
Botswana)
E-mail: blb@birdlifebotswana.org.bw
www.birdlifebotswana.org.bw

Brazil
SaveBrasil
Rua Fernão Dias, 219, casa 2
Pinheiros
05427-010 São Paulo, SP
Tel: +55 (11) 3815-2862
Fax: +55 (11) 3815-0343
E-mail: aves@savebrasil.org.br
www.savebrasil.org.br/

Bulgaria
Bulgarian Society for the Protection
of Birds
Musagenitza Complex
Block 104, Entrance A, Floor 6
BG-1111 Sofia
Tel: +359 (2) 971 5855
Fax: +359 (2) 971 5856
E-mail: bspb_hq@bspb.org
http://www.bspb.org

Burkina Faso
Fondation des Amis de la Nature
(NATURAMA)
Naturama
01 B.P. 6133
Ouagadougou 01
Tel: +226 37 32 40 or 62
E-mail: naturama@fasonet.bf

Burundi
Association Burundaise pour la
Protection des Oiseaux
Avenue de la Victoire n° 25
PO Box 7069
Bujumbura
Tel: +257 (24) 9470
Fax: +257 (24) 9471
E-mail: aboburundi@yahoo.fr

Cameroon
Cameroon Biodiversity Conservation
Society
c/o B P 3055
Messa
Yaoundé
Tel: +237 220 2645
Fax: +237 220 2645

Canada
Bird Studies Canada
PO Box 160
Port Rowan
Ontario N0E 1M0
Tel: +1 (519) 586-3531
Fax: +1 (519) 586-3532
E-mail: generalinfo@bsc-eoc.org
www.bsc-eoc.org

Canada
Nature Canada
85 Albert Street
Suite 900
Ottawa, ON K1P 6A4
Tel: +1 (613) 562-3447
Fax: +1 (613) 562-3371
E-mail: info@naturecanada.ca
www.naturecanada.ca

Cook Islands
Taporoporoanga Ipukarea Society
PO Box 3063
Rarotonga
Tel: +682 (21) 144
Fax: +682 (23) 513

Croatia
Croatian Society for Bird and Nature
Protection (CSBNP)
Gunduliceva 24
HR-10000 Zagreb
Tel: +385-1-4825-403
Fax: +385-1-4825-390

Cuba
Centro Nacional de Areas Protegidas
(CNAP)
Calle 18a # 4114 e/ 41 y 47 Playa
Ciudad Habana
Tel: +53 (7) 202-7970
Fax: +53 (7) 204-0798
E-mail: cnap@snap.co.cu
www.snap.co.cu

Cyprus
BirdLife Cyprus
PO Box 28076
2090 Lefkosia
Tel: +357-2-245-5072
Fax: +357-2-245-5073
E-mail: cos@cytanet.com.py

Czech Republic
Czech Society for Ornithology
Na Belidle 252/34
150 00 Prague 5
Tel: +420 (274) 866 700
Fax: +420 (274) 866 700
E-mail: cso@birdlife.cz
www.birdlife.cz

Denmark
Dansk Ornitologisk Forening
Vesterbrogade 138-140
DK-1620 Copenhagen V
Tel: +45 (33) 28-3800
Fax: +45 (33) 312-435
E-mail: dof@dof.dk
www.dof.dk

Ecuador
Aves y Conservacion
Joaquín Tinajero E3-05 y Jorge Drom
Casilla 17-17-906
Quito
Tel: +593 (2) 22 71 800
Fax: +593 (2) 22 71 800
E-mail: cecia_de@uio.satnet.net
www.cecia.org

El Salvador
SalvaNatura
33 Avenida Sur #640
Colonia Flor Blanca
San Salvador
Tel: +503 (-279) -1515
Fax: +503 (-279) -0220
E-mail: info@salvanatura.org
www.salvanatura.org

Estonia
Eesti Ornitiliigiaühing (EOÜ)
PO Box 227
Vesti Str. 4
50002 Tartu
Tel: +372 (7) 422-195
Fax: +372 (7) 422-180
E-mail: eoy@eoy.ee

Ethiopia
Ethiopian Wildlife and Natural History
Society
PO Box 13303
Addis Ababa
Tel: +251 (11) 663-6792
Fax: +251 (11) 618-6879
E-mail: ewnhs.ble@ethionet.et

Falkland Islands
Falklands Conservation
PO Box 26
Stanley
Tel: +500 22247
Fax: +500 22288
E-mail: info@conservation.org.fk
www.falklandsconservation.com

Faroe Islands
Denmark
Føroya Fuglafødifelag (Faroese
Orginithological Society)
Postsmoga 1230
FO-110 Tórshavn
Tel: +298 (352) 309
Fax: +298 (352) 301
E-mail: ffff@kallnet.fo

Finland
BirdLife Suomi-Finland
Annankatu 29A
PO Box 1285
FIN-00101 Helsinki
Tel: +358 (94) 135-3300
Fax: +358 (94) 135-3322
E-mail: office@birdlife.fi
www.birdlife.fi

France
Ligue Pour La Protection des Oiseaux
La Corderie Royale
B.P. 90263
17305 Rochefort Cedex
Tel: +33 (546) 821-234
Fax: +33 (546) 839-586
E-mail: lpo@lpo.fr
www.lpo.fr

French Polynesia
Société d'Ornithologie de Polynésie
«Manu»
B.P. 21098
98713 Papeete
Tahiti
Tel: +689 (50) 62-09
E-mail: sop@manu.pf
www.manu.pf

Georgia
Georgian Center for the Conservation
of Wildlife
PO Box 56
Tbilisi 0160
Tel: +995 (32) -32-64-96
Fax: +995 (-32) -53-74-78
E-mail: office@gccw.org
www.gccw.org

Germany
Nabu Nature and Biodiversity
Conservation Union (NABU)
Herbert-Rabius-Str. 26
D-53225 Bonn
Tel: +49-228-40-36-0
Fax: +49-228-40-36-200
E-mail: claus.Mayr@NABU.de
www.NABU.de

Ghana
Ghana Wildlife Society
PO Box 13252
Accra
Tel: +233 (21) 663 500
Fax: +233 (21) 670-610
E-mail: wildsoc@ighmail.com
www.ghanawildlifesociety.org/

Gibraltar
Gibraltar Ornithological and Natural
History Society
The Gibraltar Natural History Field
Centre
Jews Gate
Upper Rock Natural Reserve
PO Box 843
Tel: +350-72639
Fax: +350-74022
E-mail: gonhs@gibnet.gi
www.gonhs.org

Greece
Hellenic Ornithological Society
Vas. Irakleiou 24
GR-10682 Athens
Tel: +30 (210) 822-7937
Fax: +30 (210) 822-7937
E-mail: info@ornithologiki.gr
www.ornithologiki.gr

Hong Kong
Hong Kong Bird Watching Society
GPO Box 12460
Tel: +852 2377-4387
Fax: +852 2314-3687
E-mail: hkbws@hkbws.org.hk
www.hkbws.org.hk

Hungary
Hungarian Ornithological and Nature
Conservation Society
Kolto u. 21.
1121 Budapest
Tel: +36 (1) 275-6247
Fax: +36 (1) 395-8327
E-mail: mme@mme.hu
www.mme.hu

Iceland
Fuglavernd - BirdLife Iceland
PO Box 5069
IS-125 REYKJAVIK
Tel: +354-652-0477
Fax: +354-551-6413
E-mail: fuglavernd@fuglavernd.is
www.fuglavernd.is

India
Bombay Natural History Society
Hornbill House
Shaheed Bhagat Singh Road
Mumbai
400 023
Tel: +91 (22) 2282-1811
Fax: +91 (22) 2283-7615
E-mail: bnhs@bom4.vsnl.net.in
www.bnhs.org

Indonesia
Burung Indonesia
PO Box 310/Boo
Bogor 16003
Tel: +62 (251) 357-222
Fax: +62 (251) 357-961
E-mail: birdlife@burung.org
www.burung.org

Ireland
BirdWatch Ireland
1, Springmount
Newtown Mount Kennedy
Co. Wicklow
Tel: +353 (1) 281-9878
Fax: +353 (1) 281-9763
E-mail: info@birdwatchireland.ie
www.birdwatchireland.ie

Israel
Society for the Protection of Nature
in Israel
Hashfela 4
Tel-Aviv 66103
Tel: +972-3-638-8666
Fax: +972-3-687-7695
E-mail: ioc@netvision.net.il

Italy
Lega Italiana Protezione Uccelli
via Trento n. 49
IT-43100 Parma
Tel: +39 (0521) 273-043
Fax: +39 (0521) 273-419
E-mail: info@lipu.it
www.lipu.it

Japan
Wild Bird Society of Japan
Head Office
Maruwa Building
3-9-23 Nishi-Gotanda
Shinagawa-ku, Tokyo 141-0031
Tel: +81(0)3 5436 2620
Fax: +81(0)3 5436 2635
E-mail: haramoto@wbsj.org
www.wbsj.org/

Jordan
Royal Society for the Conservation of
Nature
PO Box 6354
Jubeiha-Abu-Nusseir Circle
Amman 11183
Tel: +962 (6) 533-7931
Fax: +962 (6) 534-7411
E-mail: adminrscn@rscn.org.jo
www.rscn.org.jo

Kenya
NatureKenya
PO Box 44486
00100 GPO
Nairobi
Tel: +254-2-374-9957
Fax: +254-2-374-1049
E-mail: office@naturekenya.org
www.naturekenya.org

Kuwait
Kuwait Environment Protection Society
PO Box 1896
Safat 13019
Tel: +965 (-484) -8256
Fax: +965 (-483) -7856
E-mail: q8environment@yahoo.com
www.keps74.com

Latvia
Latvijas Ornitologijas Biedriba
PO Box 1010
Riga 1046
Tel: +371 (7) 221-580
Fax: +371 (7) 603-100
E-mail: putni@lob.lv
www.lob.lv

Lebanon
Society for the Protection of Nature in
Lebanon
Awad Bldg, 6th Floor
Abdel Aziz Street
P.O.Box: 11-5665, Beirut
Tel: +961 (1) 748-308 or 309
Fax: +961 (1) 344-814
E-mail: spnlorg@cyberia.net.lb
www.spnlb.org

Liberia
Society for the Conservation of Nature
of Liberia
Monrovia Zoo
Lakpazee
PO Box 2628, Monrovia
E-mail: fatuwhite@yahoo.com

Liechtenstein
Botanish-Zoologische Gesellschaft
Im Bretscha 22
FL-9494 Schaan
Tel: +41 (75) 232-4819
Fax: +41 (75) 232-2819
E-mail: bzg@adon.li

Lithuania
Lietuvos Ornitologu Draugija
Naugarduko St. 47-3
LT-03208 Vilnius
Tel: +370 (5) 213-0498
Fax: +370 (5) 213-0498
E-mail: lod@birdlife.lt
www.birdlife.lt

Luxembourg
Letzebuerger natur-A Vulleschutz-Liga
Kraizhaff
rue de Luxembourg
L-1899 Kockelscheuer
Tel: +352 (29) 04-041
Fax: +352 (29) 05-04
E-mail: birgit.jacoby@luxnatur.lu

Malaysia
Malaysian Nature Society
PO Box 10750
Kuala Lumpur 50724
Tel: +60 (3) 2287-9422
Fax: +60 (3) 2287-8773
E-mail: mns@mns.org.my
www.mns.org.my

Malta
BirdLife Malta
57 Marina Court
Flat 28
Abate Triq Rigord
MT-Ta' Xbiex, MSD 12
Tel: +356 (21) -34 7646
Fax: +356 (21) -34-3239
E-mail: office@birdlifemalta.org
www.birdlifemalta.org

Mexico
Pronatura A.C.
Aspergulas 22 (antes Pino)
Colonia San Clemente
C.P. 01740
Tel: +52 (55) 563-55-054
Fax: +52 (55) 563-55-054
E-mail: pronatura@pronatura.org.mx
www.pronatura.org.mx

Myanmar
Biodiversity and Nature Conservation
Association (BANCA)
14A Bawga Lane
9th Mile
Mayangon Township
A/6-2 Anawrahtar Housing, Hledan
Ward No.2, Kamayut Township,
Yangon
Tel: +09 (51) 661-658
E-mail: banca@yangon.net.mm

Nepal
Bird Conservation Nepal
House Number 388 KHA,
Uttardhoka Marg,
Lazimpat,
Kathmandu (150 meters from Lazimpat
Chowk towards Gairidhara), North side
of the Royal Palace.
Tel: +977 (1) 441-7805
Fax: +977 (1) 441-3884
E-mail: bcn@mail.com.np
www.birdlifenepal.org

Netherlands
Vogelbescherming Nederland (VBN)
PO Box 925
3700 AX Zeist
Tel: +31 (30) 69-37799
Fax: +31 (30) 69-18844
E-mail: fred.wouters@vogelbescherming.nl
www.vogelbescherming.nl

New Caledonia
Société Calédonienne d'Ornithologie
Responsable du projet IBA
Immeuble le Richelieu
12 bis, rue du Général Mangin
Centre Ville
BP 31 35
98846 Nouméa cedex
Tel: +687 (26) 24 48
E-mail: sco@sco.asso.nc
www.sco.asso.nc

New Zealand
The Royal Forest and Bird Protection
Society
P O Box 631
Wellington
Tel: +64 (4) 385-7374
Fax: +64 (4) 385-7373
E-mail: office@forestandbird.org.nz
www.forestandbird.org.nz

Nigeria
Nigerian Conservation Foundation
PO Box 74638
Victoria Island, Lagos
Tel: +234 (1) 264-2498 ext 7903
Fax: +234 (1) 264-2497
E-mail: ncf@hyperia.com

Norway
Norsk Ornitologisk Forening
Sandgata 30 B
N-7012 Trondheim
Tel: +47 (-73) -52-60-40
Fax: +47 (-73) -52-40-90
E-mail: nof@birdlife.no
www.birdlife.no

Pakistan
Ornithological Society of Pakistan
PO Box 73, 109/D
Dera Ghazi Khan 32200
Tel: +92 (641) 462-339
Fax: +92 (641) 462-408
E-mail: aleembzu@yahoo.co.uk

Belau (Palau)
Palau Conservation Society
PO Box 1811
Koror, Palau 96940
Tel: +680 (-488) -3993
Fax: +680 (-488) -3990
E-mail: pcs@palaunet.com
www.palau-pcs.org/

Palestine
Palestine Wildlife Society
Beit Sahour
PO Box 89, Bethlehem
Tel: +972 (2) 2277-4373
Fax: +972 (2) 2277-4373
E-mail: wildlife@palnet.com

Panama
Sociedad Audubon de Panamá
Apartado Postal 2026
Balboa, Ancón
Tel: +507 224-4740
Fax: +507 224-4740
E-mail: info@panamaaudubon.org
www.panamaaudubon.org

Paraguay
Guyra Paraguay: Conservación de Aves
Coronel Rafael Franco 381 c/ Leandro Prieto
Casilla de Correos 1132
Asunción
Tel: +595 (21) 229-097
Fax: +595 (21) 227-777
E-mail: guyra@guyra.org.py
www.guyra.org.py

Philippines
Haribon Foundation
2/F, Santos and Sons Building
973 Aurora Blvd., Cubao
Quezon City 1109
Tel: +63 (2) 434-4642
Fax: +63 (2) 434-4696
E-mail: act@haribon.org.ph
www.haribon.org.ph

Poland
Ogólnopolskie Towarzystwo Ochrony Ptaków
ul. Odrowaza 24
PL 05-270 Marki Warszawy
Tel: +48 (22) 761-8205
Fax: +48 (22) 761-8205
E-mail: office@otop.org.pl
www.otop.org.pl

Portugal
Sociedade Portuguesa para o Estudo das Aves
Avenida da Liberdade 105-2ºEsq
1250-140 Lisboa
Tel: +351 (213) 220-430
Fax: +351 (213) 220-439
E-mail: Spea@spea.pt
www.spea.pt

Romania
Romanian Ornithological Society
Str. Gheorghe Dima 49/2
RO-400336 Cluj Napoca
Tel: +40 (-264) -438-086
Fax: +40 (-264) -438-086
E-mail: office@sor.ro
www.sor.ro

Russia
Russian Bird Conservation Union
Shosse Entuziastov 60, Building 1
Moscow
111123
Tel: +7 (495) 672-2263
Fax: +7 (495) 672-2263
E-mail: mail@rbcu.ru

Rwanda
Association pour la Conservation de la Nature au Rwanda
PO Box 4290, Kigali
Tel: not available
Fax: +250-7-7845 (c/o M Muramira)
E-mail: acnrwanda@yahoo.fr

Samoa
O le Si'osi'omaga Society Incorporated
PO Box 2282
Apia, Western Samoa
Tel: + 685-25897
Fax: +685 -21993
E-mail: ngo_siosiomaga@samoa.ws

Saudi Arabia
National Commission for Wildlife Conservation and Development
PO Box 61681
Riyadh 11575
Tel: +966 (1) 441-0369
Fax: +966 (1) 441-0797
E-mail: ncwcd@zajil.net
www.ncwcd.gov.sa/

Seychelles
Nature Seychelles
PO Box 1310
Suite 202
Aarti Chambers
Mont Fleuri
Mahe
Tel: +248 (22) 5097
Fax: +248 (22) 5121
E-mail: nature@seychelles.net
www.seychelles.net

Sierra Leone
Conservation Society of Sierra Leone
PO Box 1292
Freetown
Tel: +232 (22) 229-716
Fax: +232 (22) 224-439 (fax bureau)
E-mail: cssl_03@yahoo.com

Singapore
Nature Society (Singapore)
510 Geylang Road
#02-05 The Sunflower
Singapore 389466
Tel: +65 (6741) 2036
Fax: +65 (6741) 0871
E-mail: contact@nss.org.sg
www.nss.org.sg

Slovakia
Slovak Ornithological Society/BirdLife Slovakia
Mlynske Nivy 41
821 09 Bratislava
Tel: +421-2-55-422-185
Mobile: +421 (905) 256-184
Fax: +421-2-55-422-186
E-mail: vtaky@vtaky.sk
www.birdlife.sk

Slovenia
DOPPS - BirdLife Slovenia
(Društvo za opazovanje in proucevanje ptic Slovenije)
p.p. 2990
TRŽAŠKA 2
SI-1001 Ljubljana
Tel: +386 1 426-5875
Fax: +386 1 425-1181
E-mail: dopps@dopps-drustvo.si
www.ptice.org

South Africa
BirdLife South Africa
PO Box 515
Randburg
Johannesburg 2125
Tel: +27 (11) 789-1122
Fax: +27 (11) 789-5188
E-mail: secretary@birdlife.org.za

Spain
Sociedad Española de Ornitología
Melquiades Biencinto 34
E-28053 Madrid
Tel: +34 (91) 434-0910
Fax: +34 (91) 434-0911
E-mail: mjarmesto@seo.org
www.seo.org

Sri Lanka
Field Ornithology Group of Sri Lanka
Department of Zoology
University of Colombo
Colombo 03
Tel: +94 (75) 342-609
Fax: +94 (75) 337-644
E-mail: fogsl@slt.lk

Suriname
Foundation for Nature Preservation in Suriname
Cornelis Jongbawstraat 14
PO Box 12252
Paramaribo
Tel: +597 271-856
Fax: +597 421 850
E-mail: stinasu@sr.net
www.stinasu.sr

Sweden
Sveriges Ornitologiska Förening
Stenhusa Gård
380 62 Mörbylånga
Tel: +46 (8) 612-2530
Fax: +46 (8) 612-2536
E-mail: info@sofnet.org

Switzerland
Schweizer Vogelschutz SVS-BirdLife
Schweiz
ASPO BirdLife Suisse
Wiedingstr, 78
PO Box,
CH-8036 Zürich
Tel: +41 (0) 44 457 70 20
Fax: +41 (0) 44 457 70 30
E-mail: svs@birdlife.ch
www.birdlife.ch

Taiwan
Wild Bird Federation Taiwan
1F, No. 3, Lane 36 Chinglung St.
116 Taipei
Tel: +886 (2) 8663-1252
Fax: +886 (2) 2930-3595
E-mail: mail@bird.org.tw
www.bird.org.tw

Tanzania
Wildlife Conservation Society of
Tanzania
PO Box 70919
Dar es Salaam
Tel: +255 (22) 211-2518
Fax: +255 (22) 212-4572
E-mail: wcst@africaonline.co.tz

Thailand
Bird Conservation Society of Thailand
43 Soi Chokchairuammit
Viprawadee-Rangsit Rd
Samsaen-nok
Dindaeng
Bangkok 10320
Tel: +66 (2) 691-4816
Fax: +66 (2) 691-4493
E-mail: bcst@bcst.or.th
www.bcst.or.th

Tunisia
Association «Les Amis des Oiseaux»
Avenue 18 Janvier 1952
Ariana Centre - Office C 208/209
2080 Ariana
Tel: +216 (71) 717 860
Fax: +216 (71) 717 860
E-mail: aao@topnet.tn

Turkey
Doga Dernegi
PK: 640 06445
Yenisehir
Ankarae
Tel: +90 312 (448) 05 37
Fax: +90 312 (448) 02 58
E-mail: doga@dogadernegi.org
www.dogadernegi.org

Uganda
NatureUganda
P O Box 27034
Kampala
Tel: +256 (41) 540 719
Fax: +256 (41) 530 134
E-mail: nature@natureuganda.org
www.natureuganda.org

Ukraine
Ukranian Society for the Protection of
Birds
PO Box 33
Kiev-01103
Tel: +380 (44) 284-7131 or 284-9063
Fax: +380 (44) 284-7131 or 284-9063
E-mail: uspb@birdlife.org.ua
www.birdlife.org.ua

United Kingdom
Royal Society for the Protection of
Birds
The Lodge
Sandy
Bedfordshire
SG19 2DL
Tel: +44 (0) 1767-680551
Fax: +44 (0) 1767-693265
E-mail: enquiries@rspb.org.uk
www.rspb.org.uk

Uruguay
Aves Uruguay (GUPECA)
Casilla de Correo 6955
Correo Central, Montevideo
Tel: +598 (2) 902-2362
Fax: +598 (2) 908-5959
E-mail: gupeca@adinet.com.uy
www.avesuruguay.org.uy/

USA
Audubon
700 Broadway
New York, NY 10003-9562
Tel: +1 (212) 979-3000
Fax: +1 (212) 979-3188
E-mail: join@audubon.org
www.audubon.org

Venezuela
Sociedad Conservacionista Audubon de
Venezuela
Apartado 80.450
Caracas 1080-A
Tel: +58 (212) 992-3268
Fax: +58 (212) 991-0716
E-mail: audubon@cantv.net

Yemen
Yemen Society for the Protection of
Wildlife
29 Alger Street
PO Box 19759, Sana'a
Tel: +967 (1) 44 74 23
Fax: +967 (1) 44 74 24
E-mail: wildlife.yemen@y.net.ye

Zambia
Zambian Ornithological Society
Lusaka 10101
Tel: +260 (125) 5981
E-mail: zos@zamnet.zm
www.wattledcrane.com

Zimbabwe
BirdLife Zimbabwe
PO Box RVL 100
Runiville, Harare
Tel: +263 (4) 490 208
E-mail: birds@zol.co.zw
www.fisheagle.org

Black Stilt. Photo: © Bruce Winslade

Species-finders

Jonathan C Eames and elephant owner,
northern Kachin State Myanmar, 4 December 2006.

- the lives
and adventures
of four field
ornithologists

SO FAR THIS CENTURY, in just seven years, around 45 bird species new to science have been added to the world's list. Fortunately, only four are considered Critically Endangered (CR). They are all South American: the Iquitos Gnatcatcher *Polioptila clementsi* (see p. 220) , the Carrizal Seedeater *Amaurspiza carrizalensis* (see p. 240), the Pernambuco Pygmy Owl *Glaucidium mooreorum* (see p. 170) and the Munchique Wood-wren *Henicorhina negreti* (see p. 219). Some of the 45 new species were discovered by museum and laboratory workers, but for others we have to thank a few dedicated and knowledgeable ornithologists working in the field, in some of the world's least known –and least comfortable –places. Here are the stories of four individuals of this increasingly rare species.

In the early days of ornithological exploration, it was relatively easy to find new species. Much of the ornithological map of the world was uncharted. The science of systematics was based on plumage characteristics and anatomy, and specimens, often several individuals, had to be collected in order for a new species to be recognised. The bird skins could be prepared in the field and sent overseas for later examination, perhaps by a museum ornithologist living a comfortable life in a contemporary scientific metropolis in Europe or America.

Many prominent ornithologists of the day had a network of collectors in the field which they relied on. The only equipment required for collecting new species was a gun or traps to collect the birds, and materials for preparing the skins. And, of course, they needed sponsors for an expensive trip to a remote and dangerous place where local porters and support staff could be hired. But it was in fact not even necessary to make the trip to take part in the glory of describing a species new to science: the Madagascar Pochard was described by a museum curator who never set his foot on Madagascar. He just happened to be in the right museum in the right time.

Nowadays, voice, biology, distribution and DNA are also important factors for separating species, and the brutal custom of killing many individual birds of the same species has been abandoned. The recent advances in DNA classification of birds, for which a blood sample or a loose feather is enough, have of course contributed to new species being described (and, indeed, some old ones being lumped into already existing species, to the dismay of avid listers). Some of these newly described species were collected as skins almost a hundred years ago, which shows that the scientific value of these important collections is still very high. The science of DNA-based systematics has not become completely stable yet, nor has the birds' evolutionary tree been completely established, so it is likely that new species will still emerge from skins already lying in museum drawers,

or from birds trapped in the field and that more species will be lumped into already existing ones.

But for the most groundbreaking work in new species discovery, we are indebted to a group of highly qualified birders who combine field work and scientific research in poorly known areas of the world. Here we take a closer look at four of the most proficient of these high-profile conservationists, and the forces that drive them.

Paul Salaman

Paul has described four new species to science, all from Colombia: the Endangered Chocó Vireo *Vireo masteri*, the Endangered Chestnut-capped Piha *Lipaugus weberi*, the Endangered Upper Magdalena Tapaculo *Scytalopus rodriquezi* and the Critically Endangered Munchique Wood-wren *Henicorhina negreti* (which you can read more about on p. 219). He was also involved with Fundacion ProAves in the rediscovery of several long-lost species, such as the Critically Endangered Dusky Starfrontlet *Coeligena orina* (see p. 176) which had vanished for over 50 years, the Tumaco Seedeater *Sporophila insulate*, lost for over 90 years, and Fuertes' Parrot *Hapalopsittaca fuertesi* which had not been seen since1910.

Paul was born in Australia in 1971 and started birding at the tender age of six. The defining bird moment had come a year earlier, when he saw Little Blue Penguins jump out of the sea at dusk and waddle in lines up the beach to nesting burrows in Victoria, Australia. In 1978 his family moved to the UK and a meeting with Sir David Attenborough inspired Paul, then aged eight, to work for conservation. By the age of 14, he was already managing a small nature reserve owned by the London Wildlife Trust, and he began ringing birds three years later. According to friends, he also became very adept at climbing the fences surrounding London reservoirs and escaping pursuing Thames Water officials in his quest for rare birds.

Photo: © Fundacion ProAves, www.proaves.org

Paul has been heavily involved with Gorgeted Woodquail conservation

III, who confirmed that the vireo was unknown to science." The bird was named Chocó Vireo.

The year after Paul discovered the vireo, he established a nature reserve in Colombia to protect it, and received the prestigious BP Conservation Award. In 1995 Paul commenced a PhD with Professor Christopher Perrins at the University of Oxford, on threatened bird populations of southwest Colombia. While leading a month-long bird tour across Colombia in October 1997, tallying over 1,000 species (itself a remarkable record), Paul encountered a flock of two dozen Yellow-eared Parrots *Ognorhynchus icterotis* (see p. 161). The famous Danish ornithologist Niels Krabbe, also active in South America, persuaded Paul to start a project on the species. Almost ten years later, and after extraordinary efforts led by Paul, the Yellow-eared Parrot's global population has climbed from just 81 birds to over 600 individuals, representing one of the most successful Critically Endangered species recoveries in Latin America. Paul's work on the Yellow-eared Parrot led to the creation in 1999 of Fundacion ProAves (www.proaves.org), an NGO with 65 staff and some 20 projects, aiming at protecting Critically Endangered species across Colombia. In 2005 he became Director of International Programs in the American Bird Conservancy.

A year's birding around the world made Paul realize that instead of spending £100 on a 'twitch' in the UK for one rare species, he could spend a little more and see a hundred lifers. This global experience whetted his appetite for international conservation and ornithology. As an undergraduate in 1991 he found himself traveling in Colombia, and discovered a species new to science when he was only 19.

"Suddenly, a small bird appeared before me amongst the undergrowth and, obligingly, flew into a mist-net. I retrieved the bird and upon later examination tentatively identified it to the vireo group. However, I was perplexed as to its precise identity, as the bird I was holding clearly did not exist in my identification guides. The basic features of the bird corresponded to the vireo genera, however the combination of a broad creamy double wing-bar and long pale supercilium stripe were unknown in the genus. Little did I know at the time that I was experiencing the greatest ornithological privilege, the discovery of a bird species new to science. This only became apparent upon returning to the UK, where I consulted numerous Neotropical ornithological experts, particularly the late Theodore A. Parker

Photo: © Fundacion ProAves, www.proaves.org

Always on the lookout

Are there any species in the pipeline which you are about to describe?

Yes – a new species of antpitta (*Grallaria*) which was collected in 1880 and probably is already extinct. I am describing this with Thomas Donegan and Robert Prys-Jones from the British Natural History Museum where the specimen is held.

What is your main concern when it comes to bird protection in the future?

My main concern is that the protection of key sites and habitats for threatened species does not get side-tracked or marginalised in an attempt to work with local communities, without first ensuring protected areas are established and protected. As the global human population continues to spiral upwards, and associated social and economic demand for forested lands by man increases, it is clear that conservation will lose out. Now is the time to urgently conserve the most important sites and habitats not already well represented in protected areas.

Which is the most exciting still undescribed, species, and why?

We have a new Megascops "Screech-owl" from the ProAves' El Dorado Bird Reserve in Sierra Nevada de Santa Marta. It is exciting as it was found within the new bird reserve created in 2006 and further highlights the importance of the site for bird conservation and research. There are further surprises awaiting at the site thanks to the work of ProAves and Niels Krabbe!

What is it that makes certain people find and describe birds?

Basically, what is required to find a new species is a lot of luck, nothing more! Many people wish they could find a new species for science, but very few do. When you find a new species you are certainly compelled to describe it - your name is forever attached to the species.

Frank Lambert

Frank was born in Brighton (UK) in 1958. He was always interested in nature and from the age of around 10 started to watch birds in his garden, using his grandfather's old opera glasses.
"There were two events I can remember that got me interested in foreign birding. The first was the publication of Ben King's Field Guide to the Birds of Southeast Asia, containing Martin Woodcock's great plates of incredible birds. That got me hooked on the idea of going to Asia. The second event was a birding trip to the Camargue and southern France, when I was about 16-17, with Tim and Carol Inskipp, and Pete Grant amongst others. It was my first real birding trip out of the UK."

Exploring North Peru with Huw Lloyd and Colin Bushell

At age 19 he and friends Richard Grimmett, Dick Filby and Les Norton drove from the UK to Nepal and Assam in India, and managed to bird in Afghanistan and elsewhere on the way. Five years later he had obtained a First class BSc Honours in Ecology and in 1987 went on to complete his PhD at the University of Aberdeen on *Fig-eating and dispersal by birds in a Malaysian lowland rain forest*. Frank is a tropical forest ecologist, specialising in ornithology, forest policy and natural resource use and management, and has gained most of his experience in tropical parts of South-east Asia and South America. In 1983 he wrote the landmark Pica press book Pittas, Broadbills and Asities. He left Southeast Asia in 2002 and is now based in South America (currently in Peru) where he now leads birding and wildlife tours and assists with various conservation and research projects.

Frank has described three new species to science, the Endangered Talaud Rail *Gymnocrex talaudensis* and Talaud Bush-hen *Amaurornis magnirostris*, and the Least Concern Sangihe Scops Owl *Otus collari*, and has co-described a new species of Tyrant in the genus *Cnipodectes*.

In Frank's own words, the discovery of the tyrant flycatcher was perhaps the most surprising as it was found in Manu National Park, within the trail system of the famous Cocha Cashu Biological station, which has been visited by many notable Neotropical birders, some of whom must surely have either heard or seen the species but not realised it was new.
"I managed to get a video of the bird, but being unable to contact anyone from Cashu, had to wait until I returned to Cusco about two months later. I immediately went to see Barry Walker with the video - it turned out that, unknown to me, Dan Lane, whilst working on skins in Cusco, had uncovered the existence of this new species just before I had found it in the field. The fact that there was a specimen, of course, meant that it could be described immediately,

and, as the only person to have found the species in the field, I collaborated with Dan on the description. The only specimen at that time was of a bird that was originally mist-netted in Manu and misidentified at the time, lying for some ten years in a museum drawer. I think that finding a new species in such a well-worked site goes to show just how much there is still to learn about Neotropical birds. Manu National Park is one of the most visited birding sites in South America, yet it may still harbour undescribed species! Indeed, a very distinct new tanager has recently been found on the main birding route into the park!"

Birding can be full of incidental adventure. Frank broke his back in Borneo, floated for an hour in waters infested with piranhas after a speedboat flipped over in Colombia, had a huge tree fall on his canoe in New Guinea, and endured a close shave with the Khmer Rouge in Cambodia.

"Jonathan Eames and I did some survey work together, on Tonle Sap, Cambodia. This was when the Khmer Rouge were still active, and perhaps we should not have taken the risks we did. At the time, however, Giant Ibis was still a key bird that had not been found, and we were keen to be the first to find it. So we did some surveys on the lake near where we knew that there was a large waterbird colony. We had to travel on small boats with a large machine gun mounted at the front on a big tripod, just in case. That was worrying enough, but when we reached the area that we had hoped to survey we had to stay in a floating police or army house. The first thing they showed us was a trap door, through which we were to escape if the Khmer Rouge attacked, straight down into the murky waters. I don't think we slept too well, and we left the area the next day. I heard that the Khmer Rouge attacked that area about a week after we were there....".
It took another decade or so before Frank and Jonathan got to see Giant Ibis.

What is your main concern when it comes to bird protection in the future?

Climate change and the number of people on the planet are surely the main factors that are going to determine which species survive the coming century. Unfortunately, conservation organisations tend not to say much about human population growth and it seems like a bit of a taboo subject, even though it is going to have as much an impact on wildlife, on mankind and our environment as climate change will have. I read recently that mankind is growing by 1.5 million people a week. Everyone seems to be preoccupied with how to reduce carbon emissions, without mentioning that we also need to find a way to gradually reduce the number of people on the planet, not let it increase.

What is it that makes certain people find and describe birds?

Experience, perseverance, and a degree of luck are all important, but if you want to find new species, you need to look carefully and critically at everything you see and, especially in the Neotropics, get tape recordings for comparison with other taxa. This is important because there are probably significant numbers of cryptic species to be found – that is, species that look remarkably similar to others but might sound different, or have subtle differences that one could easily overlook. Another factor for finding new species, of course, is the amount of time you spend looking for birds; I have spent a considerable amount of my life in the field, including much of my free time. Right now, for example, I am probably averaging about 280 days a year in the field. I just spent three straight months visiting the fantastic reserve system of ProAves in Colombia, for example.

Photo: © Frank Lambert

Frank taping a Tapaculo in Colibri del Sol reserve of ProAves, Colombia

Jonathan Charles Eames

Born in 1958 Jonathan is BirdLife International's Programme Manager for Indochina, based in Vietnam and also covering Cambodia, Laos and Myanmar. He has a BA Hons in development studies from the University of East Anglia in the heart of Norfolk, the UK's premier birdwatching county. After finding a Booted Warbler *Hippolais caligata* on Scilly, a Scaly Thrush *Zoothera dauma* on Shetland and Israel's first Black Bushchat *Cerotrichas podobe*, Jonathan graduated to finding three new species of bird in Vietnam: Chestnut-eared Laughingthrush *Garrulax konkakinhensis*, Golden-winged Laughingthrush *Garrulax ngoclinhensis* and

Black-crowned Barwing *Actinodura sodangaorum*. He has also been involved in describing another 14 subspecies, including a new subspecies of Chestnut-headed Partridge, *Arborophila cambodiana chandamonyi*, and rediscovered, with colleagues, the Imperial Pheasant *Lophura imperialis*, Grey-crowned Crocias *Crocias langbianis* and Sooty Babbler *Stachyris herberti* in Vietnam. The latter species had not been recorded for 74 years. More recently he rediscovered Gurney's Pitta *Pitta gurneyii* (see pp. 190-191) in Myanmar and estimated that up to 8,000 pairs remain. His quest for the possibly extinct Pink-headed Duck *Rhodonessa caryophyllacea* (see p. 90) continues and we hope to report in another volume of this book that it has been successful!

Jonathan has been interested in birds and wildlife since he was a small boy. He grew up in Leicestershire, a classic English shire county of rolling hills. It has a mosaic landscape with a mixture of arable and pasture, with beef, dairy and sheep, and woodland and small copses. Family walks in the nearby countryside meant he grew up with wildlife in mind, watching Lapwings displaying on the plough, Jackdaws plucking wool from the backs of sheep, primroses and bluebells in the woodland in spring, and Brown Hares boxing in the fields. Evenings and weekends after school were spent across the fields, which included many wild flower meadows full of cowslips, pushing always a little further to the next copse or rough grassland looking for things new, finding inspiration.

"Looking back now I think I worked those fields pretty well to find nesting Grasshopper Warblers, Common Snipe, Hobby and Barn Owl and Great Crested Newts", says Jonathan. "Of course you can forget about finding most of those species now thanks to the Common Agricultural Policy which led to agricultural intensification."

His first foreign trip was in 1973 when, at the age of 15, he joined an expedition to survey seabirds on the Faeroe Islands, which lie between Iceland and Scotland but belong to Denmark. One of the highlights was a visit to the island of Mykines, which at the time held the only known gannetry on the Faeroes. He was also there to look for Leach's Petrel. The first literal taste of birds was when he sampled young gannets, which he thought tasted awful, while puffins and guillemots appealed more (he recommends them par-boiled, then sauted in butter). Being dive-bombed by bonxies (as Great Skua *Catharacte skua* is known in Shetland) and Arctic Skuas *Stercorarius parasiticus* was delightful, and made a lasting impression on him. All the precious film he had taken with him was used on taking photos of skua chicks, which did not impress his parents.

Being an ornithologist in remote areas can be quite nerve-wrecking at times, as Jonathan found in Pakistan in the early nineties. After discovering that the Palas valley in the North-west Frontier Province held the largest population of Western Tragopans *Tragopan melanocephala*, he and his colleagues

Jonathan C Eames with Seng Kim Hout, Wildlife Protection Office, Forestry Adminstration, in western Siem Pang District, Stung Treng Province 24 January 2003.

Photo: © J C Eames

Jonathan C Eames with Tim Appleton MBE on elephant back in Kachin Province, Myanmar 2004.

headed back to Islamabad via the Karakoram Highway which was a long four-day drive through wild inhospitable country.

"There had been a strike amongst the taxi drivers on the highway and the road was deadly quiet and devoid of traffic. After three days of patiently waiting in a roadside village a pick-up truck belonging to the Government of Pakistan Geological Survey went past. My Pakistani government colleagues hailed the driver and arranged a ride. Relieved to be on the road at last after such a long wait, we rounded a corner after a few kilometres to find the road blocked by vehicles and about 250 angry Pathan tribesman waving AK47s in the air. They surrounded the pick-up. I was a little apprehensive but my colleague Muneer bravely stood up in the back of the open vehicle and gave a speech. After a few moments the mob fell silent and they parted and let the pick-up through. Astonished and relieved I asked Muneer what he had said. 'I told them we were Englishmen and Pathans and they must either kill us or let us through', he replied".

For Jonathan, finding his first new species had its own special thrill.

"In my case the thrill was the Black-crowned Bar-wing, but it all happened quite quickly and unex-pectedly. On arriving in a village we rested, and later in the afternoon Roland Eve and I went out to stretch our legs before sun-down and look for a few birds. The first bird I put my binoculars on that afternoon was a Long-tailed Shrike, the next bird was new to science! I found the Chestnut-eared Laughingthrush lying in a mist-net shelf. It was on the last net round of the last day in the field of a month-long trip! What luck! It was a male and on my next trip I got a female in the nets and a juvenile."

Are there any species in the pipeline which you are about to describe?

I have my eyes on a couple of things.

What is your main concern when it comes to bird protection in the future?

Too few of us are involved in bird conservation and there are too many folk devising strategies for conservation and too few of us out there with their sleeves rolled up. I always thought there would be hundreds of younger people with the same realisation following behind me and others of my generation. My biggest worry is that after us there is no one. There should be at least sufficient people in enough numbers to make a difference. Why aren't younger people inspired as our generation was?

Which is the most exciting, still undescribed, species and why?

The most exciting undescribed species is one that will radically change the way we perceive life on Earth and the way we relate to one another.

What is it that makes certain people find and describe birds?

Imagination. You must have the realization that any isolated 2,000 m plus peak anywhere in the world may hold an undescribed taxon. Being able to identify birds has nothing to do with it. For me finding birds is exciting but identifying them is a routine chore. I knew when we explored Mount Bi Doup in the central highlands of Vietnam that it must support an undescribed taxon and it did.

Per Alström

Per has described or co-described the following species; *Phylloscopus sichuanensis* (now Chinese Leaf-warbler *Phylloscopus yunnanensis*), Hainan Leaf-warbler *Phylloscopus hainanus*, Emei Leaf-warbler *Phylloscopus emeiensis*, Alström's Warbler *Seicercus soror* and Mekong Wagtail *Motacilla samveasnae*.

Per Alström has made his mark on taxonomy in Asia. He was born in 1961 and made his first notes of birds when he was 11, in 1972. Neither his parents nor his friends were interested in birds; a possible influence may have been a teacher in a nursery years before. He soon joined some older, more experienced birders in Gothenburg, Sweden where he grew up, and was allowed to come with them on outings. At age 11 he already recognised species such as Chiffchaff, Willow Warbler and Tree Pipit, identifications that require more than just a passing interest in birds. There is an anecdote from the seventies when, on an excursion with the local ornithological society, he corrected the leader, one of Sweden's skilled field ornithologists, on Tree Pipit *Anthus trivialis* identification in front of a group of experienced birders four times his age.

His parents took him on holidays abroad frequently, which was very exciting for a young birder, and he managed to get himself arrested for the first time at the age of 13, while studying Lesser Short-toed Larks *Calandrella cinerea* too close to Monastir airport in Tunisia. Larks and pipits and other less colourful birds, not so popular with the birding populace, have always fascinated Per, and he has authored several international papers and books on these groups. His first birding trip abroad without his parents took place in 1977, when he went to the Camargue in southern France.

Since 1980 Per has spent a total of over three years in Asia, from the extreme north to the extreme south, west to east. He has returned frequently to the same sites, enabling him to carry out long-term, high-quality research. Apart from birds he has had fantastic encounters with other wildlife - including around 25 meetings with Tigers, and the time he has spent with distant people and tribes has had a great bearing on his global outlook on life.

Per interrupted a trip in China in 1985, after having spent the autumn of 1984 ringing birds in Japan, because he had been admitted to the Faculty of Medicine in his home town of Gothenburg. He found he needed a sabbatical after the first term, and travelled to Eilat in Israel for ringing. Then he studied for a further term before he had to take a new sabbatical, to finish writing his book on pipits, wagtails and larks together with Krister Mild and Dan Zetterström. It was another 17 years before the pipits and wagtails book was published, and the larks are still waiting. That sabbatical grew so long that he eventually decided to study biology instead, so that he could combine ornithological trips with his studies. Per obtained a PhD at Uppsala University. Today he is Associate Professor at the University of

Well-equipped and ready for action, steppes of Kazakhstan 2006

Photo: © Andrew Lassey

Stockholm/Swedish Museum of Natural History and a taxonomist at the Swedish Species Information Centre at the Swedish University of Agricultural Sciences.

During his Asian trips in the mid-1980s, Per and colleague Urban Olsson recorded that the species known as Lemon-rumped Warbler *Phylloscopus chloronotus* had two types of song which both differed markedly from Pallas' Warbler *Phylloscopus proregulus*, of which Lemon-rumped was considered a subspecies at the time.
"A few years later we heard another seemingly Lemon-rumped with a third type of song as well. It is very unusual for warblers of the genus *Phylloscopus* to have different songs within one species. This made us suggest already in 1990 that perhaps Pallas' and Lemon-rumped Warblers should be split into two species. In June 1989 I observed a bird that sang with the third and a fourth type of song, together with ornithologist Peter Colston from the British Museum. We could observe it well and saw that it differed in appearance from Lemon-rumped. Then I realised it was an unknown species we had been puzzled by. A few years of intensive field studies of the new species followed, involving playback, habitat choice and biology where it bred sympatrically with Lemon-rumped Warbler. This resulted in a publication of *Phylloscopus sichuanensis*, named after the Sichuan province of China where most observations had

been made. My joy was marred a bit a few years later when it surfaced that the famous French-born ornithologist La Touche already had described this species as *Phylloscopus proregulus ynnanensis* 70 years previously. He had however based his description on a few samples collected during migration, so my studies still provided plenty of new knowledge on this taxon, which now is known as Chinese Leaf-warbler *Phylloscopus yunnanensis*".

Per has, together with Urban Olsson, spent 12 years studying the Asian *Seicercus* species, another greenish warbler genus. They not only took advantage of long-since collected skins in museums in Europe, America and China, but also performed extensive field work which incorporated biological studies, voice recordings and playback, altitudinal distribution and taking blood samples from captured birds. They found that the genus could be divided into five groups, and that in some places three groups could breed on the same mountain, but at different altitudes, and be indifferent to playback of the neighbouring taxa's songs. This resulted in the separation of five species of *Seicercus*, including the newly described Alström's Warbler *Seicercus soror* (*soror* means sister), and two subspecies of two of the species. Naming was difficult, as they did not want to repeat the mistake with La Touche's warbler, so this time an exhaustive search after old type skins was made. Since Per's and Urban's paper, a sixth species has been described by German biologists.

Photo: © Ulrica Alström

Descending the Annapurna, Nepal 2004

Are there any species in the pipeline which you are about to describe?

At least one.

What is your main concern when it comes to bird protection in the future?

The brutal destruction of habitats worldwide and the lack of opportunities to practically protect reserves and national parks from poaching, illegal logging etc. It is all about lack of commitment and will, and unscrupulous greediness among large companies combined with local poverty and overpopulation.

Which is the most exciting still-undescribed species, and why?

Probably a species I recently saw on an image by an Asian colleague, which apparently is undescribed and quite common where it was found.

What is it that makes certain people find and describe birds?

This question is difficult to answer without sounding somewhat boastful. However, it seems obvious that it's a combination of pure luck - being in the right place at the right time - and a good knowledge of all of the taxa in a certain group. A thorough knowledge of vocalisations has proven increasingly important in the last few decades. Analyses of DNA will also reveal a number of new species in the future. A sense for detail and a good memory also helps.

Four global ornithologists who all got hooked at an early age and have described over 25 new species and subspecies between them. They are all in their late thirties or above.
Are they too Critically Endangered, or are there any young ornithologists out there 'with their sleeves rolled-up' who will respond to Jonathan Eames call and follow in their footsteps?

The Madagascar Pochard

- a rare diving duck resurfaces

The secret breeding site of the newly
discovered Madagascar Pochards

SIX SPECIES OF DUCK ARE CLASSIFIED AS Critically Endangered in the 2007 IUCN Red List. Several others have been wiped from earth's surface over the centuries. The extinct ducks include not only species occurring on exotic and remote islands, such as the Mauritian Duck *Anas theodori* and the flightless Amsterdam Island Duck *Anas marecula*, which both disappeared several hundred years ago, but also the Labrador Duck *Camptorhynchus labradorius* of Canada and the USA which disappeared as recently as in the mid-to-late 1870s. The extinction of these three species is directly attributable to man; the island-residing ducks were presumably killed for food by starved visitors who had travelled across the seas and saw a good opportunity for varying their diet. The Labrador Duck, which lived in less remote areas and wintered in Cheaspeake Bay, was over-hunted in its winter quarters, and its eggs and chicks were over-harvested in the Canadian breeding areas.

The Madagascar Pochard *Aythya innotata* belonged to that uncertain category of species described as "Critically Endangered (Possibly Extinct)", until it was sensationally rediscovered in late 2006. It was first described in 1894 by the famous Italian zoologist Count Adelardo Tommaso Salvadori (1835-1923), who was curator at the Museum of Turin. He published several books, including volumes 20-21 and 27 (including ducks) of the catalogue of birds in the British Museum at Tring. Salvadori presented a number of new duck species as skins at a British Ornithologists' Club meeting, attended by contemporary ornithological dignitaries such as Henry Seebohm and R. Bowdler-Sharpe, in the restaurant Frascati at 32 Oxford Street in London on 24 October 1894. The pochard skin probably came from Tring, as Salvadori apparently never visited Madagascar himself. The bird was of course known to the people of Madagascar, where it carried the names Onjy or Fotsy Maso in the Malagasy language. Salvadori gave it the specific name *innotata* which means "unremarkable", and it is an unremarkable species, which makes little impression with its uniform colouring. But the story of its return from possible extinction is anything but unremarkable.

Madagascar Pochard superficially resembles Ferruginous Duck *Aythya nyroca*, with rusty-brown plumage, pale abdomen and, in the male, a white eye. But it is thought to be more closely related to the Australian Hardhead or Australasian White-eye *Aythya australis* than the Ferruginous Duck. Its relative dullness and the restricted range may both explain why it has not occurred commonly in captivity. It feeds mainly on plants or small invertebrates, and it is thought that it has played a role in spreading water plants from lake to lake. It is also thought to be sedentary, although subfossil records of a duck on nearby Réunion may belong to this species.

It was never very common, although Lake Alaotra, some 200 km north of the capital, was a stronghold where it was considered common in the 1920s and 1930s. Before 2006, the last sighting of a flock had been in June 1960 when 20 birds (one of them obtained as a specimen) were reliably recorded at Ambatosoratra. In 1991, a male was caught in a fishing net and held in captivity in Madagascar until it died a year later, this being the last record for 15 years. The Pochard was also reported from Lake Itasy, Antananarivo and Maevatanana. There are nearly 60 museum specimens around the world. The last wild specimens, before the 1960 and 1991 individuals described above, were collected in the 1930s. It seems that any captive population died out during the Second World War.

The decline

It is still not clear why numbers have fallen so dramatically over the last century, but human activities have undoubtedly played a major part. Man settled on Madagascar approximately 1,200 years ago, arriving initially from Indonesia and then Africa and Europe and, habitats were raidly modified as the settlers spread over the island. From the 14th century rice paddies were created, rice being a staple diet of the increasing population. The last 1,000 years have also seen decreased rainfall, which has resulted in the original habitat becoming drier. Wetlands have been especially affected by anthropogenic changes in combination with drought; as deforestation has taken place, wetlands have become shallower due to siltation, thereby becoming suitable for modification into rice paddies.

Lake Alaotra, at the centre of the rice-growing district on Madagascar, is no longer an ideal habitat for Madagascar Pochard. Situated in the northern half of Madagascar, it is Madagascar's largest lake,

Half of the known offspring in 2006.

plants typically congest the clear water surfaces and also lead to deoxygenation, which severely affects the animal life. The deforested hills around the lake contribute strongly to silting and the lake bottom is soft, consisting of layers of sand, clay and mud. There are natural marshes surrounding the lake, in particular in the southern area where papyrus *Cyperus* and reeds *Phragmites* dominate.

Historically the lake has always been rich in waterfowl, but habitat changes and introduced fish have reduced the numbers. Herbivorous fish, such as species of carp, were released into the lake in the early 20th century. They were followed by exotic cichlids, particularly Tilapia species, in the mid 20th century. These introduced species changed the floral composition, competing not just with Madagascar Pochard for food, but also with over 30 indigenous, endemic fish species. In the 1960s, the North American Black Bass *Micropterus salmoides* was introduced. A carnivorous species, its introduction coincided with a rapid decline of waterbirds and it is suspected to have predated on ducklings. Later, another carnivorous fish, the Asian Snakehead *Ophiocephalus striatus*, was introduced, and this species not only predates waterbirds but

approximately 40 by 9.5 km and with depths ranging from 1,5 to four metres at high-water. Many endemic bird species are found on the lake; including the Alaotra Grebe *Tachybaptus rufolavatus*, another Critically Endangered (Possibly Extinct) species (see p. 106). Large areas of inaccessible swampland make Lake Alaotra very difficult to survey.

The vegetation of Lake Alaotra was originally dominated by water lilies *Nymphaea* but water-hyacinth *Eichhornia crassipes* and water-fern *Salvinia auriculata* have now taken over, even though a comeback of water lilies has been noted recently on the southern parts of the lake. These introduced

39

Lily Réné Arison Roland from The Peregrine Fund, who found the species, and Glyn Young from Durrell Wildlife Conservation Trust.

may have caused the extinction of North American Black Bass! It seems that some less-threatened species of waterbirds such as Allen's Gallinule *Porphyrio alleni*, African Pygmy Goose *Nettapus auritus* and Madagascar Jacana *Actophilornis albunucha* have also had to retreat from the lake.

With an increasing human population, fishing became more intensive, and death through entanglement in monofilament gill-nets is probably another element in the pochard's decline. Duck hunting also took its toll. The locals regularly hunt ducks using snares. The use of guns is not especially common and is usually restricted to foreigners and expatriates. The hunting season is officially from May to July, but often starts in April, and coincides with the dry period, though some hunting also takes place during the wet season between October and January. It is estimated that almost 20% of the total adult population of Meller's Duck *Anas melleri* is killed annually at Lake Alaotra alone.

Chemicals banned in Europe are still used in Madagascar and these contribute to polluting Lake Alaotra with residue. With all these pressures on the lake, it is unsurprising that intensive searches (including major publicity campaigns) at Alaotra during 1989-1990 and 1993-1994 failed to discover any evidence of Madagascar Pochard.

The new site and the discovery

In November 2006, a team from the Peregrine Fund were surveying biodiversity in remote parts of Madagascar in connection with work on the Madagascar Harrier *Circus macrosceles*, a species classified as Vulnerable.
The Peregrine Fund (www.peregrinefund.org) is a worldwide conservation organisation running some 20 projects aimed at conservation of raptors on all continents. The team included the National Director of the Peregrine Fund, Dr. Lily-Arison Rene de Roland, who manages the Madagascar project with Dr. Russell Thorstrom.

At a small volcanic lake 330 km from Lake Alaotra, Lily and local biologist Sam Thé Seing found a flock of pochards, consisting of nine adults, and four young which were determined to be approximately two weeks old. At last there was concrete evidence that the species was still alive and breeding, a good start for conservation. Follow up surveys located around 20 mature individuals with up to nine ducklings at the same site. Five birds were seen at a second lake three to four kilometres from the site, but these may be part of the 20 individuals counted previously. This lake is undisturbed by rice paddies, and according to local people does not contain fish, and is therefore rarely disturbed which further raises hopes that the species will be able to survive there.

In July 2007, breeding recommenced and four nests were found.

The future

The Durrell Wildlife Conservation Trust (Madagascar) is primarily responsible for co-ordinating conservation efforts for the Madagascar Pochard. Richard Lewis and Glyn Young are directing the efforts to save the pochard from extinction, including further surveys of montane lakes. A PhD student and Durrell employee, Felix Razafindrajao, is planning to undertake a project clarifying the causes of extinction from its better-known habitats such as Lake Alaotra.

BirdLife International is cautiously optimistic about the survival of such a tiny population.
"There do not appear to be any immediate threats to the species at the site of its rediscovery, but given that it has a tiny known population, it faces significant risk from stochastic (random) events and genetic factors, particularly inbreeding depression", says Dr. Stuart Butchart.

Efforts are also underway to conserve the last vestiges of suitable habitat at Lake Alaotra. The Malagasy government has ratified the Ramsar Convention, and Lake Alaotra may be proposed as a Ramsar Site. Implementation of any conservation policy for the area will be very difficult because of Alaotra's huge economic importance for agriculture and fisheries. But there are hopeful signs, since some of Madagascar's endemic species have already re-populated from other parts of their ranges as water-lilies and other emergent vegetation have made a comeback along the lake's southern edge.

Other ducks in line for rediscovery

Two other Critically Endangered duck species are categorised as "Possibly Extinct", though since they live in poorly surveyed areas there are hopes they may still occur in the wild.

The Crested Shelduck *Tadorna cristata* (see p. 90) of north-eastern China and adjacent parts of Russia and Korea was last seen reliably in 1964 near Vladivostok. Massive publicity campaigns involving distributing over three million printed leaflets in the region have only produced rumoured occurrences. Its range is poorly known and some of the assumed breeding areas are remote and rarely visited by ornithologists.

The other species is the Pink-headed Duck *Rhodonessa caryophyllacea* of Bangladesh, India, Nepal and Myanmar (see p 90). It was last seen in 1949, but a possible sighting was made in Myanmar in 2003, so there is a small chance that the species may survive in the remote wetlands of northern Myanmar. The last individual in captivity lived on until in 1945.

Let us hope that these two species will feature in a future edition of this book as "good news" stories, like the one you have just read.

Falling off the edge of the world

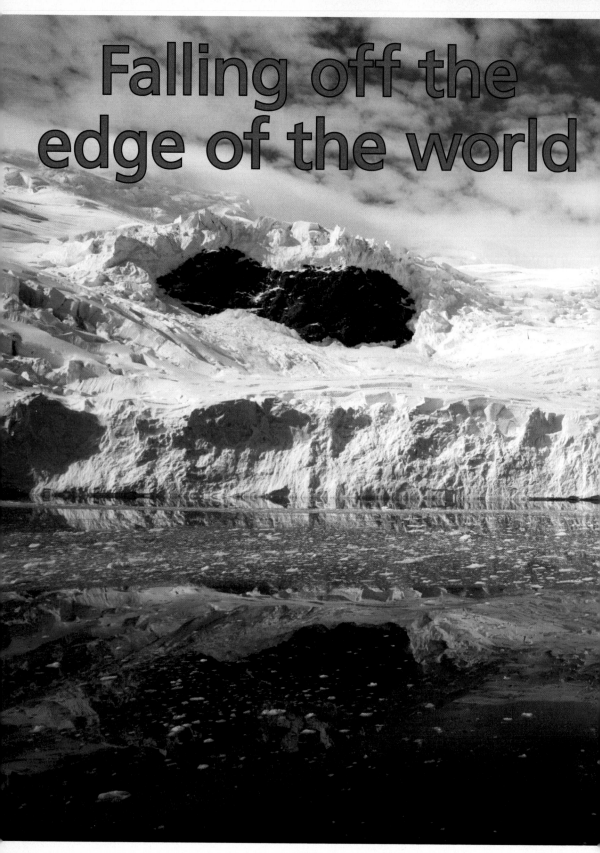

the impact of climate change on birds and their ranges

THE WORLD HAS UNDERGONE MANY MAJOR climatic changes throughout history. But today these changes are taking place far more rapidly than ever before, and it is we humans who affect the biosphere by our activities. Climate change is already impacting on biodiversity, and by the end of the century climate change and its impacts may be the dominant direct driver of biodiversity loss. More severe effects, including bird extinctions, are predicted. A study in the journal Nature, published in 2005, estimated that without urgent action, almost one third of land-based species could be committed to extinction as a result of climate change by the middle of this century.

Birds have long been used as indicators of the state of the world's ecosystems. Here we take a look at changes in the ranges, movements and seasonal behaviour of a number of species which provide grim evidence of the speed and extent of global warming.

The amount of carbon dioxide in the atmosphere is now at its highest in 400,000 years, having risen by 30% since the mid 19th century. Seven of the top ten warmest years in the 20th century occurred in the 1990s. The Intergovernmental Panel on Climate Change forecasts that average global surface temperatures will be between 1.4 and 5.8 Celsius (with some variation) above 1990 levels by 2100, and will continue to rise after that even if emissions stabilise. For comparison, the average change in temperature between the peak and trough of a major ice age is 4 or 5 Celsius. The consequences for ecosystems and wildlife which are already being felt include increased extreme weather (floods and droughts), the retreat of mountain glaciers, the thawing of permafrost, the release of sweet water into the oceans which affects the marine life, later freezing and earlier break-up of ice on rivers and lakes, lengthening of mid- to high-latitude growing seasons, poleward and altitudinal shifts of plant and animal ranges (resulting in declines in some plant and animal populations) and earlier flowering of trees, emergence of insects and egg-laying in birds. These changes, particularly the shifts in range and abundance, will have profound impacts on species, sites and habitats.

Long travels and murky waters

The effects are already being felt in the Arctic, where since the 1970s the ice cover has been retreating at a rate of 3% per decade. The Black Guillemot Cepphus grylle, a circumpolar species of auk which is categorised as Least Concern (for today that is!) breeds on Copper Island in remote north Alaska. The colony on that island has been carefully studied since the 1970s. During the breeding season the guillemots here feed on the cod that live under or at the edge of the ice pack. With retreating ice and hungry young in the nests, the birds must travel further from

their breeding grounds to obtain their food. This species depends on just one food resource, and with local contraction of the pack ice of just below 10% a decade, they will soon be unable to bring up their young at this colony. At the same time as the Black Guillemot adults are being forced to expend more energy, and spend more time way from the nest in search of food, the sub-arctic and more aggressive Horned Puffin Fratercula corniculata is spreading north and taking over its nest sites.

Slightly further south, in the Bering Sea between America and Russia in the northern Pacific Ocean, hundreds of thousands of Short-tailed Shearwaters Puffinus tenuirostris died in 1997. Their main food source, krill, was plentiful as usual in the sea but white microalgae had bloomed, causing the water to become turbid, which prevented the birds from seeing the krill. This algal blooming was caused by unusually high sea temperatures. It is believed that the shearwaters, which are generalists in their feeding, quickly adapted to taking small fish in shallower water instead, and similar mass deaths have not, as far is known, taken place since. The total population of this species is estimated at around 30 million and it is considered of Least Concern. Here, warming did not affect the supply of food, it just made it more difficult to find.

The United Kingdom case

In February 2004 large numbers of Fulmars Fulmarus glacialis turned up inland in the United Kingdom. This was unusual for a bird usually to be seen far out at sea at that time of year. Shortly afterwards, large numbers of dead Fulmars washed up on the coasts not just of the UK, but also of other European states such as France, Belgium and the Netherlands. Post-mortems revealed that the birds were starved, and that they had arrested or not completed their

Kittiwake (Rissa tridactylus) above and Black Guillemot (Cepphus grylle) below

moult. Under normal circumstances, the moult should have been completed by October the previous year, but moulting is energy-consuming, and birds which have difficulties finding food may suspend their moult. The stage at which the moult had been interrupted showed that the birds had encountered serious energy problems at least four to five months before they died. That was the first indication that something was wrong in the North Sea in 2004.

Another indication came as seabirds returned to their UK breeding colonies such as Bempton Cliffs, North Yorkshire, the Farne Islands off Northumberland and Sumburgh Head on the Shetlands in spring 2004. Atlantic Puffins *Fratercula arctica*, Northern Guillemots *Uria aalge*, Sandwich Terns *Sterna sandvicensis* and Kittiwakes *Rissa tridactyla* were among them. In June 2004, the equivalent of half the previous June's total rainfall fell on the Farne Islands in just two days, resulting in 1,000 dead Sandwich Tern chicks. Since the average clutch of a Sandwich Tern pair is just above one egg, and there were 2,000 breeding pairs there, this means that half of that year's chicks succumbed to the heavy rain. Some 1000 chicks survived the rains, of which normally around 900 would survive to fledge and head off to west Africa for the winter. The terns breed first at three or four years old, and only 300 of the fledged birds are expected to survive these years and return for breeding. Terns are quite long-lived birds (the oldest Sandwich Tern recorded was 20 years old) so single crashes like this one may not have a great effect on the whole population. But to be subjected to these hardships year after year will probably have a very serious effect.

At the same time, at Bempton Cliffs, Kittiwakes only managed to produce one young per five nests. British Kittiwakes lay on average two eggs, meaning that out of ten eggs only one fledged. The full effect will take years to become apparent, since those lucky few that fledged in 2004 and have survived will only return to breed for the first time this year (2008). Meanwhile in the Shetlands, neither Kittiwakes nor Arctic Terns managed to produce any young in 2004. The reason is believed to be the lack of sandeels, an important food source during breeding which in its turn can be connected to a shortage of plankton due to rising sea temperatures. The plankton is also an important food source for Fulmars in winter.

North American songbirds

Well-documented studies of American songbirds show that ranges have been changing in accordance with rising average temperature since the 1970s. Seven out of 35 species have shifted their ranges on average more than 100 km north in the last quarter of a century. Baltimore's state bird, the Baltimore Oriole *Icterus galbula*, may in fact stop breeding in Baltimore altogether and shift its range into new areas to the north. This could of course bring about competition with other species inhabiting the same niche (compare Black Guillemot and Horned Puffin

American Robins (Turdus migratorius) now arrive earlier to some breeding grounds, before the snow has disappeared.

Tortuga Bay, Santa Cruz, Galapagos

Photo: © iStockphoto / Morley Read

above). Also in America, spring migrants from the South American tropics are in some cases arriving up to three weeks earlier than 30 years ago. We know this thanks to long, uninterrupted series of standardised counts at migration hotspots, by both amateur birders and professional ornithologists. An interesting North American study showing how short-distance migration has been affected has been published by David W. Inouye and his colleagues. They followed American Robins *Turdus migratorius* in Colorado as they migrated between low-level wintering areas and high-altitude breeding areas in the Rocky Mountains. The growing season at the lower altitudes has become considerably longer during the last quarter of a century, and triggers the birds to migrate earlier to their breeding grounds, where the growing season has not increased as much. The date of the first sighting at the breeding grounds could differ by over a month, but on average has become gradually earlier over the years. But due to increased winter precipitation, the higher grounds do not become bare of snow until at about the same time as before. So the birds now have to wait 18 days longer for the snow to disappear and create favourable feeding conditions for breeding. This means that they must be well-stocked with fat when they arrive, and the delay, which requires them to call on their energy reserves, could severely affect their physical condition and consequent breeding success.

The El Niño phenomenon

Off the western coast of South America, changes in the natural phenomenon known as El Niño are affecting bird populations. El Niño is a strong combination of climatological and hydrological phenomena, and usually occurs every fourth to seventh year. Beginning around Christmas time, it lasts for 12-17 months and its effect can be felt all over the globe. El Niño is caused by cold water upwelling on the Pacific side of the South American coast, which lowers air pressure. The change in air pressure weakens the trade winds, which then change direction and thereby influence the water temperature. Off Peru, with its normally cold and fish-rich waters, warm water streams in from the Ocean and results in rain and much less fish than usual. Across the Pacific, in Australia and South East Asia, the pressure rises and creates warm and dry conditions, leading to drought and forest fires.

Far-away places such as eastern Africa can be affected by floods and plentiful rainfall, while southern Africa may receive much drier weather than normal. Southern California and Mexico receive colder and wetter weather, while winters in central and eastern USA become much warmer and drier during El Niño years. In 1998, during the last El Niño, the highest average temperatures ever were measured all over the world. It is anticipated that 2007 will be another such year, and what we have seen so far certainly points at it. There is much speculation whether global warming will reinforce El Niño. The most pessimistic commentators believe that global warming may escalate the El Niño effect so much that rain forests will dry out, thereby releasing even more carbon dioxide into the atmosphere. Historical disasters such as a famine in Mesopotamia and the demise of the Moche civilization in Peru coincided with strong El Ninos.

The Endangered Galapagos Penguin *Spheniscus mendiculus* is regularly affected by El Nino. In 1982-83, over 75% of the population starved to death because of the lack of food in the warmer-than-usual waters. After this, the population entered a slow recovery phase. However, the 1997-1998 El Niño caused a further decline of 66%. The population may now be in another recovery phase. But in 2006 only 2007 individuals were thought to remain, which is almost 60% lower than record numbers in the seventies.

South African range contractions

In Africa, a continent holding a high degree of endemism and deemed to be much affected by climate change, there is one comprehensive study by Robert E. Simmons and his colleagues at the Percy Fitzpatrick Institute in Cape Town. Simmons et al suggest that small-bodied birds with short generation times will be more likely to adapt to climate change than larger-bodied birds with longer generation times. Migrant species, and those with very specialised feeding habits, are also prone to be affected as they can turn up in newly hostile environments on their travels, while species with small ranges, restricted to very special biomes, such as the Succulent Karoo or the Cape Floral Kingdom, are entirely dependant on what happens to the biomes. The beautiful Blue Swallow *Hirundo atrocaerulea*, so far classified as Vulnerable globally with a population of around 2000 pairs, is one species that is likely to be affected by climate change in Africa. It is an intra-African migrant that breeds in south-eastern Africa and migrates to Uganda and Kenya. In South Africa there are very few breeding pairs (65 pairs) and its typical biome of grassland is threatened by increased bush-encroachment in its whole African range.

Several formerly abundant Asian vulture species have found a place in this book after a catastrophic decline in numbers in recent years. In South Africa, research on the Lammergeier or Bearded

Coal power plant, Germany

Galapagos Penguin (Spheniscus mendiculus) is affected by El Niño events and currently classified as Endangered.

Vulture *Gypaetus barbatus* and Cape Vulture *Gyps coprotheres* has shown that climatic change over the last 50 years may also be a factor, and that it is has been hidden by more obvious causes of population decline such as mass poisoning, veterinary use of the drug diclofenac, and changes in livestock welfare and carcass disposal practices. The effects of warming can be predicted to include vultures which breed in shadier areas having a higher success than those breeding on sites exposed to the sun. For the Lammergeier, which begins breeding in January or even earlier, warm winters could be less favourable than normal winters.

Long-distance migrants are out of synch with their food

For long-distance migrants, the conditions at the breeding grounds are unknown when they leave their often tropical wintering grounds. Birds such as Pied Flycatcher *Ficedula hypolecua* often arrive in northern latitudes late in the spring, to coincide with peak availability of food. If these birds continue to arrive at the same time but spring arrives earlier, they may be too late to take advantage of the abundant food they need to take them through the energy-intensive activities of establishing and defending a territory, nesting, egg-laying and feeding the young. There is always some variation in the arrival times of these intercontinental migrants, and birds that arrive early will be able to exploit the earlier availability of food sources, which will perhaps favour these individuals and their offspring in an evolutionary way. Perhaps this also explains why for example records of American Tree Swallow *Tachycineta bicolor* show a trend of arriving progressively earlier year by year (now up to three weeks earlier than 30 years ago).

As seen from these examples, climate change will affect birds in many ways. Studies suggest that many species will not be able to keep up with their changing climate space. As species move at different rates, the community structure of ecosystems will also become disrupted. The most susceptible species will be those with restricted ranges, bounded distributions (on the edges of continents, mountain-tops or small islands), specialised habitat requirements or small populations. While bird species differ greatly in dispersal abilities, most are relatively mobile compared to other organisms which will be impacted even more severely.

We do not yet have the knowledge to predict with certainty how and when individual species will respond to climate change, or how ecosystems will change. However we do know that efforts now to improve the resilience of species and habitats through strengthening populations and addressing existing pressures will help them to adapt.

To keep global warming below the level of 2 degrees Celsius –the level beyond which catastrophic environmental change will be inevitable –requires immediate action at personal, local, national and international levels. Readers of this book, with our bird's-eye view of climate change, have less excuse than many for inaction. We should already have begun to make changes in our own lives, to spread the word among our communities, and to put pressure on our governments. For most of us, protected in the short term by our wealth and technology, it's an issue of losing the biological diversity that enriches our lives and makes them worth living. But for many of the species we treasure, and for our fellow human beings in the less developed world, it's a matter of life and death.

Further reading

Dewytt, L. 2004. A Birds Eye View of Climate Change. Audobon Naturalist News. www.audubonnaturalist.org/cgi-bin/mesh/naturalist_news/featured_articles/flight_risk

Inouye, D.W., Barr, B., Armitage, K. B. and Inouye B. D. 2000 Climate change is affecting altitudinal migrants and hibernating species. Proceedings of the National Academy of Sciences of the Untied States of America. Vol. 97: 1630-1633.

Lehikonen, E., Sparks, T. H. & Zalakevicius, M. 2004. Arrival and Departure Dates. Advances in Ecological Research 35: 1-31.

Price, J. T. & Root, T. L. No Orioles in Baltimore? Climate change and Neotropical migrants. Bird Conservation 16:12.

Simmons, R, E., Barnard, P., Dean, W.R.J., Midgley, G. F., Thuiller, W. & Hughes, G. 2004. Climate change and birds: perspectives and prospects from southern Africa. Ostrich 75/4:295-308.

Simmons, R. E. & Barnard, P. 2005. Too Hot to Handle? The impact of climate change on African birds. Africa - Birds and Birding Nov. 2005:52-60.

Simmons, R. E. & Jenkins, A. R. 2007. Commentary. Is climate change influencing the decline of Cape and Bearded Vultures in Southern Africa? Vulture News 56:41-51.

Wormworth J. & Mallon, K. 2006. Birds and Climate Change. World Wide Fund for Nature Australia.

Migration studies split the atom

THE WONDERS OF BIRD MIGRATION have fascinated people for thousands of years. Where do these feathered creatures come from, where do they go, and why do they migrate? Knowledge of these patterns of movement and the reasons behind them can have a great impact on conservation, not least because for migratory, threatened birds with large or unknown breeding ranges we need to know which populations we should concentrate our conservation efforts on. We also need to know exactly what threats they face, not just in their breeding areas, but also in their winter quarters and along their migration routes. Most of the existing data comes from ringing (banding) and more recently from satellite tracking, but now there is a new, lab-based technology which can draw essential information from feathers, even from centuries-old museum skins.

The first person on record to comment on bird migration was the ancient Greek historian Herodotus (d. 424 BC/BCE), who travelled extensively in Asia Minor and the Middle East. He was thus able to make observations of birds in a large geographical area. In *An Account of Egypt* he wrote "…and cranes flying from the cold weather which comes on in the region of Scythia come regularly to these parts for wintering,…." (*Histories*, Book II, Chapter 22). Scythia is what we know today as the area to the north and east of the Black and Caspian Seas, and Herodotus was apparently well aware that the migration of cranes was triggered by climate.

Aristotle (384-322 BC/BCE) and Pliny the Elder (24-79 AD/CE) gave further comments on migration in their publications *History of Animals* and *Historia Naturalis* respectively, mixing facts with superstition, and introducing novel ideas such as the underwater hibernation of swallows. The concept of hibernating swallows actually lived on into the era when the evidence for bird migration was well understood, and even the great Linnaeus, "the Father of Taxonomy", was a follower of it. It was observed that in autumn, swallows would gather in large flocks in reedbeds for roosting. The reeds would become so heavily laden with swallows that they bent towards

the surface, and, the theory went, eventually submerged the swallows, which then supposedly entered an underwater torpid state until the next spring. As recently as 1897, the prominent American ornithologist Dr. Elliot Coues, who compiled a bibliography of 182 papers dealing with the topic of swallow hibernation, wrote: "I cannot consider the evidence as inadmissible, and must admit that the alleged facts are as well attested, according to ordinary rules of evidence, as any in ornithology."

As we know today, swallows prefer roosting in reeds outside the breeding season because they are safe there, and often have a convenient and rich supply of insect food to stock up on before continuing the next leg of their journey. But Linnaeus was also well aware of the need to actually track individual, migrant birds, and wrote in his *Migrationes Avium* in 1757 that it "would demand great effort, diligence and time by future generations spread over the world to solve the riddles of bird migration". We belong to those generations today.

Marking individual birds

It is of course essential to have knowledge of birds' origins, movements and habits in detail if we wish

Starling (Sturnus vulgaris) was the first bird to be ringed, on 5th June 1899

to conserve them successfully for future generations to enjoy. But individual birds of a species, and indeed sometimes of different species, look very alike. How can we recognise the individual Western Sandpiper *Calidris mauri* we saw on the tundra of Alaska in summer, when it stops over in Vancouver, or winters on the beach of Mexico? If numbers of wintering sandpipers in Mexico diminish, does that mean that the population in Alaska is decreasing, or are the breeding grounds in north-eastern Siberia involved? Can we be sure that a Woodcock *Scolopax rusticola* shot in its wintering site in France comes from Finland, or are other breeding populations of woodcock being affected by the scale of hunting of this species in France? Many parts of birds' ranges are largely uninhabited by people, and even less so by ornithologists. So how can we discover the unknown breeding sites of Slender-billed Curlew *Numenius tenuirostris*, a Critically Endangered species, or even know in which region they may lie?

One way is to mark individual birds. The first bird known to have been marked was a swallow in the second Punic War (some 200 years after Herodotus's crane observations). Quintus Fabius Pictor, a Roman senator who was apparently well aware that swallows could re-orientate themselves, tied a thread on the leg of a swallow taken from a nest in a besieged town. The knots on the thread indicated to the town's inhabitants the date when they would be relieved, and he released the swallow knowing that it would fly back to its nest and relay the message.

It was the Dane Hans Christian Cornelius Mortensen (1856-1921) who responded in earnest to Linnaeus' call for future generations to solve the riddle of bird migration, and developed the technique known in Europe as ringing, and in America and Australia as banding. After having experimented with zinc bands, he attached a metal ring to the leg of a Starling *Sturnus vulgaris* on 5 June 1899 in Viborg, a small, picturesque town in mainland Denmark. He had studied the breeding biology of Starlings and was eager to learn more of their migration habits. When he died he had managed to ring over 5,000 birds of different species, of which there were some 500 recoveries, a very high percentage. Amazingly, he obtained 18 recoveries of White Storks *Ciconia ciconia* from Africa, as well as many from neighbouring countries and provinces. The high success rate can be explained by many local recaptures and his involvement with species that lived close to humans.

The method of ringing was quickly adopted as a scientific tool thereafter: in 1901 in East Prussia (now the Russian enclave of Kaliningrad on the Baltic coast), 1904 in the United Kingdom, 1908 in Hungary and 1909 in Portugal and the United States. Today the method is used worldwide.

New techniques have evolved, such as satellite telemetry, which involves placing miniature transmitters on captured birds or nestlings. Another technique is to gather knowledge of unique feather moult patterns among different populations of the same species. An example of that is the Dunlin *Calidris alpina*, a small shorebird which looks the same in winter plumage worldwide. Populations from different breeding areas winter at the same site, but can be distinguished race-wise by how their flight feathers have been moulted. Yet another method is to let migrant birds fly their whole migration route in wind tunnels with artificial magnetic fields, and see how they orientate themselves.

What are stable isotopes?

In the late 20th century, molecular analysis of the occurence of isotopes in bird´s feathers emerged as a technique for tracking birds. To understand this we need to know how feathers are constructed, and what stable isotopes are. Bird feathers are made of a protein called keratin, which is also found in the fur, scales, exoskeletons and claws of other animals, and in our own hair and nails. Keratin is made of aminoacids which in turn are made up mainly of carbon (C), hydrogen (H), nitrogen (N) and oxygen (O).

These elements occur in nature as different isotopes, which are variations of an atom that have different numbers of neutrons. Isotopes can be stable or unstable. The unstable ones decay over time, at rates ranging from fractions of a second to thousands of years, and have a variety of scientific applications, such as carbon dating.

Stable isotopes, as the name suggests, do not decay. They are picked up through the food the bird eats and the water it drinks, and because they are stable, they remain in the feathers until the next moult, in the same state as when they were absorbed.

Birds change their feathers once or twice a year. Moulting patterns vary with age and species. Some, like large birds of prey, may be in continuous moult, even on migration, while others have clearly defined moult periods when they are resident in specific areas, which may be breeding sites, wintering sites or intermediate stopover sites. Other species may moult certain feathers at certain times (e.g. flight feathers just before embarking on migration, and body feathers in the wintering quarters). Ducks and geese gather in certain areas and moult all their feathers at once, which renders them flightless and vulnerable. This means that stable isotope patterns in any of the migratory Eurasian eagle species' feathers are less likely to say something about the bird's origin than the feathers of, for example, a Northern Pintail *Anas acuta*, a species with a wide range which undertakes a 'moult migration' to wetlands, lakes and estuaries, where it gathers in large numbers.

During migration the feathers (with the exception of species like the large birds of prey described above) will not absorb any stable isotopes, since they are already fully grown. So if we have detailed knowledge of a species' moult habits, we can be certain that the isotopes in its feathers come from the area where the feathers were regrown – its

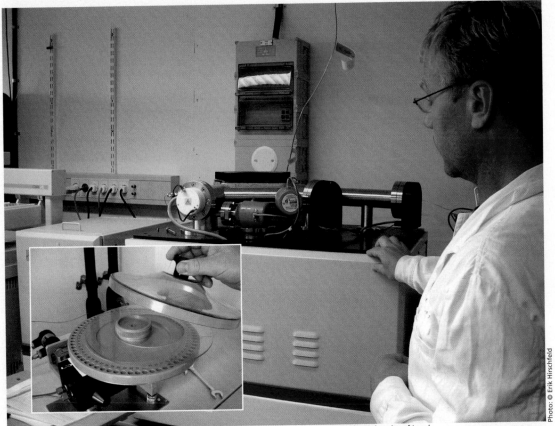

Professor Staffan Bensch and his isotope analysis equipment at the University of Lund

breeding or wintering grounds, depending on the species.

Isotopes wander up the food chain, through plants or other animals that are devoured and from the water a bird drinks, so it is important to know exactly where in the food chain the species is when interpreting the stable isotope signature, as well as knowing what it eats. A bird that feeds on refuse produced by humans, such as a Critically Endangered Slender-billed Vulture *Gyps tenuirostris*, may breed in India, but is likely to end up with an isotope signature from other areas, since its diet feeds may include items that have been brought in from outside the breeding area. For similar reasons, the feathers of birds of prey that feed on migrant songbirds, such as Eleonora's Falcon *Falco eleonorae* or Sooty Falcon *Falco concolor* (both of Least Concern) will tell us little about their origins. On the other hand, a berry-eating young thrush, hatched and growing its feathers in Canada, will reflect an isotope pattern true to its breeding ground.

Stable isotopes are distributed differently over the Earth depending on geological (e. g. soil), biological (e. g. plants) and climatic (e.g. wet or dry) conditions. After water has evaporated at the equator, the heavy *Deuterium* isotope of oxygen falls back to earth as rainfall relatively quickly, so that the further away

from the equator, the less *Deuterium* will show up in precipitation. It may vary from one side of a mountain range to another, depending on which side of the mountains receive most rainfall. There are even variations in the great oceans, caused by different temperatures, the inflow of glacial water and amount of precipitation. In general, one can say that the lowest amounts of *Deuterium* are found in large, dry inland regions of the world, far away from the sea, such as interior Siberia and Mongolia.

Isotope patterns are regularly mapped in some places, for example North America where maps are produced annually. In other places these maps hardly exist. The International Atomic Energy Association (IAEA) and World Meteorological Organization (WMO) have produced such maps going back 40 years, taking measurements in rain and snow at several hundred sites all over the world. However, the distribution may vary locally and differ significantly a few kilometres away from the measurement sites. It has also been suggested that in areas of local heavy precipitation, such as the tropics, isotopes of hydrogen and oxygen may vary too greatly in to be usable as tracers. In south-east Asia for example, rain comes from many different directions. Rain falls in the Himalayas and then enters the sea via rivers, while other weather systems come with the monsoon from the oceans, which distorts

Ringing (banding) has been an established method of tracing individual birds for over a century

Old skins of Aquatic Warbler (Acrocephalus paludicola) top and Slender-billed Curlew (Numenius tenuirostris) bottom, lying in museums, can still be very useful for isotope research.

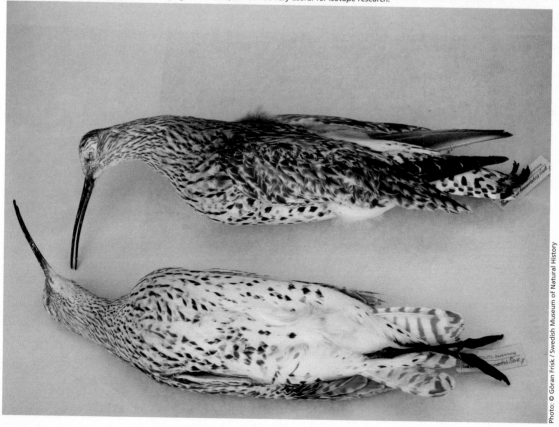

the patterns. Annual fluctuations in rainfall may also affect the patterns. But in general, by knowing the pattern of the stable isotopes in the birds' breeding or wintering areas, we can find out roughly where an individual bird has come from.

Another way of knowing the distribution of isotopes is to study the patterns of a commoner reference species occurring in the same area and feeding on the same food as the species we wish to study. This method has been used with Europe's rarest songbird, the Vulnerable Aquatic Warbler *Acrocephalus paludicola*, using the resident Winding Cisticola *Cisticola galactotes* as a reference species on the wintering areas in Africa. This research has already revealed that Aquatic Warblers from Poland have different wintering grounds to those hatched in Belarus and Ukraine.

How can this method be used in the future?

When birds cannot easily be found in the field – and even when they can – we can draw on easily available information from the large numbers of birds lying dormant in dusty drawers in natural history museums all over the world. Their feathers will still, after perhaps hundreds of years, show stable isotope patterns which tell us more about their lives. This modern method can also be used when trapping live birds which then can be released, albeit with a missing feather or two. Dr Debbie Pain of the RSPB, who has been involved in the Aquatic Warbler project, says "With this research, all you need is to snip off the end of one tiny feather - we're not engaged in a mass feather-pulling exercise."

This method has also been used when studying the Critically Endangered Slender-billed Curlew, with the Least Concern Eurasian Curlew *Numenius arquata* as a reference species. Feathers from museum skins of a dozen Slender-billed juveniles, taken on migration or at wintering sites, have been analysed. Results indicate that they come from the steppes of Kazakhstan, a conclusion reached by comparing the isotope patterns with those of large numbers of Eurasian Curlews which we know originated in roughly the same area. This could help explain why earlier searches for the breeding grounds of Slender-billed Curlews have been unsuccessful, since they focussed on areas in other habitats in western Siberia, and on the region where the only two known nests were found, north of Omsk.

To analyse the isotopes involves expensive laboratory equipment and great care. Basically, one takes a feather off a bird, living or dead, and splits it into minute pieces. Each piece is crammed into a small metal container, which is then burnt. The resultant gases are transported by a carrier gas, helium in this case, in a small pipe to an electronic gun, which fires the molecules in a magnetic field. The molecules' trajectories are affected differently by the magnetic field depending on weight, and they will end up in different containers, where they will be analysed and the result presented in an Excel spreadsheet.

This is less easy than it sounds. As we have seen earlier, there are large variations, both locally and in larger regions, in isotope patterns over the world. If we use just one individual bird, there is always the risk that it comes from an atypical area. Instead we need a series of feathers from many different birds, so that we get a large body of data which can be used to say where the populations we wish to study more closely are most likely to come from. This knowledge can then be used to focus ground searches for unknown breeding or wintering areas.

The large number of specimens required can be a big problem for the world's rarest migratory birds. We believe the surviving Slender-billed Curlew population to number fewer than 50, so we may not be able to find enough feathers to determine its origins, even when augmented by historical skins in museums. The method works best in cases where there are many skins of a species from a certain range in museums, or where population numbers are high and the birds easily trapped, so that we can get an adequate sample. There are plenty of diminishing species in less endangered categories that still show good numbers, where we can use stable isotope signatures to direct our conservation efforts, as with the Aquatic Warbler.

"Isotope work can help to tie up wintering, breeding grounds and migration routes, or can be used to look at habitats used when birds were growing their feathers, so there are a range of potential uses relating to habitat quality and body condition etc," says Debbie Pain.
"So, I imagine that isotopes will continue to be of use for work on Critically Endangered species, but their utility will depend upon the species and the specific questions that we need to answer."

Linnaeus' assertion 250 years ago that it "would demand great effort, diligence and time by future generations spread over the world to solve the riddles of bird migration" is as valid as ever. It is likely that methods such as ringing/banding, satellite telemetry and stable isotope analysis will work closely together in the future to aid conservation of the world's rarest migratory species, such as Slender-billed and Eskimo Curlew *Numenius borealis* and Sociable Lapwing *Vanellus gregarius*. Linnaeus is probably following the developments with great interest, and smiling broadly at us from his heavenly nature reserve, surrounded by those birds technology and awareness came too late for.

Balearic Shearwater

- newly recognised species goes straight on the Critical list

Lyme Bay, Dorset, UK, 2006

Photo: © Tom Brereton

IT IS A WARM, QUIET SPRING DAY on the Balearic island of Majorca, the popular European holiday destination off the Mediterranean coast of Spain. The sun rises slowly over a calm sea. Street cleaners and gardeners start work in the holiday resorts, sweeping up pine needles around the pools, arranging deck chairs, getting rid of last night's glasses and beer cans by the poolside. The early risers among the tourists leave their rooms for breakfast and morning coffee. The night-owls are coming back to bed after a full night of partying. A local fisherman leaves the small port in his open boat to go beyond the small offshore island for today's catch. Straight ahead of the boat comes a small line of dark birds, flying in a perfect line close after each other, wings beating swiftly in the windless conditions just centimetres above the sea surface: Balearic Shearwaters!

The Balearic Shearwater *Puffinus mauretanicus* was only recently recognised as a species. It was first described in 1921, as a subspecies of Manx Shearwater *Puffinus puffinus*, by Dr. Percy Roycroft Lowe (1870-1948) who was in charge of the bird collection at the British Museum from 1919 to 1935. He was a surgeon by profession and was well respected for his studies of the anatomy of birds. In 1990 the other Mediterranean subspecies of Manx Shearwater was split into a new species called Yelkouan Shearwater *Puffinus yelkouan*, and Balearic Shearwater then became known as a subspecies of it. Finally, in the early 21st century, research into DNA, morphology and biology by Spanish and German scientists determined that there were enough differences from Yelkouan Shearwater for Balearic Shearwater to receive specific status.

The Yelkouan Shearwater breeds from France and Algeria eastwards across the Mediterranean to Turkey, but occurs regularly in the Black Sea and has also bred there. Birds showing characteristics of possible hybrids between Yelkouan and Balearic Shearwater occur as breeders on Menorca. The two forms probably separated 1 or 2 million years ago.

Shearing the waves

It is one of the mid-sized shearwaters. (The English word shearwater is derived from the birds' habit of seemingly cutting the waves with their long, thin, pointed wings.) The wingspan is around 85 centimetres. Its colouration is mainly dark both above and below, in contrast to many other shearwaters which show paler underparts, sometimes with distinct borders to their darker upperparts. The Balearic Shearwater's underparts are a shade paler than its upperparts, but in the field it can give an impression of being completely dark, and therefore gets confused with the South Pacific-breeding Sooty

Shearwater *Puffinus griseus*, which also occurs in the Atlantic and Mediterranean at certain times of the year.

Shearwaters, in common with other *Procellariiforme* seabirds, have paired tubular nostrils on the upper mandible of the bill. Through them they can eject an oily and foul-smelling secretion, and it is also believed that they have a strong sense of smell, with which they can detect nest sites at night and which they also use to locate food. It has been suggested they may even be able to avoid oil spills thanks to their well-developed olfactory sense. Silent at sea, except when competing for food with congeners and other seabirds, they are quite vocal at the nesting sites. Their walking ability on land is very poor, but these are birds that can swim and fly perfectly.

Good divers

Shearwaters have hooked bills with sharp mandibles which facilitate the cutting of their food. They catch their prey by plunge-diving or picking it from the surface of the sea. They have been recorded diving to depths of 26 metres in dives lasting up to 40 seconds.

Balearic Shearwater feeds on small fish such as anchovies and pilchard, and sometimes also on squid and plankton. It is, however, not known exactly what proportions of these different foods make up its normal diet. A study in the Mediterranean off north-eastern Spain by biologists José Manuel Arcos and Daniel Oro has shown that several feeding strategies are used during the breeding season. One is to approach floating objects, which attract fish, and investigate them. Another is to follow fishing vessels to pick up discarded catch and offal. This has also been recorded in the Bay of Biscay by Dr. Pierre Yésou.

As Balearic Shearwaters can dive to considerable

depths they can often pick up pieces which are not competed for by, for example, gulls. They have also been seen to follow schools of dolphins which drive prey towards the surface, and to feed on plankton during hours of less light, although they do not generally feed nocturnally. Interestingly, waste from fishing vessels in the Mediterranean can account for nearly half of the energy intake, although variation in this is great, and it may only be a secondary source of food. It is apparent that discards from fishing vessels are locally important, while small shoaling fish are essential.

Nocturnal breeders

Balearic Shearwaters breed from February to June, and the birds are at least three years old when they breed for the first time. In the Balearics, one can find the species on islets off the main islands, where it nests in crevices, ledges and caves which it visits at night. According to fossil remains, it has bred historically on the main islands. There is probably some competition for nest sites with the larger Cory's Shearwater *Calonectris diomedea* which may be the reason for finding Balearic Shearwaters breeding on islands or islets with rats, while Cory's Shearwaters usually shun these. At the breeding sites introduced land-based predators such as cats, genets or rats may be a serious concern, as is the case on the islet of Cabrera off south-western Majorca. However, a possible ancestor of Balearic Shearwater, *Puffinus nestori*, apparently cohabited with rat-sized rodents millions of years ago.

Populations are difficult to assess accurately, because of the inaccessibility of some colonies and the birds' nocturnal habits when attending the nests. Current estimates, based on breeding counts, assume that there are around 2 000 breeding pairs and a total of 10 000 birds, but other authors provide more conservative estimates, below 8 000 birds (Oró et al., 2004; BirdLife International, 2007). However, recent counts by the Migres programme in Spain suggest that there may be more Balearic Shearwaters than previously thought (see below).

However, there is strong evidence that the breeding population has experienced a remarkable decrease in the last decades. The island of Formentera off Ibiza is a stronghold and may hold as many as 70% of the rapidly decreasing total population. Adult survival is relatively low, and it has been suggested that the species may become extinct by 2040. What is clear is that in the last decade numbers have halved in traditional winter quarters off north-east Spain and in post-breeding waters in the Bay of Biscay.

The trip up north

Most Balearic Shearwaters depart their breeding areas in late spring, leaving the Mediterranean via the Straits of Gibraltar between mid-May and mid-July, when the passage rate may surpass 200 birds/hour. The movements along the Atlantic coast of the Iberian Peninsula increase from May to September, when concentrations or "rafts" of more than 100 Balearic Shearwaters may be found off the Portuguese coast and in the Galician "rías" (open estuaries). These movements follow the coast northwards to the Bay of Biscay and the Brittany coast of France, some of them reaching the seas off the British Isles and the south of the Scandinavian peninsula. The return into the Mediterranean starts progressively from September, when adult birds begin to reoccupy their colony, and extends to January. Part of the population, mainly adult birds, may remain within, or not move far from, the Mediterranean,

The moult takes place after breeding, in June-October, when most birds have dispersed into the Atlantic. The Bay of Biscay off France and Spain has been an important moulting and feeding area for these birds, even though some remain around the Balearic Islands and in the Mediterranean off north-eastern Spain. In the nineties it was discovered that traditionally large numbers off the French coast of the Vendée had diminished, and that the birds had shifted their whereabouts north to the western Channel between France and England.

In Scandinavia, where the species is extralimital, records increased in the nineties and the early part of this century and at the same time sightings increased in the United Kingdom and Ireland, from hundreds to several thousands annually. Bearing in mind that Balearic Shearwater has only recently been elevated to specific status, one would suspect that this would generate a higher interest among 'seawatchers', as birders counting seabirds from strategic headlands are known, and consequently lead to more sightings being recorded. But the fact that there have actually been fewer records of Balearic Shearwaters off the Vendée in France, which has been well-studied for a long time, together with increased numbers at places such as Cape Clear Island in Ireland and Portland in England, where seabirds have also been counted for many years, indicates that this shift in distribution is real. The southern limits of its range is, as far is known, the coast of Morocco, but records have been made down the African west coast to Senegal.

Why has the distribution changed? A reason for this may be that water temperatures rose above the range (probably around 16-18C) which is favoured by Balearic Shearwaters. The shearwaters' preference for this is probably affected by the availability of prey, and of the food which the shearwaters' prey feeds on, at these temperatures. An indication of this comes from the Vendée, France, where temperatures rose to 20C in 1999, and numbers of warm water species such as Cory's Shearwaters increased at the same time as Balearics decreased.

Threat picture

There are a number of threats to the species. The main ones are lack of food resources, lack of protection of breeding sites and predation at breeding sites by introduced mammals. Oil spills are,

Counting shearwaters leaving the Mediterranean, October 2006.

Badia de Roses, off Catalonia, Spain, 2004

Isla Dragonera, off Majorca, is one breeding site for Balearic Shearwater

Photo: © José Manuel Arcos

as always with seabirds, a high-potential hazard too. On the good side, human disturbance does not rate highly as a threat, even though the species is still locally predated in some areas. From having been harvested in thousands at breeding sites 30 years ago, probably no more than a few hundred are now taken annually. Accidental by-catch of Balearic Shearwaters in the fishing industry also seems rather low but work is needed to ascertain its true impact.

Since non-breeding distribution has moved further away from the breeding areas, the birds have to spend more energy migrating to the new moulting areas, and as the moult is also energy-consuming, they need be able to find adequate food in their new areas. Human over-fishing of the main food source, anchovies and pilchards, is known to have forced the birds away from their traditional areas off the French coast, and in combination with global warming of the sea this has forced their northward shift. There are also new hazards in these waters, such as windfarms; and as the species often is found feeding on waste from fishing vessels, (perhaps more so when the natural food resource disappears), new regulations on how to handle fish offal at sea could also have a negative impact.

The way forward

The actions to protect this species can be summed up as :

- Protect breeding sites from predators (rats, cats).
- Obtain protected status of the breeding sites.
- Protect hotspots along migratory corridors (for example, establishing marine IBAs).
- Integrate breeding population surveys and migration counts for long-term monitoring of populations, estimates and trends.
- Perform more surveys to determine movement patterns and ecology, as water conditions change.
- Study how to improve adult survival rate.

It may be difficult to protect seabirds as they not only breed in carefully chosen, very special places, but also because when not feeding they roam over large areas of sea. In the case of the Balearic Shearwater this incorporates, as we have seen above, parts of the Atlantic Ocean and the western Mediterranean. Closer to the breeding areas, the most important foraging places for the Balearic Shearwater, and indeed many other seabirds, is the area off the Ebro delta, a major river in Spain entering the Mediterranean near Barcelona. The Cape La Nao region further to the south is also important in this respect. Out of the breeding range, some important migratory hotspots along the migratory flyway, like the Straits of Gibraltar, the Galician "rías" and others sites along the Portuguese coasts are also key points for the survival of the species, being particularly sensitive to serious threats, like overfishing, maritime traffic or oil spills.

Tallying today's totals at Tarifa, Spain with Jebel Moussa, Morocco in the background

The situation in 2007

The breeding results in monitored colonies on the Balearics indicate that breeding success was low in 2007 and in order not to jeopardize this further, plans for colour-marking fledglings which then could be followed from Atlantic watchpoints were abandoned.

We are not yet fully aware of Balearic Shearwaters' detailed migration patterns, but in 2007 a chain of seawatchers were monitoring the species' movements throughout western Europe. Counts have taken place in Gibraltar, where the species exits the Mediterranean after breeding, and at strategic sea-watching points off the Spanish, Portuguese, French, British and Irish coasts. The efforts are coordinated by national BirdLife partners in Spain, Portugal, the UK and France as well as by other organisations such as the National Oceanography Centre (www.noc.soton.ac.uk) in the UK, Fundacion Migres (www.fundacionmigres.org) in Spain and the ornithological service Birdguides (www.birdguides.com).

The counts at Gibraltar, which were not daily but took place from mid-May to mid-July, showed that the total numbers of Balearic Shearwaters leaving the Mediterranean and flying into the Atlantic numbered over 12,500 birds (with only 600 flying in the reverse direction). This number requires more investigation and can be explained in at least three ways: either undiscovered breeding colonies of the species exist, or the non-breeding population is bigger than previously expected or exiting birds pass back into the Mediterranean unseen in a loop that is too far from shore to be detected.

In France, there have been counts of rafting birds in Vendée as usual, which peaked at 1500 individuals on 14 September. 2007 may be one of the poorest years ever; however fishing practices have also changed in recent years and may affect the number of birds seen in traditional places.

The British figures (daily and site-specific) can be seen at www.seawatch-sw.org. Project results show that over 1,000 Balearic Shearwaters were recorded in UK waters between July and September, with movements into the North Sea and Irish Sea. Some birds even made it as far north as the Orkneys and Hebrides. Previously, it has been thought that 10-35% of the world population occurs in UK waters annually, and the new 2007 data validate these results; it is therefore of great importance to identify the roosting and feeding areas of the species.

So what does the future hold for this species? To conclude, we asked two of the researchers working with the species for their thoughts.

Pierre Yésou of the **Office National de la Chasse et de la Faune Sauvage**, an agency under the super-vision of France's Ministries of Environment and Agriculture

What, in your opinion, are the main issues to sort out when it comes to understanding the life and movements of non-breeding Balearic Shearwaters? Which of these may have the greatest bearing on conservation?

"Prior to a better understanding there is a strong need for better description of what is occurring. The sea-watch effort currently developed both in Britain and the Iberian peninsula will make the picture clearer, but important parts of the scene remain in the shadows (for example, how many birds move south to Atlantic Morocco and further south, and where do they forage? What is the true distribution in Biscay, where monitoring from the coast does not describe the situation fully enough?)."

"Obtaining such information implies that at-sea surveys must be organized, which will involve some cost. Well-planned at-sea surveys will allow the gathering of significant data associated with the birds' distribution (oceanography, fisheries, behaviour)."

"Meanwhile, high-tech means should be used, providing information about individual birds to be coupled with population information obtained through more traditional survey methods. The limitation is that we do not know how to catch these birds at sea; thus any electronic equipment should be fitted to either breeding birds or fledglings. Satellite tracking and data loggers have been tried in the course of the EU Life project and are worth developing again on a larger sample. The use of alternative techniques such as GPS or light detector must be considered. Another technique worth investigating is the analysis of fat composition, which should inform us about the main dietary components at different time scales (recent markers circulating in blood, older markers in various fat tissues)."

Maite Louzao Arsuaga, Institut Mediterrani d'Estudis Avançats &Universidad de Oviedo, Spain

Can you list the main research areas where we need more knowledge of the species for conservation?

"In relation to conservation priorities for species preservation, conservation agencies should establish long-term monitoring programmes at the breeding colonies (1) to continue with the protection of the breeding habitat (i.e. elimination of introduced species), and (2) to implement standard protocols to establish population trends, (3) as well as to obtain robust population estimates. At sea, it is important (4) to estimate the real impact of fishing gear on the mortality of shearwaters, and if this is significant,

to reduce it, and assess the effect of other factors (pollution) and (5) to evaluate the effect of fishing over-exploitation on the species."

"In summary, it is necessary to have an ecosystem-based management approach for Balearic Shearwater conservation, both in the Mediterranean during breeding and around the Atlantic coast of south-west Europe, during its dispersal."

Further reading

Arcos, J. M. & Oro, D. (2002). Significance of fisheries discard for a threatened Mediterranean seabird, the Balearic Shearwater *Puffinus mauretanicus*. Marine Ecology progress Series Vol.239: 209.-220.

BirdLife International (1999) Species action plan for the Balearic Shearwater in Europe.

BirdLife International (2007) Species factsheet: *Puffinus mauretanicus*. Downloaded from http://www.birdlife.org on 6/9/2007

Cuenca, D., Arroyo, G.M., Sandoval, A., and Noivo, C. 2006. Phenology of Balearic Shearwaters *Puffinus mauretanicus* along the Atlantic coast of the Iberian Peninsula. Proceeding of the Seabird Group 9th International Conference. University of Aberdeen, Scotland, UK.

Fundación Migres. Programa MIGRES MARINAS. In: www. fundacionmigres.org
Genovart, M., oro, D., Juste, J. & bertarolle, G. (2007). What genetics tell us about the conservation of the critically endangered Balearic Shearwater? Biological Conservation 137: 283-293.

Heidrich, Petra; Amengual, José F. & Wink, Michael (1998): Phylogenetic relationships in Mediterranean and North Atlantic shearwaters (Aves: *Procellariidae*) based on nucleotide sequences of mtDNA. Biochemical Systematics and Ecology 26(2): 145–170.

Mourino, J., Arcos, F., Salvadores, R., Sandoval, A. & Vidal, C. (2003). Status of the Balearic Shearwater (*Puffinus mauretanicus*) on the Galician coast (NW Iberian peninsula). Scientia Marina 67:135-142.

Oro, D., Aguilar J. S., Igual, J. M. & Louzao, M. (2004). Modelling demography and extinction risk in the endangered Balearic Shearwater. Biological Conservation 116:93-102.

Yésou, P. (2003). Recent changes in the summer distribution of the Balearic Shearwater *Puffinus mauretanicus* off western France. Scientia Marina 67:143-148.

Ecotourism
- following the green road
to enjoy birds in a beneficial way

Sea-watching in Oman

ECOTOURISM AS A WORD WAS FIRST COINED in 1972 but as an activity, it probably began in Africa 20 years before. Its development into a fully working (and recognised) conservation tool is a relatively new concept and the effects, function and methodology of ecotourism have only recently been studied. It was in the 1990s that ecotourism really came into its own and since then the number of tour companies genuinely offering a 'green' way to enjoy travelling and watching wildlife has hugely increased. Ecotourism is now able to offer an essential lifeline for much of the world's endangered wildlife, and especially for birds.

One definition of ecotourism is 'the practice of low-impact, educational, ecologically and culturally sensitive travel that benefits local communities and host countries'. It is often summed up with phrases like 'Take nothing but pictures, leave nothing but footprints and waste nothing but time'. This is in stark contrast to many holidays which go to places that have destroyed every vestige of natural habitat to provide a totally unsustainable, resource-hungry, experience that profits only the companies involved and often exploits the local populace.

Threats to the world's birds come in many forms but habitat loss is one of the greatest. This may be as a result of removing a natural resource – logging forests to profit from the wood or draining wetlands to use the land for other purposes. Catching wildlife for sale, either alive, or as products manufactured from the animal or plant, also poses a great threat. These activities provide a short-term income and leave areas devoid of value for the future. The only reason for such wanton destruction is that a greater value is placed on the commodity that can be sold than on the continued existence of the habitat or wildlife. What ecotourism does is to give such places a new value (and a long-term one!).

To work, ecotourism has to have a market to appeal to. A large number of the world's ecotourists come from Europe and North America, and so ecotourism will always work best in areas that they visit the most. Africa, and North and South America have a large share of existing ecotourism projects, while Asia, Oceania and Australasia have least. To attract sufficient ecotourists, any project must have the special wildlife that acts as the initial draw. As well as this a country must be accessible, politically stable, and have good facilities and infrastructure. Even with all of this it must also be marketed effectively.

Ecotourism has to have a focus. This can be an existing nature reserve, rich in wildlife, with all the facilities for visitors to enjoy, or it could be a specially created, privately-run reserve, perhaps with built-in accommodation. Wildlife has to be a part of the attraction and this can be rich in variety and spectacle, or have prominent species - the African

savannah offers all of this. It can be a selection of venues and activities in the form of a trail - the Inca Trail of Peru is a classic example, and there are now many birding trails that seek to emulate it.

Successful ecotourism will:
- generate increased local revenue
- provide income nationally
- improve existing or establish new conservation areas locally
- conserve biodiversity by providing an alternative to destructive activities
- promote the sustainable use of wildlife, by providing jobs to local populations
- share benefits with local communities with their consent and participation in the ecotourism activities
- evoke a positive attitude among the local community by maximizing the incentives
- minimize its own impact on the environment
- be affordable and economical in its use of local resources

Successful ecotourism should never:
- damage habitat for the provision of its facilities, eg accommodation, or by any other action
- exclude the local community or fail to involve them
- adversely affect the conservation status or well-being of any species
- fail to generate enough income to help conserve the wildlife it depends on

The wildlife must be easy to see – although there are never any guarantees, enough interesting species should be viewable in a relatively short period of time, without too much effort involved if high numbers of tourists are to be attracted.

A good example might be a South American parrot clay-lick. Many of these exist and if made easily accessible with adequate viewing facilities, then they are an almost guaranteed spectacle and could be linked to visiting a remoter but rarer species nearby. Activities other than viewing the wildlife could also be utilised to bring an conservation income and this

Chaparri Ecolodge - home of the Critically Endangered
White-winged Guan *Penelope albipennis*

in itself can act as a draw by telling clients that a particular trip will directly benefit the local wildlife if they do certain things, or stay in certain places. And if possible try to show them where some of the benefit will go as this is an extra 'feelgood' factor.

Some species will only be attractive to the true devotee. Not part of the 'megafauna' or 'flagship species' they are of interest to the keenest birder only. Steve Rooke, Managing Director of Sunbird, a UK-based bird tour company, is philosophical about the lure of Critically Endangered species to birding tourists: "These rarest of birds are a factor but they probably only influence a few people. A trip to Cambodia, for example, will try to see White-shouldered Ibis, but most birders want to see the other birds as well and the trip will not be a failure through the lack of this one bird. If there is the chance to see one of these endangered birds on a trip we build this in and use this in our promotion, but to structure a tour around just one species risks extreme disappointment if it is not seen. There are only a few birders who would take a trip just to see the one bird - only the keenest of world listers - most like to see a wide range of birds and if they are lucky enough to see something very rare then this is the icing on the cake. "

Monitoring is important as a part of any ecotourist project. It is essential that any potential problems can be detected early before they have a lasting impact that could damage both the wildlife and the local

economy that depends on it. Some areas are more sensitive that others and will only sustain a certain level of visits before some damage is done.

There can often added value from ecotourism. Often the tourists themselves have an awareness of conservation and the need to protect wildlife and habitats. Their interest may well encourage them to become involved beyond the life of the trip itself, becoming a long-term supporter of a conservation organisation or project.

Ecotourists should always beware of tour companies that are not what they seem. While they offer what are called 'sustainable', 'green' and 'eco-friendly' tours, they may not be actually putting anything back into the local community, nor benefiting the local wildlife in any way. This so-called 'green-washing' can easily be identified with a few well placed questions.

Impacts of ecotourism

Ecotourism is growing at about 10 to 15% per year, and it is estimated that it now accounts for nearly one in five tourists worldwide.

But while many conservation organisations and governments may try to ensure that projects are sustainable and beneficial, many ecotourism projects simply pay lip service the important issues and merely

The Refugio Amazonas Lodge used by Rainforest Expeditions

Tambopata Research Centre, Peru is situated by the world's largest macaw clay-lick

hint that they are based on environmentally friendly policies and operations. They may take care not to do any direct damage to habitat while ensuring that wildlife is not scared away, but in reality they are having a detrimental effect overall.

The impacts of tourism are not always obvious. Having daily visits from groups of tourists, no matter how well-intentioned they are, can have a negative impact simply by introducing unwanted stress. Just a slight change to normally daily life, on a regular basis, can result in reduced breeding success due to extra predation, or disruption of feeding or other parental care.

In areas that attract large numbers of ecotourists, care must be taken not to overexpose the wildlife. Studies have shown that visitors, even in a controlled situation, can cause stress to the birds and this can impact of breeding success and survival. Regular disturbance to a daily routine, even if only slight, can have a cumulative effect.

There are several seabirds on the Critical list, and the one most likely to benefit from ecotourism has to be the Waved Albatross *Phoebastria irrorata* (see pp. 94-95) of the Galapagos. These famous islands have used their wildlife as a draw to tourists for a considerable time. With the accessibility and tameness of the birds, many of which are large and entertaining, plus other high profile species like the giant tortoise, marine iguanas and others. The Galapagos have, in many ways, become a victim of their own success. Galapagos ecotourism is of huge economic benefit to Ecuador and will continue to be so as long as it is managed in a low-impact way. The potential

problems come from the by-products of tourism – pollution, disturbance, overuse of resources. To be truly sustainable there has to be some form of regulation to limit the numbers of tourists at popular sites and to ensure that the wildlife does not suffer. Many tourists like to experience wildlife 'in the wild' and the enjoyment can be lessened if there are large numbers of people at a particular wild site.

A study on juvenile Hoatzins *Opisthocomus hoazin* in the Cuyabeno reserve in the Ecuador showed that those visited by tourists had double the levels of corticosterone (a stress hormone) when compared to chicks in areas where no tourists are allowed. The tourists appear to be affecting the chicks' survival as the researchers also found that of the nests in restricted areas raised at least one fledgling, while the number dropped to just 15 per cent in areas that tourists visited. Another study suggests that tourists may be scaring Hoatzin chicks, which nest on branches hanging over water, causing them to jump into rivers and lakes infested with predators.

In another study, on Yellow-eyed Penguins *Megadyptes antipodes* in New Zealand, chicks in areas frequently visited by tourists weigh on average three-quarters of a kilogram less than chicks with no tourists. The adult penguins tend to delay their landing with food if they see people on the beaches where they land and will literally wait until the coast is clear. This may mean that they digest some of the food meant for their chicks, as well as reducing the amount of feeding time per day. As lighter chicks are less likely to survive, tourists could be having an extremely detrimental effect on this species. Transmission of disease, and even introduction of foreign wildlife by visitors could also be a problem.

Ecotourism in action

The Peruvian government-run tourist authority, Prom Peru, has been very active in publicising Peru as the best birding destination in South America. With more than 1,800 species, Peru contains 16% of the world's birds, and many endemics. Two species are critically endangered, and one of these is scarcely known. With its famous Inca Trail, Peru attracts hundreds of thousands of visitors keen to see the antiquities like Machu Picchu. The Amazon Basin is also a great draw, with specialist holidays to navigate the great river and experience its wildlife. With increasing access to the whole of the country, there is a risk that wildlife might suffer from the development of inappropriate tourism. But here Peru is leading the way, with an expanding tourist infrastructure based on sustainability and use of natural products and local people.

They have developed a Northern Birding Trail that visits the best sites for the wealth of endemics and regional rarities. This gives birders the opportunity to see the White-winged Guan *Penelope albipennis* (see p. 84) and Iquitos Gnatcatcher *Polioptila clementsi* (see p. 220). There is a well established Southern Birding Trail with tour companies like Rainforest Expeditions using local lodges for accommodation, local transport to the more isolated areas, and local guides to lead visitors to the very best places, giving employment and income to the local community, and providing the added value that should ensure protection for these areas in the future. A central trail is also planned which will give access to the remaining areas that birders want to visit.

One of the world's most endangered birds, the Iquitos Gnatcatcher was first described in 2005, and its known population is only 10-15 pairs that live within an area of 20 square kilometres in the north-east of Peru. The people of the city of Iquitos have taken it to their hearts – they have declared the gnatcatcher (called locally Perlita de Iquitos) as the city bird and held an Iquitos Gnatcatcher Festival in November 2006. Although it lives in Allpahuayo-Mishana, a 'Reserved Zone' and 'National Reserve', the species is still at high risk with agriculture and timber extraction posing the greatest threats.

But there is hope. CANATURA (Club Amigos de la Naturaleza), is a local student-run nature club that organized the Gnatcatcher Festival as well as the first Amazonian Biodiversity Festival. By publicising the special wildife of the area, and giving it a positive value, they encourage local public support for the reserve. They recognise that one key activity that will help is birding with visiting birders bringing important revenue to the region. If this is directed straight to the local communities it will encourage them to value the habitat and its wildlife as it stands resulting in long-term benefits, rather than a quick one-off profit from logging or other destructive activities.

Also in the north of Peru, the White-winged Guan is a special bird that attracts birders and there are several projects to help it. The Chaparri Ecolodge is set in a private conservation area that is community owned and was established in 2001. It has a small amount of accommodation built traditionally from local materials and most staff and services are sourced locally. Solar generated energy and a reedbed water treatment system ensure that the lodge is truly 'green'. Part of the profits go to the social projects in the area as well as conservation work. At Chaparri the White-winged Guan has been reintroduced - there are now seven breeding pairs there, so everyone who stay will not only see the guan and other wildife, but will directly help to support its survival.

Ecotourism began early in the Seychelles with wildlife visits to Cousin Island beginning in 1972. The island now attracts about 10,000 tourists each year, as well as educational groups and local visitors, and is managed by Nature Seychelles. It has won several awards for conservation and ecotourism. As well as its popular marine life, including turtles it has several flagship bird species including Seychelles Warbler *Acrocephalus sechellensis* and Seychelles Magpie-Robin *Copsychus sechellarum*, both of these listed as Vulnerable and Endangered respectively. Cousin Island is kept free from development and the reserve is managed by local staff. There is no overnight accommodation and all visits are strictly monitored to ensure that no alien predators or other wildlife are accidentally introduced. Tourism brings in a large proportion of the Seychelles' income and many of the islands are trying to attract tourists with visits that offer a wildlife experience that is both sustainable and beneficial to the local economy as well as the flora and fauna.

The Zululand Birding Route is a celebrated ecotourism initiative that has been running for 10 years. The Route has received praise from around the world for its economic benefits to local communities through its use of "birder-friendly" establishments and its team of 20 local bird guides. The Zululand and Greater Limpopo Birding Routes bring in a combined income of ZAR 50 million (USD 6.8million) per year in direct economic value to the South African region. It also brings clear environmental benefits in the form of habitat protection and bird conservation. Many vulnerable species benefit, including Blue Swallow *Hirundo atrocaerulea* and Wattled Crane *Bugeranus caruncalatus*.
Pelagic trips to see whales and other marine life have been successful and attractive forms of ecotourism for many years. Pelagic birding is also increasing in popularity and as well as supporting use of local boats etc, in one case it has direct conservation benefits for a Critically Endangered species. In New Zealand, the rediscovery of the New Zealand Storm-petrel *Oceanites maorianus* (see p. 104) has heralded an increase in people wanting to look at seabirds. Pterodroma Pelagics is one company that takes tours to see the storm-petrel, and much of what is known about the species has been found out such tours. Chris Gaskin, of Pterodroma Pelagics, said: "Through

Looking for tigers with local guide, India

Photo: © Magnus Ullman / AviFauna, www.avifauna.se

Moroccan desert

Photo: © Magnus Ullman / AviFauna, www.avifauna.se

Kristianstads Vattenrike, Sweden, World Heritage Area

New Zealand Storm Petrel (top right) and Siberian Crane

Photo: © Brent Stephenson

Photo: © Pete Morris / Birdquest

our trips we have contributed a great deal to what is known about New Zealand Storm-petrels, their distribution, behaviour and so forth. Many of the 100 or so trips we have made have been as a direct result of paying participants."

Birdfinders is just one of the bird tour companies in the UK that is trying to ensure that its tours bring benefits to local communities and conservation in the areas they visit. One of the areas they run tours to is the steppes of Kazakhstan especially to see the Sociable Lapwing *Vanellus gregarius* (see pp. 136-137). These directly benefit the local community with payment for accommodation, spending in local shops and employment.

As a result of the birding trips there, the Akim of Astana (president of region) has become interested in who is visiting the area and why, and this has significantly increased the profile of eco-tourism in the region and protection of Sociable Lapwing to the extent that many groups are now staying with local villagers who realise that preserving this critically endangered species is beneficial to their economy.

Although there is no BirdLife partner in Colombia yet, there is a bird conservation organisation, ProAves, that manages reserves for many of the Critically Endangered species found in the country, like the Blue-billed Curassow *Crax alberti* (see p. 85). Ecoturs is a company that was set up specifically to organize safe birding tours in a country whose reputation does not lend itself to large-scale tourism. All of the profits from Ecoturs are donated to ProAves for their conservation work and they find that the visitors they bring to ther reserves will also donate money. Ecoturs uses local labours and goods whenever possible and even sell local handicrafts to bring even more income to the local communities. On the El Dorado reserve the lodge is built from non-native pines which are being replaced with native species.

The way forward

The key to successful ecotourism is in having a market that desires it, the high profile species to attract interest, the infrastructure to support it and the local community to work with. There are many new initiatives around the world that are trying to bring these areas of interest together.

The Azerbaijan Ornithological Society (AOS), the local BirdLife partner, has been running a nature-based tourism educational campaign since the start of 2006, with funding from the European Union Institutional Building Partnerships Programme. It has been working, with both local and national authorities and stakeholders, on a project called 'Career Development for Azeri people on nature tourism at protected areas' - raising awareness and providing training and support in eco-based tourism to local people around three protected regions of the country. With support from the Minister for

Tourism, AOS has also formed a strategic relationship with AtaTourizm, a leading Azeri tourist company, who will help to promote eco-tours to the country. Azerbaijan supports breeding Sociable Lapwing and Siberian Crane *Grus leucogeranus* (see p. 132) on passage.

In the Philippines, where a quarter of Asia's Critically Endangered species are found, there is action to employ ecotourism as a way to help the wildlife. On Cebu, where the remnant population of only about 100 Cebu Flowerpeckers *Dicaeum quadricolor* (see p. 228) survive, there are moves to encourage ecotourism in the area of Mt Lantoy where the flowerpecker has been found. In September 2007 the third Philippines Bird Festival was held on Cebu to raise awareness of the need to protect this species. It brought together local people with Philippine conservation groups and other organisation from within Asia.

In 2006 BirdLife International's World Bird Festival was held in Los Haitises National Park, an IBA in the Dominican Republic which provides the last refuge for the Critically Endangered Ridgway's Hawk *Buteo ridgwayi* (see pp. 128-129). This was an opportunity for bird conservation organisations, community groups and ecotourism guides to talk about common aims realting the conservation of the area, and its important birdlife. With only 80 to 120 pairs of Ridgway's Hawk surviving, confined to about 200 square kilometres of native rainforest, urgent action is needed. Studies published in 2006 show alarming levels of encroachment on the park by farmers, and high levels of human disturbance leading some hawks to abandon their nests. Ecotourism has been recognised as one obvious way to halt this.

Finally, in 2008, funds will be made available for the conservation of four Critically Endangered birds in the Americas – Belding's Yellowthroat *Geothlypis beldingi* (see p. 237), Junin Grebe *Podiceps taczanowskii* (see p. 107), Royal Cinclodes *Cinclodes aricomae* (see p. 198) and Puerto Rican Nightjar *Caprimulgus noctitherus* (see pp. 172-173). For the yellowthroat, work includes an education and public awareness campaign, involving community projects, and the training of local bird guides to promote nature-based tourism in the reserve and bird festivals, targeting the endemic birds of the region. For the grebe, work includes a National Pride Campaign using the Junin Grebe as a symbol of the Andes and the development of a birdwatching tourism infrastucture and training with local communities.

Ecotourism is now firmly established as a conservation tool of the future.

References:
Krüger, O. (2004) The role of ecotourism in conservation: panacea or Pandora's box? Biodivers. Conserv. 14: 579-600

Categorisation
of the species

THIS BOOK TREATS THE CRITICALLY ENDANGERED birds of the world. They are thus the rarest living birds, many on the border of the next level above, which is *Extinct/Extinct in the wild*. The category *Critically Endangered* belongs to a classification system of species by the IUCN (The International Union for the Conservation of Nature and Natural Resources) also known as the World Conservation Union.

The IUCN Red List of Threatened Species provides taxonomic, conservation status and distribution information on species that have been globally evaluated using the IUCN Red List Categories and Criteria (see below). This system is designed to determine the relative risk of extinction, and the main purpose of the IUCN Red List is to catalogue and highlight those species that are facing a higher risk of global extinction. The IUCN Red List also includes information on species that are categorized as Extinct or Extinct in the Wild, Data Deficient and Near Threatened.

IUCN Classification System

EXTINCT (EX)
A taxon is Extinct when there is no reasonable doubt that the last individual has died.

EXTINCT IN THE WILD (EW)
A taxon is Extinct in the Wild when it is known only to survive in cultivation, in captivity or as a naturalized population (or populations) well outside the past range.

CRITICALLY ENDANGERED (CR)
A taxon is Critically Endangered when the best available evidence indicates that it meets any of the criteria for Critically Endangered, and it is therefore considered to be facing an extremely high risk of extinction in the wild. Possibly Extinct (PE)

ENDANGERED (EN)
A taxon is Endangered when the best available evidence indicates that it meets any of the criteria for Endangered, and it is therefore considered to be facing a very high risk of extinction in the wild.

VULNERABLE (VU)
A taxon is Vulnerable when the best available evidence indicates that it meets any of the criteria for Vulnerable, and it is therefore considered to be facing a high risk of extinction in the wild.

NEAR THREATENED (NT)
A taxon is Near Threatened when it has been evaluated against the criteria but does not qualify for Critically Endangered, Endangered or Vulnerable now, but is close to qualifying for or is likely to qualify for a threatened category in the near future.

LEAST CONCERN (LC)
A taxon is Least Concern when it has been evaluated against the criteria and does not qualify for Critically Endangered, Endangered, Vulnerable or Near Threatened.

DATA DEFICIENT (DD)
A taxon is Data Deficient when there is inadequate information to make a direct, or indirect, assessment of its risk of extinction based on its distribution and/or population status.

NOT EVALUATED (NE)
A taxon is Not Evaluated when it is has not yet been evaluated against the criteria.

The species in this book are considered Critically Endangered and that means that they meet any of the following criteria:

A. <u>Reduction in population size based on any of the following</u>:

1. An observed, estimated, inferred or suspected population size reduction of > 90% over the last 10 years or three generations, whichever is the longer, where the causes of the reduction are clearly reversible AND understood AND ceased, based on (and specifying) any of the following:
   (a) direct observation
   (b) an index of abundance appropriate to the taxon
   (c) a decline in area of occupancy, extent of occurrence and/or quality of habitat
   (d) actual or potential levels of exploitation
   (e) the effects of introduced taxa, hybridization, pathogens, pollutants, competitors or parasites.

2. An observed, estimated, inferred or suspected population size reduction of > 80% over the last 10 years or three generations, whichever is the longer, where the reduction or its causes may not have ceased OR may not be understood OR may not be reversible, based on (and specifying) any of (a) to (e) under A1.

3. A population size reduction of > 80%, projected or suspected to be met within the next 10 years or three generations, whichever is the longer (up to a maximum of 100 years), based on (and specifying) any of (b) to (e) under A1.

4. An observed, estimated, inferred, projected or suspected population size reduction of > 80% over any 10 year or three generation period, whichever is longer (up to a maximum of 100 years in the future), where the time period must include both the past and the future, and where the reduction or its causes may not have ceased OR may not be understood OR may not be reversible, based on (and specifying) any of (a) to (e) under A1.

B. <u>Geographic range in the form of either B1 (extent of occurrence) OR B2 (area of occupancy) OR both</u>:

1. Extent of occurrence estimated to be less than 100 km², and estimates indicating at least two of a-c:
   (a) Severely fragmented or known to exist at only a single location.
   (b) Continuing decline, observed, inferred or projected, in any of the following:
      (i) extent of occurrence
      (ii) area of occupancy
      (iii) area, extent and/or quality of habitat
      (iv) number of locations or subpopulations
      (v) number of mature individuals.
   c. Extreme fluctuations in any of the following:
      (i) extent of occurrence
      (ii) area of occupancy
      (iii) number of locations or subpopulations
      (iv) number of mature individuals.

2. Area of occupancy estimated to be less than 10 km², and estimates indicating at least two of a-c:
   a. Severely fragmented or known to exist at only a single location.
   b. Continuing decline, observed, inferred or projected, in any of the following:
      (i) extent of occurrence
      (ii) area of occupancy
      (iii) area, extent and/or quality of habitat
      (iv) number of locations or subpopulations
      (v) number of mature individuals.
   c. Extreme fluctuations in any of the following:
      (i) extent of occurrence
      (ii) area of occupancy
      (iii) number of locations or subpopulations
      (iv) number of mature individuals.

C. <u>Population size estimated to number fewer than 250 mature individuals and either</u>:

1. An estimated continuing decline of at least 25% within three years or one generation, whichever is longer, (up to a maximum of 100 years in the future) OR

2. A continuing decline, observed, projected, or inferred, in numbers of mature individuals AND at least one of the following (a-b):
   (a) Population structure in the form of one of the following:
      (i) no subpopulation estimated to contain more than 50 mature individuals, OR
      (ii) at least 90% of mature individuals in one subpopulation.
   (b) Extreme fluctuations in number of mature individuals.

D. <u>Population size estimated to number fewer than 50 mature individuals</u>.

E. <u>Quantitative analysis showing the probability of extinction in the wild is at least 50% within 10 years or three generations, whichever is the longer (up to a maximum of 100 years)</u>.

Source: www.iucnredlist.org

Critically Endangered
- the 189 rarest birds in the world

Using the directory

References

The directory section is compiled from several sources. The primary source has been BirdLife International's factsheets which are available for each species at **www.birdlife.org**. They have been developed from, and update, *Threatened Birds of the World*, published by BirdLife International and Lynx Edicions in 2000. The factsheets include much more detail than the directory of this book, and also supply references for each piece of information. The Rare Birds Yearbook aims at giving a general and less technical overview for each Critically Endangered species, so readers wishing to cite information or find out more about a species should in general cite the factsheets rather than the book. BirdLife International also kindly supplied their latest draft accounts that were being compiled for the *2008 IUCN Red List* and *Threatened Birds of the World 2008*. For some species this has been supplemented with, new, unpublished information received from correspondence with experts. This information has been forwarded to BirdLife International, and will be considered by them for incorporation into the factsheets and *Threatened Birds of the World 2008*. BirdLife cannot assume any responsibility for factual errors in the directory: these are the sole responsibility of the Editor.

Handbook of the Birds of the World volumes

1-11, published by Lynx Edicions, **www.hbw.com**, has also been used and is a very important source for anyone interested in the world's birds. The volumes include species up to Old World Warblers so far and are still under publication.

BirdBase, **http://birdbase.hokkaido-ies.go.jp/1_eng/index.html**, an experimental database for facilitating electronic data storage and data sharing of bird surveys, has been very useful for Asian species.

Other published material, including scientific papers cited in BirdLife International's fact-sheets, has also been used. Internet searches and electronic bulletins have also provided information from less formal publications, particularly for the most recent news on a species.

Acknowledgements and references

Many persons have corresponded with the Editor and provided additional information and are acknowledged on pp. 10-11. Many others contributed to BirdLife International's factsheets, and are listed under 'contributors' in the factsheets. Specific references in the directory have been avoided for reasons of space and readability.

Page coverage

The species in the directory are featured on either a half page, a full page or two pages. Two species, Madagascar Pochard and Balearic Shearwater, feature separately in articles in the first part of the book. The decision on how much coverage a species receives has been made taking into account the amount of information available, whether there have been recent developments and the number of photographs available. It is envisaged that the full-covered species in this year's edition will be covered in less space next year while species with a low coverage this year may increase the next, although interesting developments may of course override this.

Population estimates

Population estimates are given in the header for each account, and arrows indicate whether a population is increasing, decreasing or stable.

These data come from BirdLife International's draft 2008 factsheets, plus more recent updates for some species.

Photographs

Photographs are acknowledged with the photographer's name. Most of the images here were submitted through the photo competition which ran at **www.rarebirdsyearbook.com** during May to July 2007. Besides that, some photographers with species that have not been submitted through the competition have been targeted with specific requests for use in this book and kindly given me permission to reproduce them. I have avoided reproducing images at nests, with single exceptions, as I believe that birds should not be disturbed by their nests, especially if they are already struggling for their survival. This is also why I do not accept nest images to the photo competition. In those cases where I show birds at nests, the images have either been taken by scientists working with the species' conservation and thus been near nests anyway, or been taken before the competition and offered to us outside of the competition context.

Paintings

For some species, no suitable photographs were available, so illustrations have been used. I have chosen not to use photos of specimens from museum drawers, as they bear very little resemblance to what a living bird actually looks like, feather details excepted. In some cases, however, I have used images of birds in the hand; these images were taken in connection with conservation work on the species. There is only one case of a mounted specimen from a museum, Pink-headed Duck.

Maps

Satellite images taken from Google Earth Pro have been used for the background for the maps. The distribution polygons were kindly provided by BirdLife International. Corrections and updates should be sent to science@birdlife.org. In general, only the breeding range has been depicted, as the majority of species covered are non-migratory. Where species migrate or occur over wider areas, this has been mentioned in the text.

White-winged Guan
Penelope albipennis
Population: 50-249 ↓

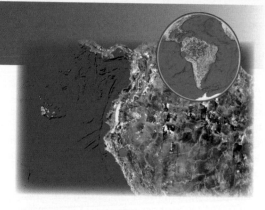

Photo: © Alejandro Tabini

Chaparrí, Lambayeque, Peru, 2007

History
1876 – the first White-winged Guan is discovered in Tumbes mangroves by Polish ornithologist Jean Stolzmann (1854-1928).

1877 – Polish naturalist Wladyslaw Taczanowski (1819-1890) describes the species for science.

1969 – local hunter and conservationist Gustavo del Solar starts searching for the species.

1973 – no records since and the species is treated as lost to science.

1977 – on 13 September, del Solar, Dr. John O'Neill and local farmer Sebastian Chinchay, spot around 8 individuals in a valley.

1978 – Solar sets up a captive breeding centre and the first bird is kept there.

1986 – on June 1, the first captive bred White-winged Guan was born.

1999 – 97 birds held in the captive breeding programme.

2001 – first group of 16 birds reintroduced in Lambayeque.

2002 – first chick born in the wild from reintroduced parents.

2007 – first group of 8 birds reintroduced in Laquipampa Wildlife refuge and the first two wild-born chicks are hatched.

Range & Population
The Peruvian stronghold of White-winged Guan is in Lambayeque, Piura and Cajamarca in north-west Peru. Historically, the species probably had a larger distribution across the Tumbesian dry forest. Today, it inhabits dry wooded slopes and ravines in a strip approximately 180 km long and 20 km wide at elevations of 600-1 400 metres. It favours valleys with small permanent streams or waterholes, and dry deciduous forest with dense cover and little human disturbance. There are possibly fewer than 300 individuals in the wild, and a captive-breeding programme holds 75 birds that are used for reintroduction and supplementation programs.

Threats
It declined partly as a result of hunting but habitat destruction, through clearance for agriculture and cutting for timber, charcoal and firewood, is probably the greatest threat. Enforcement of legal protection is low.

Conservation actions to date
Surveys have been conducted over a wide area of north-west Peru where the species and its habitat are legally protected. Laquipampa Reserved Zone at Laquipampa was established in 1982 specifically to protect the guan and the populations appear to be reasonably secure there. In July 2006 the area was declared as Peru's first Wildlife refuge. There has been a training workshop for park guards involving members of the Laquipampa and Santa Catalina communities. Small-scale experimental re-introductions commenced at Chaparri Private Conservation Area in Lambayeque when 16 individuals were released in 2001 in an effort to fill a gap in its range. Thirteen birds were released in 2003/4, bringing the total population in the Conservation Area to 26 individuals in 2004, with successful breeding by captive-raised parents recorded. Efforts are continuing to identify additional sites across its former range to host reintroductions at a rate of ten birds a year. El Angolo Hunting Reserve, near the centre of the guan's projected former range, was identified a few years ago as a suitable reintroduction site capable of holding c. 6 pairs owing to its favourable protection status and floristic composition. Education campaigns have been conducted on the guan's range by Asociación Cracidae Peru from 2005, focusing on increasing public awareness of the status.

Conservation actions required
- Surveys of Cerros de Amotape National Park and Arenillas Military Reserve are required.
- To develop ecotourism.

Photo: © Nigel Voaden

Quebrada Limon, Peru, 2005

Trinidad Piping-guan
Pipile pipile
Population: 70-200 ↓

Trinidad, 2006

Photo: © Peter Coe

Range & population
Trinidad Piping-guan is endemic to Trinidad (Trinidad and Tobago), where it was once abundant throughout the Northern Range and the southern Trinity Hills, and also occurred in lowland areas. It is now extinct in the lowlands, and almost certainly extinct in the Trinity Hills where surveys have failed to find the species since 1994. The only extant population is in the eastern portion of the Northern Range, where just c. 150 km² of suitable habitat remains. The population is probably closer to 200.

Threats
Illegal hunting and, to a lesser extent, habitat destruction through timber extraction and conversion to plantation agriculture are the chief causes of this species' decline.

Conservation actions to date
It has been legally protected since 1963. Much of the present range is within forest reserves and state forests, but the laws protecting both species and areas are generally not enforced. Species-specific ecotourism is having a positive effect in the Grande Riviere, providing financial support for local communities and developing a sense of collective responsibility.

Conservation actions required
- Survey areas of historic occurrence.
- Monitor the population in areas of known occupancy.
- Determine ecological requirements and breeding biology.
- Enforce the protection of current forest reserves.
- Formally establish the Matura National Park.
- Develop further education/public awareness campaigns to ensure the success of site protection

---

Blue-billed Currasow
Crax alberti
Population: 1,000-2,500 ↓

RNA El Paujil, 2004

Photo: © Alonso Quevedo

Range & population
This species historically occurred in northern Colombia. Two of the few large lowland forest areas remaining in its range have produced recent records: two sites on the west slope of the Serranía de San Lucas, Antioquia and the Serranía de las Quinchas, Boyacá. It inhabits humid forest up to 1,200 m and breeds in the dry season, nesting in December-March, with parties of adults and chicks observed in March-August. It feeds on fruit, shoots, invertebrates, and perhaps even carrion.

Threats
Colonisation and deforestation for coca farming are the principal threats acting around the El Paujíl Bird Reserve. In 1996, there was a gold rush in the Serranía de San Lucas and most of the eastern slopes have since been settled, logged

and converted to agriculture and coca production. Hunting and egg-collecting for food have contributed to past and present declines, and surveys since 1998 have failed to locate mature males in the field, suggesting that hunting remains a severe threat.

Conservation actions to date
El Paujíl Bird Reserve was established in 2004 and local authorities have introduced penalties for shooting or trapping the species. Protection of forest, campaigns to limit hunting and raise awareness of conservation and habitat reconstruction are needed. In 2007, Fundacion Ecolombia has eight birds for captive breeding.

Conservation actions required
- Determine its population and distribution more accurately.
- Protect forests on the Serranía de San Lucas and Serranía de las Quinchas.
- Implement effective conservation measures in existing protected areas.
- Initiate educational campaigns.

Djibouti Francolin
Francolinus ochropectus

Population: 250-999 ↓

Day forest in Goda mountain, Tadjourah region, Djibouti, July 2006

Photo: © Houssein Rayaleh

History

1952 – a bird is collected on 22 February by Captain Albospeyre and is shortly thereafter described by Jean Dorst (1924-2001) and Christian Jouanin (born 1925) as a new species of Francolin.

1977 – an estimated 5,600 birds are present in Forêt du Day.

1985 – an estimated 1,500 birds are present in Forêt du Day. The species is recorded in the Mabla mountains for the first time.

1998 – an estimated 500-1,000 birds are present in Forêt du Day.

2004 – surveys indicate a total of c. 115-135 individuals in Forêt du Day.

2006 – World Pheasant Association estimate numbers to 612-723 adults.

Range and population

The Djibouti Francolin is endemic to Djibouti, where it is known from only two sites. Forêt du Day in the Goda Massif, totalling 15 square kilometres, is probably the only viable site, but the population has decreased significantly in the last 30 years due to habitat change. The size of the population at the nearby Mabla Mountains is unknown.

It occurs in small groups in dense vegetation in juniper woodland with records between 700 and 1,500 m and has also been found in secondary woodland. It feeds on seeds, berries and termites, and also figs from the forest edge. The breeding season is from December to February. It is probably monogamous and lays a clutch of 5-7 eggs. The only known nest was a shallow grass-lined depression on an inaccessible mountain ledge.

Threats

At Forêt du Day, woodland is in poor condition. Figures published in 2006 indicate that 95% of the preferred habitat of plateau juniper was either dead or dying and did not support the species. The reasons for this are unclear, but the high level of grazing by cattle, camels and goats is certainly a problem in much of the woodland, possibly exacerbated by acid rain, climate change and fungal disease. Other concerns include collection of firewood on lower slopes, hunting and human disturbance. At Mabla, there are signs of significant human disturbance in the remaining stands of woodland, which have been heavily exploited for firewood and grazing.

Conservation actions to date

Part of Forêt du Day was apparently declared a National Park in 1939, but the designation is no longer valid. Projects examining environmental and socio-economic issues in the Forêt du Day area have been carried out by the government and international agencies, but recommended measures have never been implemented, partly due to internal unrest since the early 1990s. Research to clarify the species range and population numbers is ongoing. A conservation education programme is being trialled in five local schools.

Conservation actions required

- Immediate implementation of protected status of the "Forêts de Day et de Mabla" as recently decreed by government.
- Conduct ecological studies to determine habitat limits and reproductive ecology, especially whether there is seasonal dependence upon juniper forest. These will be aided by the use of radio-tagging which requires development of suitable catching techniques.
- Community-based juniper forest restoration through planting and assisted regeneration, and the maintenance of local plant nurseries.
- Involve local stakeholders by convening a Protected Area Management Group in the Goda and Mabla areas.
- Create a working group within Djibouti to promote conservation of the species and its habitat.
- Develop a long-term integrated management project for the Goda massif, involving socio-economic and agro-pastoral surveys and a conservation education programme.

BirdLife Species Guardian **Houssein Rayaleh (Djibouti Nature)**

Day forest in Goda mountain, Tadjourah region, Djibouti, July 2006

Photo: © Houssein Rayaleh

Gorgeted Woodquail
Odontophorus strophium

Population: 250-999 ↓

Santander, Colombia

Photo: © David Caro Sabogal

Range & population
This species occurs on the west slope of the East Andes of Colombia, between 1,500 and 2,500 metres. Overall, it appears to be restricted to the larger oak forest remnants in the eastern Cordillera. Breeding coincides with the rainy seasons.

Threats
Since the 17th century, the west slope of the East Andes has been extensively logged and converted to agriculture, including pastures and, at lower altitudes, coffee, plantain and sugarcane plantations. Forest loss below 2,500 m has been almost complete, with habitat in many areas reduced to tiny, isolated relicts on steep slopes and along streams. In some areas habitat regeneration is beginning following the abandonment of marginal land.

Conservation actions to date
The Guanentá-Alto Río Fonce Flora and Fauna Sanctuary, protecting 100 km² of forest was gazetted in November 1993. The species is also protected by the adjacent Cachalu Biological Reserve, with frequent sightings there since 1999. Surveys are underway by Fundación ProAves including radio-telemetry studies on population densities and range size.

Conservation actions required
- Survey and estimate remnant populations.
- Assess movements and the species' need for forest connectivity.
- Develop initiatives to protect any additional sites discovered.

Himalayan Quail
Ophrysia superciliosa

Population: < 50, trend unknown

Painting: © Norman Arlott/HBW2 (Lynx Edicions)

Range & population
This species was first described in 1846 from a collection of live birds at the Earl of Derby's Estate in England, and has not been recorded reliably since 1876. The known records come from Uttaranachal in north-western India. Five possible sightings where however made in 2003 near Naini Tal. It was recorded in long grass and scrub on steep hillsides, particularly south-facing slope crests, between 1,650 m and 2,400 m.

Threats
The species was last seen 60 years before independence, indicating that hunting levels during the colonial period contributed significantly to its decline. Widespread land-use changes thereafter, particularly open cast mining for limestone and related disturbance, are other likely contributory factors to its decline. It is also hypothesised that habitat changes at lower elevations during the post-Pleistocene glaciation might have pushed subpopulations to suboptimal higher elevations, causing local extinctions.

Conservation actions to date
There have been a number of unsuccessful official and unofficial attempts to rediscover the species. In 2002 a survey used posters, interviews with locals and habitat analyses to direct field searches, but failed to find evidence of the species.

Conservation actions required
- Conduct further surveys in areas supporting Cheer Pheasant *Catreus wallichi,* which has similar habitat requirements.
- Conduct interviews with local hunters.
- Based on these interviews, continue a comprehensive series of field surveys.

Laysan Duck
Anas laysanensis

Laysan Island, 2007

Population: 391-597 ↑

History

1860 – Laysan Duck is exterminated from all other Hawaiian islands except for Laysan.

1890s – Laysan is occupied for guano-mining and workers start hunting the duck for food and fun. Three other endemic Laysan species are eradicated. Vegetation-destroying rabbits are introduced.

1892 – Lord Rothschild (1868-1937) formally describes the species.

1902 – the population is down to less than 100.

1909 – Laysan is declared part of Hawaiian Bird reserve.

1911 – only 11 birds remain.

1912 – seven individuals of Laysan duck remain after Japanese parties visit the island.

1926 – the last rabbits are exterminated from Laysan.

1930 – the one remaining female gets her eggs destroyed by a Bristle-thighed Curlew *Numenius tahitiensis*. The female astonishingly manages to lay another clutch.

1950 – 33 individuals counted.

1967 – Laysan Duck is declared an endangered species with federal protection.

1987 – 500 individuals present.

1993 – drought and disease reduce the numbers by half.

1995 – 246 adults.

2000 – 375 adults.

2004/5 – 42 birds are introduced to Midway atoll.

2006 – 56 juveniles fledge on Midway.

2007 – the Midway population is at 100.

This species has previously been treated as a subspecies of Mallard *Anas platyrhynchos*, but is now considered a species of its own.

Range & population

Laysan duck is endemic to the Hawaiian Islands (USA), where it was recently confined to Laysan island. Sixty years ago the only remaining female had its clutch destroyed. Birds have recently been translocated to the two islands that comprise Midway Atoll National Wildlife Refuge and bred successfully there in their first year. Subfossil remains indicate that it also occurred on other islands. The Laysan Duck is a species which certainly can hold the claim of having been on the brink of extinction. The population apparently fluctuates and in the past this has been attributed to differing methods and timing of censuses, but new information suggests that the population has fluctuated between 7 and 827 adults in the last century. In the 1993 drought the population dropped to 82-122 adults from a peak of 827 birds prior to the drought.

It occurs on the central hyper-saline lake on Laysan, but spends most of its time near freshwater seeps around the shore. It nests in dense stands of shrubs and grasses and only 30% of chicks survive to fledging. The principal food source is brine flies and shrimps, but it also takes invertebrates, including insect larvae, moths, terrestrial flies and spiders. It has been suggested that variation in food supplies can be one reason for the fluctuating numbers. By day the ducks prefer terrestrial vegetation but favour the lake at night.

Threats
Food shortage appears to be the main threat and leads to high chick mortality, especially on Laysan Island. Reproductive success is sometimes related to brine fly population levels which, in turn, are reduced by drought and low water-levels. However, severe drought and a disease outbreak in 1993 led to a significant die-off of adult birds. Introduced ants (e.g. big-headed ant *Pheidole megacephala*) are important competitors for terrestrial invertebrate prey. Parasitic infestation by the nematode *Echinuria uncinata* is an additional factor and alien plants have threatened nesting habitat. Its behaviour of freezing rather than taking flight if threatened has made it an easy prey for introduced predators, such as small mammals. Global warming and associated sea-level rise are further concerns which may affect this species.

Conservation actions to date
The alien grass *Cenchrus echinatus* is thought to have been eradicated through efforts of the US Fish and Wildlife Service and native bunch grass, which is used by the ducks as nesting material, has responded positively. Snow fences have been installed to stabilise the movement of sand and allow for natural revegetation and planting of endemic vegetation. A translocation programme has so far been successful. Radio transmitters and individual banding have been used to monitor breeding success and survival.

Conservation actions required
- Continue to monitor the population size and health.
- Continue to enhance nesting habitat on Midway .
- Enhance brood rearing habitat on Midway Atoll with small fish-free freshwater wetlands with abundant cover.
- Use translocation and ecosystem restoration to re-establish four additional populations of Laysan Duck to reduce extinction risks.
- On Laysan, continue to stabilise dunes by planting endemic vegetation.
- Restore freshwater wetlands, to Lisianski Island prior to potential re-introduction.

- Ensure strict procedures to prevent the accidental introduction of exotic plants, invertebrates, and animals and control exotic plants and alien predators already established.
- After restored predator-free habitat is available, create a new genetically managed captive population within Hawaii to provide birds for reintroductions to other Hawaiian islands.

Laysan Island, 2004

Photo: © Mark Alexander MacDonald

Midway Atoll NWR, 2006

Photo: © James H Breeden Jr.

Laysan Island, 2004

Photo: © Mark Alexander MacDonald

Crested Shelduck
Tadorna cristata
Population: < 50, unknown trend

Blake Twigden, www.inventas.co.nz/50rarestbirds/

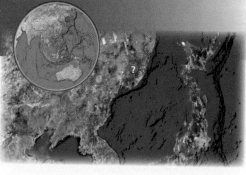

Range & population
This duck was originally thought to be a hybrid between Ruddy Shelduck *Tadorna ferruginea* and Falcated Teal *Anas falcata*. The species is known from a small number of records from Russia, Japan and South Korea and unconfirmed records from north-east China. The most recent was a sighting of a male and two females in May 1964 together with Harlequin Ducks *Histrionicus histrionicus* near Vladivostok, Russia. It may breed on mountain lakes and winter along coasts, often near river mouths.

Threats
If it still survives, its numbers are likely to be so low that it would be vulnerable to a chance or accidental extinction. Several of the historical localities are close to the area affected by the implementation of a large-scale Development Project involving the border areas of Russia, China and North Korea. Hunting is also a very possible threat.

Conservation actions to date
In 1983, three million leaflets on this species were distributed in Russia, Japan, China, South Korea and North Korea. However, there was little response, with the only result being a single unconfirmed record from North Korea. A new investigation was made in China 1986–1990, through a publicity campaign which generated some unconfirmed records.

Conservation actions required
* Continue to search for the species within its potential range through publicity campaigns and the distribution of illustrated leaflets.
* Conduct surveys at historical localities and in those areas where there have been unconfirmed sightings.

Pink-headed Duck
Rhodonessa caryophyllacea
Population: < 50, unknown trend

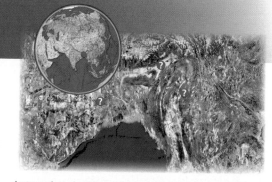

World Museum, Liverpool, 2005

Photo: © Andrew "Jack" Tordoff

Range & population
Pink-headed Duck was locally distributed in wetlands of India, Bangladesh and Myanmar, and occurred rarely in Nepal, with most records from north-east India and adjacent Bangladesh. It may still exist in Myanmar.

Threats
A combination of hunting and habitat loss has contributed to its decline. As a sedentary species, it suffered year-round persecution during a period (the late 19th and early 20th centuries) when hunting levels in India were high. Clearance of forest and drainage of wetlands for agricultural land has destroyed much of its habitat. It is likely that egg collection and disturbance also contributed to its decline. The alien invasive plant species Water Hyacinth *Eichhornia crassipes* also may have had an effect by altering wetland habitats to the detriment of this species.

Conservation actions to date
Throughout the 1950s there were attempts to clarify its status, culminating in a literature and museum specimen review. It was subsequently searched for in some key areas. Since 1956, it has been legally protected. Since 2003 BirdLife Indochina and the Biodiversity and National Conservation Association (BANCA) have conducted five separate searches in Kachin State, Myanmar.

Conservation actions required
* Locate and systematically survey any remaining remote and large tracts of suitable habitat within its former range.
* Interview local hunters.
* Take stringent protection measures should populations be discovered.

Campbell Islands Teal
Anas nesiotis
Population: 48-200 ↑

Photo: © Simon Fordham

Codfish Island, 2007

History

1810 – Campbell Island is colonised and rats are introduced shortly thereafter.

1886 – the first specimen is collected on the coast of Campbell.

1935 – Canadian ornithologist James Henry Fleming (1872-1940) describes the species.

1944 or 1958 – second and last record for many years from Campbell Island.

1972 – it is rediscovered on Dent island, a few km from Campbell.

1984 – 3 males and 1 female are taken into captivity – no breeding this year.

1990 – a survey reveals not more than 25 breeding pairs on Dent and estimates population to between 60 and 100. 4 males and 3 females are taken into captivity.

1994 – the first captive breeding takes place.

1997 – a survey on Dent locates only 3 birds, which may indicate a drop in numbers.

1999-2000 – 24 birds are released on Codfish Island as a temporary measure and start to breed almost immediately. Removal soon deemed unfeasible so the population becomes permanent.

2001 – Brown rats *Rattus norvegicus*, are eradicated from Campbell Island.

2004 – 50 birds (22 from the wild and 28 captive bred) are released on Campbell Island.

2005 – another 55 birds (22 from the wild and 33 captive bred) are released on Campbell Island.

2006 – 4 cases of breeding takes place on Campbell Island, another 54 birds, all captive-bred, are released.

This flightless and nocturnal teal has sometimes been treated as the same species as Brown Teal *Anas aucklandica*.

Range & population
Endemic to New Zealand where it has been confined to Dent Island, an offshore islet of Campbell Island, for many decades. Originally it occurred on Campbell Island but was made extinct on the main island before it could be described for science. Additional, introduced, populations have been established at Codfish Island and on Campbell Island, which now has been made become predator-free. The introduction on Codfish Island was intended as a temporary measure, but removal is not now practical so this population has become permanent.

Threats
Brown rat *Rattus norvegicus*, which has one of its densest populations in the world on Campbell Island are believed to have caused the species disappearance from this island. However, the successful eradication of this alien invasive species has allowed reintroduction of teal from captive stock. Accidental reintroduction of rats, severe weather events and the introduction of avian disease remain possible threats.

Conservation actions to date
A captive population has been built up since the first breeding in captivity in 1994. Seven males and three females caught in 1984 and 1990 formed the base for the captive population. Brown Rat has been successfully eradicated from Campbell Island since 2001 during the world's largest rat eradication programme. Birds have been successfully reintroduced to Campbell Island from the temporary Codfish Island population and directly from captivity in 2004-2006.

Conservation actions required
- Maintain wild population.
- Establish additional wild populations.
- Exclude Brown Rat from Campbell.
- Monitor the health of birds in all sub-populations to ensure that they are not suffering from disease.

Photo: © Michael Dryden

Mt Bruce Reserve, New Zealand, 2006

Brazilian Merganser
Mergus octosetaceus

Serra da Canastra, Minas Gerais State, Brazil, 2006

Photo: © Adriano Gambarini

Population: < 50-249 ↓

History

1817 – French ornithologist Louis Jean Pierre Vieillot describes the species from samples probably taken in Brazil.

1891 – the first record for Paraguay is made.

1948 – the species is rediscovered.

1984 – the second Paraguayan record is made when Nancy López sees a bird in Rio Carapá.

1993 – a survey along 376 km of river in Argentina only produces one bird.

1995 – a small population is discovered on the Rio Tibagi, Paraná, Brazil.

1998 – no records are made in Paraná despite searches.

2000 – experts from Brazil, Argentina, Paraguay, Europe and the US convene in Minas Gerais for a workshop on conserving the species.

2001/2002 – 81 individuals estimated in a survey around Parque Nacional da Serra da Canastra, Minas Gerais, Brazil.

2002 – the first record for ten years is made in Argentina in the Uruzú river. Interviews with locals in Paraguay indicate that the species may still exist there.

2007 – a new breeding site is found in Goiás state, Brazil.

Range & population

Occurs in extremely low numbers at a few, highly disjunct localities in south-central Brazil. It has occurred in adjacent areas of Argentina and Paraguay, but there are no recent records and it may be extinct there. It was previously thought to inhabit river stretches with gallery forest but is now believed to occur on unforested, undisturbed stretches of river through cerrado. It requires gallery forest, regardless of biome. The nest is placed in a hollow in a tree or among rocks in June-October.

Threats

Expanding agriculture and the construction of hydroelectric

dams are considered the principal threats to this species and dam-building has already caused severe declines across much of its range. Disturbance and pollution of rivers, which results largely from deforestation, agricultural expansion and diamond-mining, poses threats to its habitat. Mining has ceased in the immediate area of one of the localities from which it is known. In Argentina, hunting and collection of exhibition specimens have occurred during a short period of time, but its effect on the species' disappearance from there is probably not great. The impact of exotic fish species is unknown but could potentially pose a threat. Tourism and associated activities result in river disturbance and have been recorded within known territories and inside national parks.

Conservation actions to date
The species is legally protected in all States where it occurs. It is also found within three Brazilian national parks, two state parks and one 'Reserva Particular do Patrimônio Natural'. A species action plan has been published which outlines in detail its current status, ecology, threats and proposed conservation actions. A Brazilian Merganser Recovery Team has been established.

Conservation actions required
- Assess the status of the Brazilian Tibagi and Novo populations.
- Continue to monitor the Serra da Canastra population in Brazil.
- Develop and implement a fieldwork strategy using satellite images.
- Protect the watershed and riverine habitats of populations, especially in Bahia, Brazil.
- Install nest-boxes for populations outside Serra da Canastra National Park.
- Improve local awareness and promote riverbank protection.
- Assess the status of the Arroyo Uruzú population, Argentina.
- Conduct surveys in Paraguay to confirm local reports.
- Advocate for the expansion of the Chapada dos Veadeiros National Park in Brazil to include the newly discovered population in the rio das Pedras.

Photo: © Jon King

Serra da Canastra, Minas Gerais State, Brazil, November 2006

Photo: © Andy & Gill Swash

Brazil, 2005

Photo: © Adriano Gambarini

Serra da Canastra, Minas Gerais State, Brazil, 2007

Waved Albatross
Phoebastria irrorata

Española Island, Galápagos, 2005

Population: 34,694 ↓

History

1883 – the species is first described by British ornithologist Osbert Salvin (1835-1898).

1924 – first record of a Waved Albatross at Isla de la Plata, 27 km off Ecuador, in November.

1970/71 – estimated 12,000 pairs.

1990 – 10 breeding pairs reported from Isla de la Plata.

1994 – estimated 15,600 – 18,200 pairs. On 13th June, an individual ringed in 1961 being at least 5 years old was retrapped, thus establishing the longevity record of 38 years for the species.

1995 – 25,000 adults.

2001 – several non-breeding adults seen on de la Plata off Ecuador and on Isla Genovesa. Population estimated at 31,000 – 35,000 adults.

Range & population
Breeds on south Española Island in the Galápagos Islands, and perhaps on Isla de la Plata off Manabí province, Ecuador with less than 20 pairs. Breeding adults travel to the Peruvian upwelling region to feed. In the non-breeding season, birds move mainly east and south-east into the waters of the Ecuadorian and Peruvian continental shelf. It returns to breed at 5-7 years of age. On Española, the overall breeding population was considered to have been stable until recently; the breeding distribution has changed owing in part to vegetation regrowth following the eradication of goats. Breeding no longer occurs at two inland sites, perhaps through redistribution to the coast.

Threats
Recent evidence has shown a 2-3% reduction in annual adult survival compared with that in the 1960's and is thought to have driven recent dramatic declines in the breeding population. As many as 1% of the population may be killed by fishermen each year. It has been reported following fishing vessels around the Galapagos Islands to feed on discards, why long-lining can threaten the population. It can be reasonably assumed that long-line operations in the waters off Peru and

Ecuador to which it disperses may also affect it. Males are more subjected to accidents as bycatch than females and as both sexes tend to the young, this could pose a serious threat. Even if immediate action is taken to curb adult mortality the population will continue to decline for a decade or so until the current cohort of juveniles reach breeding age. Reports have also suggested that the level of harvesting by fishermen to supply food and feather markets has increased dramatically in recent years. The population on Isla de la Plata is threatened from nest-predation by rats and cats, as well as illegal collection of eggs and young. Parents do not build nests but lay their single egg on the ground. During the two-month long incubation they roll around the egg, distances up to 40 metres have been measured, which frequently results in death of the egg and mass desertions of eggs are yet to be fully explained. The species has shown susceptibility to El Niño Southern Oscillation events, perhaps due to increased adult mortality or increased negative interactions with fisheries under these conditions.

Conservation actions to date
Española is part of the Galápagos National Park and Marine Reserve. Industrial, but not small-scale, longlining is prohibited in the Galápagos Marine Reserve. In 1979, the islands were declared a World Heritage Site. Española is well protected and has no alien fauna (goats having been eradicated in 1978), and tourism is well regulated. Isla de la Plata is part of Machalilla National Park, but is insufficiently protected.

Conservation actions required
- A species action plan needs to be developed.
- Censuses and baseline studies of the breeding population need to be established, and more studies on effects of longline fishing to be performed.
- The Ila de la Plata population needs protection and the island needs to be assessed for suitability.

Española Island, Galapagos, 2006

Photo: © Nancy C Bell

At sea, Lima, Peru, 2005

Photo: © Nigel Voaden

At sea, Lima, Peru, 2005

Photo: © Nigel Voaden

Galapagos, 1996

Photo: © Andy & Gill Swash

Chatham Albatross
Thalassarche eremita
Population: 11 000 ➡

Off Pyramid Rock, 2003

Photo: © Alan Tate

Mortality levels in the non-breeding distribution area are potentially the most serious threat to the species. Illegal harvesting of chicks may occur occasionally, and although numbers are apparently small, this may have some effect on the population.

Conservation actions to date
A Threat Abatement Plan (TAP) to minimise fishing bycatch has been prepared. Measures known to be effective in mitigating seabird bycatch within the Australian Fishing Zone (AFZ) are promoted by legislation, a code of practice and education programs. A Recovery Plan has been written and a Recovery Team is in place.

Conservation actions required
- Continue accurate ground census over three consecutive years.
- Repeat census at five-year intervals.
- Work with local community to raise awareness and reduce levels of chick harvest.
- Develop and effectively implement mitigation techniques to minimise fisheries bycatch, particularly by longliners.

History
1926 – Rollo H. Beck of the Whitney South Sea Expedition collects the holotype offshore from The Pyramid.

1930 – Robert Cushman Murphy (1887-1973) describes the species.

1937 – Charles Fleming and Graham Turbott land on The Pyramid on 16th December and estimate "several thousand" adult birds.

c. 1954 – Elliott Dawson estimates that 2,500 pairs breed on The Pyramid.

1961 – Brian Bell estimates 2-3,000 pairs.

1972 – an estimated 4,000 pairs breed on The Pyramid.

1983-6 – Colin Miskelly reports adults onshore from Rima and Toru Islets, Western Chain, Snares Islands.

1995 – Jacinda Amey finds a Chatham Albatross incubating an egg on Toru Islet.

1998 – the species is split from Shy Albatross.

1999-2001 – the population on The Pyramid is accurately counted at 4,575 breeding pairs.

2001 – a bird banded in 1974 is recovered and, assuming it was banded at least seven years of age, is at least 34 years old.

This albatross has previously been considered a subspecies of Shy Albatross *Thalassarche cauta*.

Range & population
It breeds in September to April on rocky ledges and steep slopes only on The Pyramid, a large rock stack in the Chatham Islands, New Zealand. The island is privately owned and difficult to access. Satellite tracking and other observations indicate dispersal after breeding (from January) within the south Pacific Ocean west to Tasmania and east to Chile and Peru, where it winters north of 20°. It takes 11-30 days for the birds to reach this area and these waters support c. 73% of the estimated global population. It has also been recorded to the west to Tasmania and South Africa.

Threats
In 1985, a significant reduction in the extent and condition of vegetation on the breeding islet occurred due to an extreme storm, and soil was severely reduced. As a result, there was an increased probability of nest collapse, due to reduced moisture retention. There has been some improvement during the last ten years in soil and vegetation cover.

Off Gisborne, New Zealand, 2006

Photo: © Brent Stephenson

Off Valparaiso, Chile, 2007

Photo: © Pablo Caceres

Amsterdam Island Albatross
Diomedea amsterdamensis
Population: 145 ↓

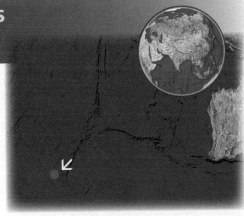

Amsterdam Island, 1982

Photo: © Eric van der Vlist

History
1983 – J. P. Roux describes the species.

1987 – the number of cattle on Amsterdam Island is reduced and a fence erected to seal off part of the island.

1992 – a second fence is erected with the aim of providing complete protection of the high plateau from possible incursions by cattle.

This species was previously considered a subspecies of Wandering Albatross *Diomedea exulans* before it was elevated to a species in its own right.

Range & population
This albatross breeds in an area of 400 hectares on the Plateau des Tourbières on Amsterdam Island (French Southern Territories) in the southern Indian Ocean. The population includes 90 mature individuals, with c. 25-26 pairs breeding annually (2004-2007). During the breeding season, mainly in February and March, birds forage both around Amsterdam Island and up to 2,200 km away in subtropical waters. Outside the breeding season birds forage in subtropical waters between western Australia and eastern South Africa. Males arrive earlier than females at the breeding sites and breeding is biannual, with first breeding taking place at 7 years of age.

Threats
Today the population is threatened primarily by the potential spread of diseases (Avian cholera and *Erysipelothrix rhusiopathidae*) that affect the Indian Yellow-nosed Albatross *Thalassarche carteri* population that exists three km from the colony. Infection risks are very high and increased chick mortality over recent years suggests that the population could be affected. Degradation of breeding sites by introduced cattle, human disturbance and introduced predators, especially cats, are presumably also to blame. There is now a fence to protect the colony from cattle, and access to the colony is strictly restricted. Interactions with long line fisheries

around the island, in the 1970s and early 1980s, could also have contributed to a decline in the population, and remain a potential threat because of the overlap between foraging birds and long line fisheries for subtropical tunas.

Conservation actions to date
All birds are banded and the population is monitored every year.

Conservation actions required
- Prevent the spread of disease.
- Eradicate cats.
- Continue detailed monitoring of the population, improve knowledge of forage zones.
- Promote adoption of best-practice mitigation measures in all fisheries within the species' range, particularly via existing and proposed intergovernmental mechanisms.

Amsterdam Island, 1982

Photo: © Eric van der Vlist

Amsterdam Island, 1982

Photo: © Eric van der Vlist

Galapagos Petrel
Pterodroma phaeopygia
Population: 2,500-10,000 ↓

Galapagos Islands, 2006

Photo: © Michael Dryden

History

1876 – British ornithologist Osbert Salvin (1835-1898) describes the species.

1978-1980 – estimated 27,000 pairs.

1979 – Galapagos Islands is declared a World Heritage Site.

1980 – the Galapagos National Park Service begins an intensive predator control programme on Floreana and Santa Cruz.

1982 – predator control is introduced in one colony at Cerro Pajas, Floreana.

1985 – 3,500 pairs estimated.

1997 – analysis of banding data since 1962 show that 3% of juveniles return to colonies on Santa Cruz and Floreana.

2005 – the population at Santa Cruz is surveyed and totals 700 pairs.

Range & population

Galapagos Petrel is endemic to the Galápagos Islands, Ecuador, where it breeds on five islands (Santa Cruz, Floreana, Santiago, San Cristobal and Isabela) with possible breeding on other islands in the archipelago. It breeds in all months but mostly in May through September in the humid highlands between 300–900 m, in burrows or natural cavities, on slopes, in craters, sinkholes, lava tunnels and gullies. Partners mate for life and young birds take 5-6 years before breeding. An analysis of ringed birds showed that of 1,000 juveniles ringed in 35 years, only 3% returned to colonies on Floreana and Santa Cruz. Birds forage around the islands, but also disperse east and north towards South America and up to 2,000 km south.

Threats

Introduced dogs, cats and pigs take eggs, young and adults, and Black Rat *Rattus rattus* and Brown Rat *Rattus norvegicus* eat eggs and chicks. Of 510 adults monitored on Santiago in 1985, over half were killed by pigs and Galápagos Hawk *Buteo galapagoensis*. On Santa Cruz the average adult life expectancy was only 6.2 years in the late seventies. Nest-site destruction by goats, donkeys, cattle and horses is also a major threat. Clearance of vegetation for agriculture and intensive grazing has severely restricted the breeding area on Santa Cruz, Floreana and San Cristóbal, and at least half the breeding range is still farmed on Santa Cruz. Adult mortality occurs when birds are killed by barbed wire fences on agricultural land. El Niño events seem to have a detrimental impact on nesting and productivity.

Conservation actions to date

The islands are a World Heritage Site which gives them protection. Predator control involving intensive rat baiting around known colonies and petrel monitoring currently continues on Floreana, Santa Cruz and Santiago

Conservation actions required

* Breeding success under various predator control regimes should be monitored to determine most appropriate management.
* Begin rat control on two islands.
* Continue searching for nesting grounds on Isabela and Pinta Islands.
* Conduct a complete census for the species.
* Study genetic variation within the population.
* Investigate and model the effects of low juvenile recruitment and combine with data on adult survivorship.

Galapagos Islands, 2006

Photo: © Jörgen Peter Kjeldsen

Black Stilt. Photo: © Dave Murray

Jamaica Petrel
Pterodroma caribbaea

Population: < 50 unknown trend

Painting: © Juan Varela/HBW1 (Lynx Edicions)

This species has sometimes been treated as a subspecies of Black-capped Petrel *Pterodroma hasitata*.

Range & population
Jamaica Petrel was a plentiful seabird up to the middle of the 19th century, but has suffered a drastic decline in numbers. The last confirmed record is of 22 birds collected in 1879. The only proven nesting was in the Blue and John Crow Mountains of eastern Jamaica bit it may have also nested on Dominica and Guadeloupe. It nests in cliff burrows and holes under trees, above 1,000 m. The courtship, mating and pre-laying period is October-December (when birds are most vocal), and young fledge by May. It visits nesting burrows nocturnally.

Threats
The presumed causes of this species' decline was predation by introduced rats (eating eggs) and mongooses (capable of taking incubating adults). Introduced pigs may also have been an important factor. It was hunted for food until the middle of the 19th century.

Conservation actions to date
The Jamaica Petrel Research Group initiated searches for the species in 1996, and this effort continued until at least 2000, but failed to find any birds.

Conservation actions required
- Search systematically above 1,000 m in the John Crow Mountains on Jamaica, coinciding searches with the beginning of the breeding season when the birds are most vocal.
- Search on Dominica and Guadeloupe.
- Continue searches at sea and photograph any dark *Pterodroma* petrels encountered in the Caribbean.

Magenta Petrel
Pterodroma magentae

Population: 120-150 ↓

Photo: © Brent Stephenson

Chatham Islands, New Zealand, 2005

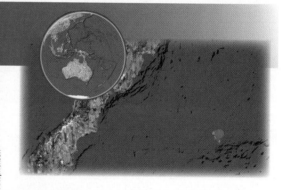

Range & population
Magenta Petrel, or Taiko as it is known locally, was re-discovered in 1978 in Chatham Island, New Zealand, 111 years after it was first collected at sea. Its range at sea is probably eastwards into the Pacific Ocean to waters off western South America and south of the island.

Threats
Historically, the pastoralisation of Chatham Island probably caused the destruction of many colonies. Introduced species of mammals take eggs, chicks and adults, or compete for, destroy or cause the desertion of burrows. Flooding of burrows may also lower breeding success. Loss of forest habitat from accidental fire represents a threat.

Conservation actions to date
Breeding areas have been protected by the Tuku Nature Reserve. Predator control was intensified in 1996 and the Chatham Island Taiko Trust was established in 1998. In 2006, a 3 ha safe colony with predator-proof fence was established at the Sweetwater Secure Breeding Site. Eight chicks were successfully moved and fledged here in April 2007.

Conservation actions required
- Continue ground searches and telemetry to locate further burrows.
- Continue night surveys for prospecting birds and to collect data on survival.
- Excavate study holes to all nest chambers to allow active intervention if chicks are undernourished or abandoned.
- Continue sustained predator and herbivore control.
- Determine importance of inshore waters for courtship and pair formation.
- Continue to study the species' ecology.

Fiji Petrel
Pseudobulweria macgillivrayi
Population: < 50 ↓

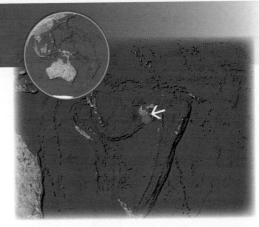

Photo: © Dick Watling

History

1855 – the medical officer on board the vessel HMS Herald collects the first specimen on the island of Gau. It is brought to the British Museum.

1860 – the species is described by British Zoologist George Robert Gray (1808-1872).

1925 – an ornithological survey of Gau, deliberately targeting Fiji Petrel, is undertaken as part of the Whitney South sea Expedition conducted by the American Museum of Natural History.

1971 – another fruitless search is conducted by J. B. Smart in October. He concludes that it most likely nests in the highland interior.

1983 – adult seen at sea close to Gau.

1984 – another adult is captured and released on the island.

2003 – an expedition in June fails to locate any Fiji Petrels. A Recovery Plan for the Fiji Petrel is drawn up with the assistance of the National Parks and Wildlife Department of New South Wales.

2004 – The National Trust, with BirdLife Fiji and the Wildlife Conservation Society, initiates a community-based project intended to attract petrels to an accessible location and thereby procure more information from grounded birds, together with an initiative to protect the Gau highlands where the petrel is believed to nest.

2005 – two birds seen by villagers on 4th May, one is captured and photographed and believed to be an adult female.

2007 – a third specimen is obtained in April after a bird lands in a village and does not survive.

Range & population

The exact breeding areas are still not known but are considered likely to be in forest or cloud-forest, perhaps amongst large numbers of Collared Petrel *Pterodroma brevipes*, in the rugged terrain of interior Gau. It may occur on other islands in the vicinity, e.g. Taveuni. Since 1985, there have been seven records of birds (all presumed juveniles) which have landed on the roofs of houses in Nawaikama and Nukuloa villages. Of these, three were released, one was injured (and preserved as a specimen at the Fiji Museum), and the fate of the others is unknown (and therefore their identification is not certain). It is thought they have been attracted to these places by artificial light. There are ten claimed sightings from observers at sea since 1960. Most of these come from Fiji waters, but there have also been claims from Tonga, Bougainville and Papua New Guinea. The first specimen was an immature male (based on undeveloped flight feathers) and probably collected in October which hints at breeding close to this month

Threats

The servicing of a recently constructed telecommunications transmitter on the summit of Gau may facilitate the movement of feral cats and rats (Pacific rat Rattus exulans and brown rat R. norvegicus) to the breeding area, and thereby increase predation. Although Collared Petrel P. brevipes seem to nest successfully (and its seasonal breeding in the first half of the year may swamp cat predation), it is possible that Fiji Petrel has a more prolonged breeding season later in the year, and it could therefore suffer disproportionately. Feral pigs have recently become established on the southern hinterland of Gau and they may represent an additional threat.

Conservation actions to date

In 1989, research on the ridge around possible nesting areas was terminated since it was felt that it, without complementary conservation action, could encourage cats to follow paths into the area. The species is well-known by local residents because it features on a Fijian bank note and because of a massive public awareness campaign which was run at Gau in 2002-2004. It is protected under Fijian law and the chiefs of the 16 villages on Gau have also signed an agreement to support the creation of a bird sanctuary for the species.

One problem with grounded birds found by local non-ornithologists has been to swiftly collect reliable data from these birds before they are released or buried. To facilitate this, a respected elder of Gau was sent to Australia to receive training in the techniques of handling and identifying seabirds, collecting morphometric data, cloacal sexing and bird banding. He returned to Gau where he conducted a workshop to pass on some of his new-found knowledge to interested islanders and is now employed as a ranger.

Conservation actions required

- Conduct surveys on Gau employing petrel specialists and using spotlighting and radio-tracking
- Develop local expertise to assist with, or carry out, surveys
- Assess the breeding success and threats to Collared Petrel and to survey seas off other suitable islands.

Chatham Petrel
Pterodroma axillaris
Population: 800-1,000 ↓

Painting: ©Juan Varela/HBW1 (Lynx edicions)

Range & population
Chatham Petrel is now restricted to Rangatira (South East Island) in the Chatham Islands, New Zealand, although it may have been more widespread. It nests in burrows amongst low vegetation and roots in lowland temperate forest and scrub, on flat to moderate sloping ground.

Threats
Intense competition for burrows with the abundant Broad-billed Prion *Pachyptila vittata* is the primary threat. Such competition may be the cause of the observed low breeding success and high rate of pair bond disruption. On the other islands in the group, exploitation by humans for food and introduced predators were the probable causes of extirpation.

Conservation actions to date
South East Island has been managed as a reserve since 1954, and cattle, sheep and goats were removed in 1961. Artificial nest-sites have been provided and burrows have been blocked to prevent occupation by Broad-billed Prions during the absence of Chatham Petrels. In 2002, a second population was created in a predator free enclosure to which over 200 chicks were transferred in four years. By 2006 four birds had returned with a pair successfully rearing a single chick for the first time.

Conservation actions required
- Locate additional breeding burrows.
- Monitor all breeding burrows annually and band all chicks.
- Estimate breeding population using additional methods.
- Develop further techniques to protect nesting birds.
- Establish another colony in the Chatham Islands.
- Use satellite tags to investigate the species' at-sea distribution.

Beck´s Petrel
Pseudobulweria becki
Population: < 50, unknown trend

Painting: ©Juan Varela/HBW1 (Lynx edicions)

Range & population
This species is known from two specimens: a female taken at sea east of New Ireland and north of Buka, Papua New Guinea, on 6 January 1928, and a male taken north-east of Rendova, Solomon Islands, on 18 May 1929. There is also a 2006 record of a bird photographed from a boat crossing the Coral Sea east of Australia's Great Barrier Reef, but it has been determined as inconclusive for a first record for Australia. Recent observations of up to 250 Tahiti Petrel *Pseudobulweria rostrata* in north-east Papua New Guinea could prove to be *P. becki*. It is assumed to breed in these two countries with speculation that it nests in the mountains of Bougainville Island, but its breeding range and at-sea distribution is unknown. Like Tahiti Petrel elsewhere in the Pacific, it probably nests on small islets and/or high mountains on larger islands.

Threats
This species is potentially threatened by predation from introduced cats and rats on its unknown breeding grounds.

Conservation actions to date
None known.

Conservation actions required
- Scrutinise and photograph all *P. rostrata* types seen within the region.
- Survey far-flung atolls and reefs north of New Ireland and the Solomons.
- Survey high-altitude forest on Bougainville.
- Investigate taxonomic validity through biochemical analysis of specimens to determine relationship wit Tahiti Petrel with which it may be conspecific.

Mascarene Petrel
Pseudobulweria aterrima
Population: 90-800 ↓

St. Pierre, 2002

Photo: © Martin Riehtmüller

Range & population
The species occurs on Réunion where it breeds in burrows on cliffs in December-March. Five breeding sites are known (with 9-10 pairs in total), all restricted to a small area which is unlikely to harbour more than c. 40 breeding burrows in total. Data collected at sea indicates that the population is probably c.1,000 of which 50-100 breeding pairs is a likely estimate.

Threats
The main threats are likely to be predation by feral cats and rats and urban light-induced mortality. Widespread light pollution such as street lamps and sport installations are responsible for the greatest majority of light-induced petrel mortality on Réunion. Mortality of juveniles is likely to affect the long term population dynamics

Conservation actions to date
Since 1996, there has been a campaign to quantify urban light-induced mortality and to rescue as many birds as possible. The rescues have been successful, with over 90% of the petrels (of various species) found on Réunion being released again. From 1996-2002 a public appeal aimed at rescuing downed birds produced 8 petrels of which 7 were banded and released.

Conservation actions required
- Develop an action plan for known breeding sites.
- Continue rescue programme of young birds attracted by lights.
- Investigate light-reduction programmes either through light-shielding or light-restriction during the fledgling period.
- Continue to search for further breeding grounds and, once found, evaluate population numbers, major threats and conservation action required.

Townsend´s Shearwater
Puffinus auricularis
Population: 46,000 ↓

Photo: © Danielle Cholewiak

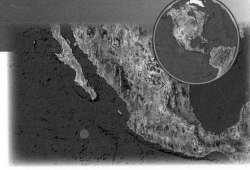

Range & population
This shearwater breeds in burrows in dense bushy areas at the forest edge on Socorro in the Revillagigedo Islands, Mexico. 46,000 individuals, including 10,600 breeding birds, were estimated during at-sea censuses in 1980-1994. It is, however, clear that the breeding range has contracted as other islands in the group (Clárion and San Benedicto) have held the species, and there are indications that numbers are declining rapidly. Birds seen immediately north of San Benedicto island in 1988 and 1990 provide some hope that a population remains on this former breeding site. Non-breeders forage largely in waters over the continental shelf of Mexico.

Threats
Cats were introduced to Socorro in the early 1970s, and more than 92% of cat scats above 500 m contain shearwater remains. Sheep are destroying nesting habitat and pigs were introduced to Clarión soon after 1979, and by 1988 numerous shearwater remains littered burrows destroyed by severe pig rooting. Sheep and rabbits have also destroyed habitat and nesting sites on Clarión. In 1952, a volcanic eruption obliterated the San Benedicto population.

Conservation actions to date
IIn 1994, the Revillagigedo Islands were declared a biosphere reserve. Surveys and monitoring are also in progress in 2007.

Conservation actions required
- Eradicate introduced mammals on Socorro and Clarión.
- Determine whether a breeding population remains on San Benedicto.
- Assist the recolonisation of Clarión.
- Continue to monitor numbers on Socorro and at sea.

New Zealand Storm Petrel
Oceanites maorianus
Population: > 200, trend unknown

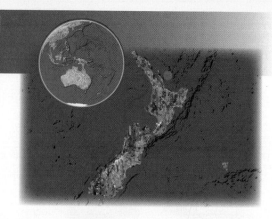

Photo: © Otto Samwald

Hauraki Gulf, New Zealand, 2006

History

1827 – the first two specimens are collected by French ornithologists J. R. C. Quoy (1790-1869) and J. P. Gaimard (1796-1858) on board the ship Astrolabe in January – March, probably along the east coast of North Island.

1895 – a third specimen is brought to the British Museum at Tring. This is the type specimen.

1932 – G. M Mathews describes the species as *Paeleornis maoriana*. The following years scientists are uncertain whether it is a subspecies of Wilson's Storm Petrel, a distinct species or a separate genus.

2003 – a storm petrel, thought to be Black-bellied *Fregetta tropica* is photographed by Brent Stephenson on a pelagic birding tour off Mercury Islands, North Island on January 25th. On 1st November a black and white storm petrel is seen in the Hauraki Gulf, just north of Little Barrier Island. On 17th November British birders Bob Flood and Bryan Thomas charter a fishing boat and photograph 10-20 storm petrels which are later confirmed as New Zealand Storm Petrels. On 13th December a number of NZ storm petrels are seen in the Hauraki Gulf.

2004-2007 – New Zealand Storm Petrels are regularly observed in the outer Hauraki Gulf (October – April) and northern New Zealand waters (March – May) by Chris Gaskin, Karen Baird and others during seabird pelagics – a number of endemic seabirds breed on Hauraki Gulf islands (most of which are now rat-free and well-protected nature reserves).

2005 – first bird in the hand is obtained when fisherman Geordie Murman captures a bird that has flown into his cabin. In November or December a bird is seen in floodlight on one of the Mokohinau Islands but eludes capture.

2006 – three birds are captured at sea by Department of Conservation staff and are fitted with transmitters.

2007 – a search of both published and unpublished historical records for black and white storm petrels has revealed a number of probable earlier sightings for northern New Zealand waters during 1969-90.
On 6th October, 10 or more New Zealand Storm Petrels are recorded, the first for the 2007/08 summer.

Range & population

The species was known only from three specimens collected in the 19th century off the east coast of North Island, New Zealand although fossil material indicate that it could have occurred at the East Cape region and South Island West Coast. It is thought to be a summer breeding seabird to the Hauraki Gulf, although a nest site has yet to be found. Four birds have been caught at sea, with all measured and DNA samples collected. Transmitters were attached to three birds, although this did not lead to the discovery of breeding sites as the transmitters only survived 4-5 weeks. The ecology of this species is unknown but it is thought to be migratory as it appears to be absent from northern New Zealand waters from June to August each year. It is readily attracted to chum slicks. At least 23 different individual birds have been identified from photos/trapping.

Threats

None are known, but the species could conceivably be impacted by introduced predators. Most of the likely islands in northern New Zealand are, however, rat-free.

Conservation actions to date

It may have already benefited from rat-eradication programmes on offshore islands. Searches for breeding grounds are underway and coordinated by NZ's Department of Conservation.

Conservation actions required

- Urgently clarify the taxonomic position of this taxon.
- Carry out further surveys at sea in the vicinity of the recent observations and elsewhere.
- Search for breeding grounds, in particular by seawatching at dusk from promontories on predator-free islands and potentially by catching individuals at sea and fitting them with radio-transmitters.
- If it is found to breed on an island with introduced predators, eradicate these as an urgent priority.

Photo: © Brent Stephenson

Hauraki Gulf, New Zealand, 2004

Guadalupe Storm-petrel
Oceanodroma macrodactyla
Population: < 50, unknown trend

Painting: © Lyn Wells / BirdLife International

Range & population
This storm petrel may persist on Guadalupe but has not been recorded breeding since 1912. Searches in 1922, 1925 and the early 1970s failed to find the species. Relatively recent reports of storm-petrels calling at night and the apparent persistence of breeding Leach's Storm-petrel *O. leucorhoa* on the island raises some hope that it may survive. Its non-breeding range is unknown.

Threats
The main cause of its demise is thought to be heavy predation by feral cats, compounded by goats destroying and degrading nesting habitat.

Conservation actions to date
Guadalupe is designated as a biosphere reserve, but there is little active management. Nearly 35,000 goats were removed in 1970 and 1971, but current numbers are conservatively estimated at 10,000 individuals. There is apparently governmental interest in eradicating introduced predators and herbivores, and non-government organisations in the region are developing the capacity to undertake eradication programmes. There is potential to remove introduced species by 2010 with fundraising for cat eradication underway. A grant has been made available to fund searches for the species on Guadalupe.

Conservation actions required
- Survey the entire island during the breeding season to ascertain if it is still extant.
- Eradicate introduced predators and herbivores.
- Birders on pelagic trips off California should be aware of this species and its identification.

Alaotra Grebe
Tachybaptus rufolavatus
Population: < 50, unknown trend

Photo: © Paul Thompson

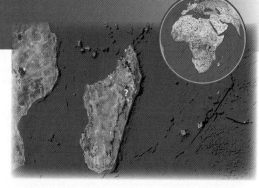

Range & population
Endemic to Madagascar and known chiefly from Lake Alaotra, but is now probably extinct as there are no records since September 1985. Individuals showing some characters of the species were also seen on Lake Alaotra in 1986 and 1988. However, unidentified grebes were seen in 2000 at the nearby Lake Amparihinandriambavy, where there is no close human habitation. The species was probably incapable of prolonged flight, so in all likelihood never occurred very far from Lake Alaotra. Usually found in pairs, sometimes in association with Little Grebe *T. ruficollis*, it feeds almost exclusively on fish. Its breeding ecology is unknown.

Threats
Two major factors have contributed recently to this species' decline; the use of monofilament nylon gill-nets and the introduction, in about 1986, of the carnivorous fish *Ophiocephalus*, which is probably capable of eating adults. Introductions of exotic plants, mammals and fish, especially *Tilapia*, have probably depleted essential foods for the species. Hybridisation with Little Grebe has occurred in the past and may have been a contributing factor in this species' decline.

Conservation actions to date
A collaborative effort is underway to conserve the last vestiges of useful habitat at Lake Alaotra. The Malagasy government has ratified the Ramsar Convention, and Lake Alaotra may be proposed as a Ramsar Site

Conservation actions required
- Conduct further searches at other sites to confirm whether or not this species is extant, particularly nearby Lake Amparihinandriambavy.
- Protect areas of least-modified wetland at Lake Alaotra.

Junin Grebe
Podiceps taczanowskii
Population: 100-300 ↓

Lake Junin (Lake Chinchaycocha)

Photo: © Alejandro Tello

and fishing is regulated but little has been done to interfere with the management of the water level, which has been in the hands of mining companies. An attempt has been made to translocate grebes to a lake north of Junín. Capture and transfer was feasible, but the chosen lake (and others) was unsuitable, because of the use of gill-nets to fish rainbow trout. In 2002, the Peruvian government passed an emergency law to protect the lake, which makes provisions for its cleaning, and places greater restrictions on the extraction of water.

History
1894 – Jean Stanislaus Stolzmann (1854 – 1928) and Hans von Berlepsch (1815 – 1950) describe the species.

1938 – the species is considered abundant.

1961 – well over 1,000 birds are present.

1977-78 – the population is estimated at 300 birds.

1992-93 – the total population may be down to 50-100 birds.

1995 – a new extrapolation method produces 205 individuals, but the next successful breeding will not take place until in 1997.

2001 – the total population is estimated at c. 300 individuals.

2007 – high mortality recorded in connection with a cold front with low temperatures.

Range & population
This flightless grebe is confined to Lake Junín at 4,080 m in the highlands of Junín, west-central Peru. Lake Junín is fairly shallow and bordered by extensive reed marshes. The grebe forages in open water, near the outer reed-border in the (wet) breeding season (November-March) and in the centre of the lake in the dry austral winter. It feeds mainly on small *Orestias* fish (which become scarce when the reedbeds dry out) supplemented with arthropods. It nests in colonies and nests are built in flooded reedbeds. The clutch size is two eggs. It is probably long-lived.

Threats
Water-level regulation for a hydroelectric plant supplying nearby mines causes nesting and foraging areas to dry out, and breeding to fail. Mining activities also pollute the lake, with the north-western part rendered "lifeless" by iron-oxide sedimentation. Relatively unstable climatic conditions, linked to El Niño Southern Oscillation events, may have contributed to large population fluctuations, with rapid population recovery in years with high water levels (e.g. 1997-1998). Its apparent inability to recover in good years suggests that a series of poor years would be very concerning.

Conservation actions to date
Lake Junín has been declared a national reserve. Hunting

Conservation actions required
* Biannual monitoring of the population and reproductive success.
* Research the species' requirements, including food, throughout its life-cycle.
* Prepare and implement a species recovery plan and involve local people in a participatory species action plan as well as environmental education and awareness raising campaigns.
* Reduce pollution (and continue monitoring water quality) and regulate water-levels for the benefit of local people and wildlife with the agreement and participation of the local mining company.
* Produce awareness material and lobby for restauration of lake Junin.
* Assess the feasibility of a sustainable habitat management programme.
* Identify a lake for potential translocation of individuals.
* Develop ecotourism in the area including involving locals and aid the population monitoring.

Lake Junin (Lake Chinchaycocha)

Photo: © Alejandro Tello

White-bellied Heron
Ardea insignis

Kachin State, Myanmar, 2005

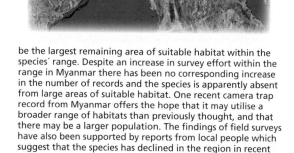

Photo: © Andrew "Jack" Tordoff

Population: 50-249 ↓

History

1878 – British ornithologist A. O. Hume (1829-1912) describes the species.

1929 – the first nest of the species is found in Myanmar.

2006 – 16 birds are believed to constitute the total population in Bhutan in February. Three active nests in Bhutan in May held eight chicks in total.

2007 – the species is upgraded from Endangered to Critically Endangered.

This heron has been treated as Imperial Heron, *Ardea imperialis*, previously.

Range & population

The range of this heron spans the eastern Himalayan foothills in Bhutan and north-east India to the hills of Bangladesh, north Myanmar and, historically at least, across west and central Myanmar. Previous reports suggest it was common in Myanmar and, although it remains locally distributed there, it has evidently declined throughout its range. The 8400 sq miles Hukaung tiger reserve in Myanmar is believed to support approximately 30-40 individuals and is thought to be the largest remaining area of suitable habitat within the species' range. Despite an increase in survey effort within the range in Myanmar there has been no corresponding increase in the number of records and the species is apparently absent from large areas of suitable habitat. One recent camera trap record from Myanmar offers the hope that it may utilise a broader range of habitats than previously thought, and that there may be a larger population. The findings of field surveys have also been supported by reports from local people which suggest that the species has declined in the region in recent years. It may also occur in south-east Tibet, China, but is now extinct from Nepal. White-bellied Herons are seen in the Brahmaputra lowlands in winter. The Bhutan population is thought to number 21 individuals in total, occurring mainly along the Puna Tsangchhu river and its major tributaries. It is primarily recorded from small or large rivers, usually with sand or gravel bars, often within or adjacent to subtropical broadleaved forest, from the lowlands up to at least 1,500 m. It tends to frequent inaccessible and undisturbed areas. A recently described nest of the species was in a Chir pine.

Threats

The main threats are widespread loss, degradation and disturbance of forest rivers. Riverine forest habitats have become degraded as a result of pollution, including of mining waste in Myanmar, human disturbance and clearance of forest along rivers and the over-exploitation of resources. Increasing disturbance and habitat degradation from settlement, conversion to agriculture, harvesting of wetland resources and, more locally, poaching are thought to present significant threats in key protected areas in north-east India, Bhutan and Myanmar. In Bhutan and Myanmar, hydro power developments and road improvements may result in habitat degradation in the future.

Furthermore, the Bhutanese government has apparently auctioned off a portion of the riverbed in Punakha-Wangdue for stone and sand quarrying which will affect the primary feeding areas for this species. Hunting, targeting waterbirds along river courses, is reported to be widespread and frequent within the species' range in Myanmar. Furthermore, rivers act as busy transport routes for the human population, exacerbating disturbance of this species. The use of fish-traps is apparently a threat to the Bhutan population.

Conservation actions to date

Some protected areas hold the species such as in Namdapha National Park, India and several other including Kaziranga, Dibru-Saikhowa and Manas National Parks, and Pabitora Wildlife Sanctuary. In Myanmar, a population is found within the Hukaung Tiger Reserve, Hpon Razi Wildlife Sanctuary and Hkakabo Razi National Park. A project studying White-bellied Heron began in Bhutan in 2003 and is run in conjunction with the Royal Society for the Protection of Nature, the World Wildlife Fund, the Felburn Foundation and the International Crane Foundation.

Conservation actions required

- Conduct extensive surveys for the species in north-east India, Myanmar and also south-east Tibet, to establish its distribution, population status and ecological requirements, particularly in breeding areas.
- Support proposals to provide more effective protection for Namdapha National Park, including creation of buffer zones.
- Support requests to maintain habitat and minimise disturbance along the Manas river and around Ada lake, Bhutan.
- Initiate conservation awareness programmes in areas supporting populations, particularly in Myanmar and north-east India, using it as a flagship species.
- Consider satellite tagging individuals to improve current understanding of the species' movements and habitat preferences.

Myanmar, 2007

Photo: © Robert Tizard

Northern Kachin State, Myanmar, November 2005

Photo: © Jonathan C Eames

White-shouldered Ibis

Pseudibis davisoni

Photo: © Jonathan C Eames

Population: 50-249 ↓

History

1836 – German taxidermist Salomon Müller (1804-1864) collects and observes the species in Borneo in December.

1875 – A. O. Hume drescribes the species in his journal 'Stray Feathers'.

1899 – an adult male is collected in Yunnan province, China in April.

1901 – several eggs are taken by collectors in Myanmar in March.

1937 – last record from Thailand.

1946 – Malaysia's only confirmed record is a bird in Sarawak in November.

1999 – last confirmed records from Vietnam.

2003 – a total of 23 are counted in Cambodia 23-24 January.

2004 – Cambodia population numbers 33 in November.

2005 – Cambodia population numbers 70 in November.

2006 – 108 birds are recorded at two sites in Cambodia on 1st November.

Range & population

White-shouldered Ibis occurs at a few sites in northern and eastern Cambodia (c. 125 birds), extreme southern Laos (c. 10 birds) and East Kalimantan, Indonesia (30-100 birds). It was previously widely but patchily distributed across much of Thailand, Laos, south and central Vietnam and Cambodia, parts of Myanmar, Kalimantan (Indonesia), Sarawak (Malaysia) and south-west Yunnan, China, but has declined dramatically during the 20th century. It is extinct from Thailand and there are no recent records from Myanmar. The principal global stronghold is in Siem Pang District in northern Cambodia where dry season counts have increased in recent years, although the reasons behind this apparent increase are unlikely to represent a genuine population increase as the number of nests recorded in the country remains very low. In Kalimantan, the population at the main locality along the Mahakam River was estimated at 30-100 individuals. It inhabits lakes, pools, marshes and slow-flowing watercourses in open, level, lowland rainforest, often subject to seasonal flooding. It also occurs in sparsely wooded, dry or wet grasslands and wide rivers with sand and gravel bars. White-shouldered ibis has been recorded along large rivers such as the Mekong in Cambodia and on the Mahakam in Kalimantan. Nesting has been recorded (during the dry season - November to April) on the edges of seasonally abandoned wet season rice paddy in Cambodia. It has been observed feeding in soft substrates on the forest floor as well as at small waterbodies. Its movements within South-East Asia are very poorly known. Large flocks, of up to 80 individuals, have been recorded in Siem Pang District, Cambodia.

Threats
It has declined as a result of habitat loss, through logging of lowland forest and drainage of wetlands for agriculture (for example, most of the Mekong floodplain in southern Laos has been converted to rice-paddies), livestock-grazing, grass harvesting, and development. Habitat loss has been compounded by hunting for food and disturbance, leading to the loss of secure feeding, roosting and nesting areas. Recent evidence suggests that forest fires in Borneo resulting from an El Niño Southern Oscillation (ENSO) event shifted the distribution of this species to unburnt stretches of rivers. There has been speculation that the species is associated with large ungulates in south-east Asia which may help to create and maintain seasonal pools within the dry forest landscape, hence, the demise of herbivores within the region may have catalysed the rapid decline of ibis. Disturbance and persecution are probably now the greatest threats in some countries.

Conservation actions to date
White-shouldered Ibis occurs in several protected areas in Cambodia and Laos and it is also depicted on public-awareness material distributed in these countries. The species was a priority species during the designation of Cambodian IBAs and priority areas for conservation in Cambodia. Research has been conducted into the species' foraging ecology and nesting in Preah Vihear Protected Forest, Cambodia.

Conservation actions required
- Prepare a proposal for the establishment of a Protected Forest in Western Siem Pang, Cambodia.
- Investigate the feasibility and value of establishing a nest protection scheme with incentives to local people for protecting nest sites, and if worthwhile, implement such a scheme.
- Continue monitoring the known population in Siem Pang and in other parts of its range as well as researching the ecological requirements of the species.

Photo: © Andrew "Jack" Tordoff

Stung Treng province, Cambodia, 2006

- Conduct further surveys in Borneo, central, northern and eastern Cambodia and south-west Vietnam to quantify remaining populations.
- Establish further protected areas or integrated conservation development projects covering landscape-level habitat tracts supporting populations, particularly in northern Cambodia and along the Mahakam river, East Kalimantan, Indonesia.
- Enforce strict protection at important permanent wetlands.
- Promote widespread conservation awareness programmes aimed at reducing wetland disturbance and large waterbird exploitation in Indo-China.

BirdLife Species Guardian   **Prach Pich Phirun**

Photo: © Jonathan C Eames

Northern Bald Ibis
Geronticus eremita

Tamri, Morocco, 2005

Population: 280 ↓

History

1504 – Archbishop Leonard of Salzburg publishes a decree protecting the species.

1555 – Konrad von Gesner of Switzerland publishes a drawing and description of Bald Ibis, widely believed to be a hoax.

1758 – first described by Carolus Linneaus (1707-1778).

1839 – William Francis Ainsworth mentions the Birecik colony.

1854 – a colony is discovered in Syria.

1930 – Moroccan population numbers 1,000 birds.

1940 – 38 colonies known in Morocco.

1975 – 250 pairs and 100-150 non-breeding birds in 15 colonies in Morocco.

1989 – 1 wild bird remains in Birecik, Turkey.

2002 – although now believed to be extinct from Syria, a new colony is discovered near Palmyra.

2005 – a wild bird, presumed originating from the Moroccan population is recorded in Extremadura, Spain February to May.

2006 – the Syrian population is down to 13 individuals, 4 birds winter in Ethiopia.

2007 – just two pairs with three chicks each plus three subadults are present in Syria in 2007.

Range & population
Revered by the Egyptians on hieroglyphs 5000 years ago, this rare ibis originally bred in southern Europe (Switzerland, Germany and Austria, possibly also Hungary, Spain and Italy) and across North Africa to Turkey. It is similar to the Southern Bald Ibis *Geronticus calvus*, but fossil records indicate that the two species split from each other very long ago. Moroccan birds, which constitute 95% of the population, are resident just moving shorter distances locally (exceptionally to Mauretania and Mali), whilst the Syrian and the former Turkish populations are migratory, to northeast Africa. Satellite-tagging of Syrian birds has revealed that this population migrates south through Jordan and Saudi Arabia; six birds spent three weeks in Yemen (July-August 2006), then wintering in central Ethiopia; migrating back to Syria, through Eritrea, Sudan, Saudi Arabia and Jordan in February 2007. Importantly, since 1980 there has been no overall decline in numbers at Souss-Massa NP in Morocco. Growing numbers and good productivity (over 500 birds in the Moroccan population after the breeding season in recent years) give cause for optimism that former areas may soon be recolonised. A semi-wild population numbering 91 individuals in 2006 exists at Birecik, Turkey. They are free-flying for five months and breed in natural nest sites on cliffs but are taken into captivity after the breeding season to prevent migration. Captive populations have been maintained in Austria (at Grünau, 22 birds, now breeding), Italy and Spain with a long-

term aim to re-establish the species in parts of its former range.

Threats
It has declined for several centuries, perhaps at least partly owing to unidentified natural causes. However, the more recent rapid decline is undoubtedly the result of a combination of factors, with different threats affecting different populations. In Morocco illegal buildings, disturbance close to the breeding cliffs and changes in farming on the feeding grounds are the threats that may have the most severe impact on the population. In Syria hunting is the main threat to the tiny population, and overgrazing has reduced habitat quality in some areas. At Souss-Massa NP, Morocco, the most recent causes of breeding failures have been loss of eggs to predators and, more importantly, poor chick survival as a result of starvation and predation.

Conservation actions to date
In 1999 The International Advisory Group for the Northern Bald Ibis (IAGNBI) was created to coordinate efforts and provide scientific advice. An international species action plan was published in 2006. Over 1,000 individuals of the western population exist in captivity worldwide, but birds from the eastern population are much rarer in captivity (four Turkish zoos hold 20 birds and participate in an *ex situ* breeding operation). An international studbook was discontinued in 1998. A breeding programme at Birecik aims to establish a partially captive population of 150 birds to provide birds for release to the wild population. Colour-ringing of young at Birecik has begun and there are plans to attach satellite transmitters to a family party in 2007. Other captive breeding schemes exist or are planned in Austria, Spain, Italy and an experimental testing phase of a potential reintroduction project is planned in Bavaria.
There have been experimental field studies of the feeding ecology of hand-raised individuals in potential summer and winter habitat in Europe. In 1991, the Souss-Massa National Park in Morrocco was designated specifically to protect nesting and feeding areas and in 1994, a monitoring and research programme was set up involving local people. The Palmyra project in Syria has initiated a research and protection programme in collaboration with local communities. Three birds were satellite-tagged there in June 2006. The project also aims to search further areas of the Syrian steppe in the near future. The breeding area in Syria was declared a protected area in 2004 by the Ministry of Agriculture and Agrarian Reform. Ecotourism and awareness-raising has been promoted throughout the range. Conservation action to date has focused on reducing the negative influences on breeding success, but it is recognised that for such a long-lived bird adult survival is also likely to be an important limiting factor on the population size.

Conservation actions required
- Conduct research into feeding and breeding biology, and habitat requirements.
- Continue to monitor numbers and breeding success.
- Protect key breeding and roosting sites from disturbance and development.
- Explore the possibility of reintroducing captive-bred birds into previously occupied sites (when detailed information on ecological requirements is available).
- Research feasibility of re-establishing a wild (preferably migratory) population in Turkey.
- Better link the Birecik and Syrian populations and projects; research potential to supplement Syrian colony with birds from Turkey.
- Continue with current husbandry at Birecik to increase colony to 150-200 birds.
- Protect wintering areas in Ethiopia.
- Determine where young birds go after leaving Syrian breeding colony.
- Raise awareness among hunters on the migration route.

Birecik-Sanliurfa-Turkey, 2007

Photo: © Soner Bekir

Tamri, Morocco, 2007

Photo: © Andy Hultberg

Tamri-Agadir, Morocco, 2007

Photo: © Roy Seadog

Giant Ibis
Thaumatibis gigantea
Population: 50-249 ↓

Cambodia, 2007

Photo: © Ron Hoff

Range & population
This species is confined to northern Cambodia and in extreme southern Laos. Singles, pairs or small parties occur in marshes, pools, wide rivers and seasonal water-meadows in open, predominantly deciduous, dipterocarp lowland forest, although historically it also frequented rice-paddies. Its diet comprises a variety of invertebrates, crustaceans, small amphibians and reptiles. Nothing is known of its breeding biology.

Threats
It has declined as a result of hunting, wetland drainage for agriculture, and deforestation. However, given that wide tracts of apparently suitable habitat remain in parts of southern Laos and central and northern Cambodia, human disturbance and hunting, particularly during the dry season when birds are concentrated around available waterholes, are almost certainly the greatest threats.

Conservation actions to date
It occurs at least seasonally in one actual and one proposed National Biodiversity Conservation Area in Laos, and at a wildlife sanctuary in Cambodia. It is depicted on public-awareness material in Laos and Cambodia as part of an ongoing campaign to reduce hunting of large waterbirds.

Conservation actions required
- Conduct further surveys to locate and quantify remaining populations in Laos and Cambodia.
- Investigate its breeding requirements, demography and seasonal movements.
- Establish further protected areas.
- Consolidate and promote further public-awareness.

Dwarf Olive Ibis
Bostrychia bocagei
Population: 50-249 ↓

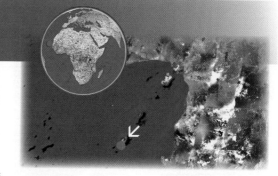

Ribeira Peixe, São Tomé, August 2006

Photo: © Nik Borrow

Range & population
This small ibis is endemic to São Tomé, São Tomé e Príncipe. The first confirmed sighting was in 1990. It is apparently relatively widely, if thinly, distributed in the south. It feeds on the forest floor in areas with sparse undergrowth and in swampy areas bordering watercourses.

Threats
Today, land privatisation is leading to an increase in the number of small farms and the clearance of trees. Road developments along the east and west coasts are increasing access to previously remote areas. Introduced mammals are all potential predators. Hunting may be the most serious threat currently with a report of 16 birds being killed in 1996/1997.

Conservation actions to date
Protection of primary forest and a national park has been proposed, but as yet the forest remains unprotected. A new law providing for the gazetting of protected areas and the protection of threatened species awaits final ratification.

Conservation actions required
- Advocacy and awareness-raising for the species and primary forest protection.
- Identification of key sites and training of staff to ensure protection.
- Field research and mapping of protection zone.
- Formulate species conservation measures and list as protected under national law.
- Ensure legal protection of all remaining lowland primary forest.

BirdLife Species Guardian  **Angus Gascoigne**
(Associação dos Biólogos Santomenses)

Christmas Frigatebird
Fregata andrewsi
Population: 2,400-4,800 ↓

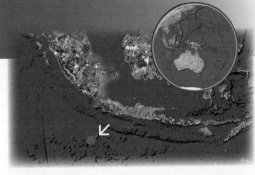

Christmas Island, 2007

Photo: © Dick Jenkin

Range & population
As the name implies, this bird is endemic to Christmas Island (to Australia), foraging at low densities over the Indian Ocean and throughout the Indo-Malay archipelago. It breeds every second year and there are indications that its population decreased by about 66% over three generations between 1945 and 2003. When not breeding, the species ranges widely across the seas of South East Asia to Indochina and south to northern Australia. Satellite tracking in 2005 showed one female undertook a non-stop 26-day 4,000 km return flight from Christmas Island and back via Sumatra and Borneo.

Threats
Future habitat loss is possible through construction of satellite launch pads and refugee transit stations. About two thirds of the nests are now located in a single colony, making the species vulnerable to cyclones or forest-fire. A possible threat is the introduced Yellow Crazy Ant *Anoplolepis gracilipes*.

Conservation actions to date
The Christmas Island National Park was established in 1980, and has since been extended to include two of the three current breeding colonies. A control programme for Yellow Crazy Ant has been successfully initiated since 2000.

Conservation actions required
- Implement the species recovery plan.
- Develop and implement appropriate techniques to monitor the total/breeding population size and population structure.
- Implement community education programme.
- Negotiate protection of all known and potential nesting habitat and appropriate buffers.
- Maintain a quarantine barrier between Christmas Island and other lands to minimise the risks of new avian diseases establishing.

Chatham Islands Shag
Phalacrocorax onslowi
Population: 540 ↓

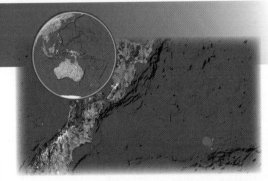

Chatham Islands, New Zealand, 2006

Photo: © Brent Stephenson

Range & population
Breeds on three islands in the Chatham Islands (to New Zealand): Chatham, Star Keys and Rabbit, with a fourth population on North East Reef. It has decreased significantly since 1997. It nests in colonies, usually high on exposed rocks on top of headlands or small islands, or on cliff-ledges.

Threats
The largest breeding colonies are found on predator-free islands. On Chatham, colonies are disturbed by humans, farm stock, feral cats, agriculture, feral pigs, introduced Weka *Gallirallus australis* and Brush-tailed Possum *Trichosurus vulpecula* as well as dogs. Birds sometimes stampede from their nests causing egg breakage and subsequent predation by gulls, and several breeding colonies have been abandoned. New Zealand Fur Seal *Arctocephalus forsteri* disturb the colony on Star Keys, and have occupied former colony sites. Visits by ecotourists can cause disturbance to colonies if not supervised carefully. Individuals are occasionally caught in crayfish pots. Inferred population declines may reflect marine changes affecting their food supply.

Conservation actions to date
The first census of this species was completed in 1997, with a follow up census carried out in 2003-2004 under the Chatham Island Shag and Pitt Island Shag recovery plan.

Conservation actions required
- Census entire adult population every 5 years.
- Monitor a Chatham Island colony yearly to determine trends.
- Fence colonies from livestock and pigs on main Chatham Island if agreement is reached with local owners.
- Educate dog owners about the possible impact of dogs on breeding grounds.
- Obtain legal protection for all colonies.

California Condor
Gymnogyps californianus

Population: 44 ↑

History

1602 – Antonio de la Ascencion, is the first non-native American to observe the species, at Monterey, California.

1792 – Scottish naturalist Archibald Menzies (1754-1842) collects the first California Condor in Monterey, California.

1805 – explorers Lewis and Clark report sighting a condor near the Columbia River in present-day Washington State.

1908 – a California condor is shot in Los Angeles County and the shooter is fined $50.00.

1924 – the last sighting of a California Condor in Arizona.

1937 – the species disappears from outside California. The 1,200 acre Sisquoc Condor Sanctuary is established by the U.S. Forest Service (USFS).

1965 – a yearly survey is initiated and runs until 1981.

1967 – the species is federally listed as endangered.

1977 – around 45 birds are known.

1985 – only 9 birds survive.

1987 – all surviving birds are moved into captivity.

2002 – first wild breeding resumed.

2003 – 138 in captivity, and 85 reintroduced in California and northern Arizona make up the population.

2005 – 17 breeding attempts in the wild are recorded.

2006 – 130 wild birds at five release sites in December.

2007 – the first chick born in Mexico for over 75 years hatched in April and a bird from the Baja population was seen in San Diego, raising hopes of cross-border interactions.

Range & population

The California Condor used to breed from British Colombia to Baja California during the 20th century. It declined rapidly throughout its historic range and in 1987 the species became extinct in the wild when the last of the six wild individuals was captured to join a captive-breeding recovery programme involving 27 birds. Breeding commences earliest at six years of age. The reintroduction programme has expanded its geographic coverage, with six birds released into Baja California, Mexico in 2002 and following years. The regular movements of the Arizona birds are confined to Coconnino County (Arizona) and Kane County (Utah), although a handful of individuals have wandered north to Flaming Gorge (Wyoming) and localities in Colorado before returning to the Grand Canyon area. The Baja California birds are largely confined to the Sierra de San Pedro Martir, where efforts are ongoing to increase the population to an anticipated carrying capacity of c. 20 pairs. It is hoped these birds will range widely enough to be effectively connected with congeners in the southern USA. Its range includes rocky, open-country scrubland, coniferous forest and oak savanna. Cliffs, rocky outcrops or large trees are used as nest sites. It scavenges on the carcasses of large mammals. Released birds have become increasingly independent in finding food and may range more than 400 km from release sites.

Threats
The drastic population decline during the 20th century is principally attributed to persecution and accidental ingestion of lead-shot from carcasses, resulting in lead poisoning. Lead poisoning remains a threat for released birds and has caused many fatalities. Shooting and accidental poisoning continue to be the principal threats to condors, but the federal government will gradually phase out the use of lead in the U.S, and shooting is becoming less of a problem for this well-publicized species. It has been particularly prone to the threat of lead-poisoning owing to its longevity and delayed onset of breeding, and given the distances it travels to forage meaning lead can build up in the blood to dangerous levels over many years having been ingested over a large area. Recently, 9 of 13 birds released at the Pinnacles National Monument in California had to be recaptured and tested for lead poisoning after feasting on a field of squirrel carcasses shot by hunters using lead-shot. Ingestion of foreign objects such as glass, fragments, electrical wiring, metal bottle tops etc has recently been found to be a threat to nestlings. Overall survival of released birds has been high, although it is estimated that rates of mortality in the wild still exceed sustainable levels. Puppet-reared birds may be more prone to exhibit problematic human-oriented behaviour such as tameness and vandalising property than parent-reared birds. In the early 1990s, a number of captive-reared birds were lost due to collisions with power lines, but this behavioural problem has been addressed using a conditioning programme with fake power poles. The spread of West Nile virus is not anticipated to be a problem for the species as most birds are vaccinated.

Conservation actions to date
A large-scale, integrated captive-breeding and reintroduction programme, managed by The Peregrine Fund (at the World Center for Birds of Prey), Los Angeles Zoo and San Diego Wild Animal Park, is preventing extinction in the wild. The success of the scheme has seen an increase from one chick hatched in 1988 to an annual hatch of 25-30 birds in recent years. Oregon Zoo has been approved as the fourth captive condor breeding institution, and received 6 pairs of condors in 2003. Aversion training to avoid power lines and humans is practised. 154 condors were released into the wild between 1992 and 2003. Clean carcasses are provided for reintroduced birds to help prevent lead-poisoning, and community education programmes aim to minimise persecution. Publicity measures include a website and near-weekly condor articles in local newspapers. The Arizona Game and Fish Department is now distributing safer lead-substitute bullets free of charge to hunters within the foraging range of the condors, and similar programs are being initiated in California. Furthermore, the Tejon Ranch Company which operates California's largest hunting programme on a 270,000 acre ranch in the Tehachapi Mountains is to phase out the use of lead shot on its land. The genetic diversity of the population has been maintained through careful distribution and representation of founder genotypes at each captive-breeding facility and reintroduction site.

Conservation actions required
- Continue the recovery plan to achieve two disjunct, self-sustaining populations of 150 individuals comprising 15 breeding pairs.
- Identify further potential release sites in southern New Mexico.
- Resume release programme in Mexico.
- Maintain and increase the productivity of the captive population.
- Continue releases of captive-bred birds.
- Maintain suitable habitat.
- Clean up sites used by condors.
- Establish condor restaurants in areas with less rubbish.
- Continue and expand information and education programmes.
- Continue supplying alternative lead-free ammunition to deer hunters.
- Advocate strongly for a ban on lead-shot and lobby the Fish and Game Commission to ensure legislation is passed.

Grand Canyon, 2005

Photo: © Marcus Lawson

Photo: © Scott Frier, USDA Agricultural Research Service

White-collared Kite
Leptodon forbesi
Population: < 50 ⬇

Painting: © Norman Arlott/HBW2 (lynx Edicions)

This species may be a subspecies of Grey-headed Kite *Leptodon cayanensis*.

Range & population
The remaining population of this kite is assumed to be tiny. It is currently known from three sites, but these are severely fragmented and there have not been any recent records. It has been recorded in Pernambuco and Alagoas, north-east Brazil. The extent of habitat loss indicates that there must have been significant declines in both numbers and range.

Threats
There has been massive deforestation in coastal Alagoas and Pernambuco, with most suitable habitat cleared or threatened. The two key sites in Alagoas are both under severe threat. The current condition of forest at Água Azul is unknown.

Conservation actions to date
The land at Murici remains privately-owned and a number of conservation initiatives have so far failed to halt forest loss. Actions required are to urgently survey all three known sites and other parcels of forest in Pernumbuco and Alagoas especially near Murici.

Conservation actions required
- Urgently survey all three known sites and other parcels of forest in Pernambuco and Alagoas.
- Designate Murici as a biological reserve and ensure its *de facto* protection.
- Protect any remaining forest at São Miguel dos Campos.
- Conduct field and museum studies to clarify its taxomonic status.

Cuban Kite
Chondrohierax wilsonii
Population: 50-249 ⬇

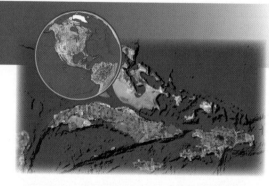

Painting: © Norman Arlott/HBW2 (lynx Edicions)

Range & population
This species, previously treated as a subspecies, has declined rapidly and now has an extremely small population, confined to a single area. There is a continuing decline in numbers and a very high chance of imminent extinction and the last record is from 1992. Cuban Kite was formerly fairly widespread on Cuba, but is now confined to a tiny area in the east of the island between Moa and Baracoa, and possibly other parts of Holguín and Guantánamo provinces. It is Cuba's rarest raptor. It is now confined to montane gallery forest, where it feeds chiefly on tree snails and slugs in the understorey. Historically, it inhabited xerophytic vegetation and montane forest.

Threats
The decline is mainly attributed to habitat destruction and alteration caused by logging and agricultural conversion. Farmers persecute the species because they (mistakenly) believe that it preys on poultry. Harvesting has apparently reduced numbers of tree snails, and thereby food availability.

Conservation actions to date
None known.

Conservation actions required
- Survey to assess distribution and population.
- Effectively protect remaining habitat.
- Protect tree snails.
- Conduct public awareness and education campaigns to help prevent persecution of the species.
- Protect the species under Cuban law.

Madagascar Fish-eagle
Haliaeetus vociferoides
Population: 233 ↓

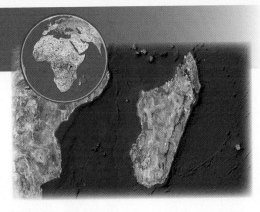

Madagascar, 2005

the tendency for pollutants to accumulate in prey tissues.

History
c. 1841 – Mr. Louis Rousseau collects a specimen which is sent to the Natural History Museum in Paris.

1845 – French ornithologist Marc Athanese Parfait Oeillet des Murs (1804-1878) describes the species.

1978-1986 – a survey along the northern coast of Madagascar by Olivier Langrand locates 40 pairs and 10 singles.

1991-1995 – surveys by The Peregrine Fund find at least 222 adults from 105 sites, of which 99 pairs bred.

2005-2006 – surveys by The Peregrine Fund find at least 233 birds.

2006 – in the Manambolomaty Lakes Complex conservation area where The Peregrine Fund works with local communities, 8 of 11 territorial pairs manages breeding, raising five young.

Range & population
Madagascar Fish-eagle survives in low numbers along the west coast of Madagascar. Surveys during 1991-1995 and 2005-2006 recorded birds apparently concentrated into three main regions: the Antsalova region, along the Tsiribihina River and south, and the coast from Mahajamba Bay north to the island of Nosy Hara and Antsiranana. The breeding population had declined slightly in some areas between both these surveys. Immature birds wander widely, making the non-breeding population difficult to assess. The species is found predominantly in wooded areas adjacent to waterbodies. It feeds mainly on fish. Breeding pairs are territorial in May-October, and nest in a large tree or rock cliff. Annual productivity is low with 0.15 young fledged per territory. Clutch-size is two but only one chick is raised, due to siblicide. In one third of breeding attempts no eggs are laid.

Threats
Deforestation, soil erosion and the development of wetland areas for rice-paddies have caused loss of nesting and foraging habitat. The species is also threatened by direct human competition for fish-stocks, persecution through the taking of nestlings for food and shooting of adults, accidental entanglement in fishing-nets, disturbance at breeding sites by human activities and, according to local people, use of eagle body parts in food and traditional medicine. Water pollution poses a potential threat given the species' reliance on fish and

Conservation actions to date
The species has been studied in the Antsalova region and at the Manmbolomaty Lakes Complex, where an ongoing conservation programme aims to increase the known breeding population, through the enforcement of existing traditional laws at the local community level and the release of captive-reared birds rescued from siblicide. In one study, the latter action almost doubled the number of young fledged per nest.

Conservation actions required
- Conduct counts in areas not thoroughly surveyed along the coast between Besalampy and Soalala.
- Monitor population size or distribution to detect changes.
- Increase awareness within local communities, to reduce persecution and protect habitat around nest sites.
- Manage the wild population to increase population size and distribution in suitable habitat.
- Investigate the factors limiting the number of available breeding territories, survival rates of immatures and adults, and reproductive productivity.

THE PEREGRINE FUND
www.peregrinefund.org

The Peregrine Fund works nationally and internationally, to conserve birds of prey in nature. They conserve nature by restoring species in jeopardy, conserving habitat, educating students, training conservationists, providing factual information to the public, and by accomplishing good science.
www.peregrinefund.org

Tsirbihina River, Madagascar, 2006

White-rumped Vulture
Gyps bengalensis

Naliya Kutch, Gujarat, India, 2007

Photo: © Arpit Deomurari

Population: 2,500-9,999 ↓

History

1788 – German physician Johann Friedrich Gmelin (1748-1804) describes the species.

1985 – White-rumped Vulture is considered to be the world's most common bird of prey numbering in the millions.

2000/01 – Toawala in Pakistan houses 445 pairs.

2003 – the colony at Keoladeo, Haryana, India becomes extinct.

2004 – the largest known remaining colony is of 160 pairs at Toawala in Pakistan, 285 pairs less than four years earlier.

2006 – Pakistan bans the use of diclofenac. The Nepalese government bans the import of diclofenac. Alternative drug Meloxicam is considered safe for vultures.

2007 – the year gets off to a good start when the first captive chick is hatched on January 1st and the second on January 9th at a breeding centre in Pinjore, Haryana, India.

Range & population

White-rumped Vulture occurs in Pakistan, India, Bangladesh, Nepal, Bhutan, Myanmar, Thailand, Laos, Cambodia and southern Vietnam, and may be extinct in southern China and Malaysia. It has been recorded from south-east Afghanistan and Iran where its status is currently unknown. It disappeared from most of South-East Asia in the early 20th century and the only viable populations in the region today are found in Cambodia and Myanmar (which both are probably in the low hundreds of individuals).

It occurs mostly in plains and less frequently in hilly regions where it utilises light woodland, villages, cities, and open areas to feed on both putrid and fresh carrion. Considerable aggregations can form while feeding and it breeds in colonies in tall trees, often near human habitation. It is social and usually found in conspecific flocks and regular communal roost sites are used. Movements are poorly known; while it is essentially sedentary, wing-tagging and monitoring of birds at vulture restaurants has shown that they will forage over a vast range. The degree of connectivity of apparently separate populations is not known.

Declines within the Indian subcontinent are ongoing at rates reported to be between 22 and 48 % per year in recent years. The status of some vulture populations in southern India is poorly known and there is some hope that these populations will have avoided the rapid declines that have occurred to the north. Southern India lies south of the "cow belt" where livestock are eaten by the human population and vultures there are therefore expected to feed largely on wild prey.

Threats
Since the mid 1990s, it has suffered a catastrophic decline of over 95% across the Indian Subcontinent (the majority of its historic range), first noticed in Keoladeo National Park, India, but mirrored in Pakistan and Nepal, to the point that the species is highly threatened with extinction. Extensive research has identified the non-steroidal anti-inflammatory veterinary drug, diclofenac, to be the cause behind this rapid population collapse. This drug used to treat domestic livestock is ingested by vultures feeding on carcasses leading to renal failure causing visceral gout. Other likely contributory factors are changes in human consumption and processing of dead livestock, and poison and pesticide use, but these are probably of minor significance. Given the lack of intensive agriculture and associated chemical use in South-East Asia, a decline predating the one in the Indian Subcontinent, and the continued presence of large areas of suitable habitat for the species, the primary reason behind its decline in that region is thought to be the demise of large ungulate populations and improvements in animal husbandry resulting in a lack of available carcasses for vultures. Furthermore, since the collapse of the vulture population the number of feral dogs in parts of India has increased by 20 times since the 1980s and rabies now poses an increased threat to human populations in the Indian Subcontinent.

Conservation actions to date
It has been reported from many protected areas across its range. The Indian government has now passed a bill banning the use of the veterinary drug diclofenac that has caused the rapid population decline across the Indian Subcontinent; their aim was to phase out its use by late 2005. Efforts to complete this process and replace diclofenac with a suitable alternative are ongoing in India, Pakistan and Nepal. Drug companies have now developed Meloxicam, a cheap alternative to diclofenac. Given that residual diclofenac in just one carcass in 250 is enough to have caused the declines seen. 'Vulture restaurants' are being used in an attempt to provide safe food sources for remaining birds. Vulture restaurants are increasingly used as ecotourism attractions in parts of the species range to raise awareness and fund supplementary feeding programmes and research. Birds have been satellite-tagged in various parts of their range to improve understanding of their movements, foraging range, site fidelity etc. to aid development of suitable conservation strategies for the species. Socioeconomic surveys in Nepal have shown that local people are strongly in favour of vulture conservation because of the associated ecological services that vultures provide. The Report of the International South Asian Vulture Recovery Plan Workshop in 2004 gave a comprehensive list of recommendations including establishing a minimum of three captive breeding centres each capable of holding 25 pairs. The centre at Pinjore, Haryana is part of a captive breeding programme established by the RSPB and Bombay Natural History Society.

A website, *www.vulturerescue.org*, has been set up to allow researchers to contribute data on known colonies to identify founder individuals for captive flocks that will ensure that the full geographical spread of the species is represented in captive breeding efforts.

Conservation actions required
- Identify the location and number of remaining individuals and identify action required to prevent extinction.
- Measure the frequency of diclofenac treated carcasses available to vultures.
- Support the ban on the veterinary use of diclofenac, and support species management or restoration, as needed.
- Initiate public awareness and public support programmes.
- Monitor remaining populations, in particular replicate conservation and research activities that have been implemented in Cambodia and Myanmar and survey southern India where it is hoped vulture populations may not have crashed to the same extent that they have in the rest of the Indian Subcontinent.
- Support captive breeding efforts at a number of separate centres.
- Promote the immediate adoption of Melixocam as an alternative to diclofenac.

Dhangdhra, 2007

Rajastahn, 2006

Indian Vulture
Gyps indicus

Near Ramanagar in Karnataka, India, 2007

Population: 2,500-9,999 ↓

History
1985/96 – population 816 birds Keoladeo National Park, India.

1998/99 – population down to 25 birds in Keoladeo National Park, India.

2001 – the species is split from Long-billed Vulture *Gyps tenuirostris*, which it previously has been considered a subspecies of.

2002 – the species is listed as Critically Endangered.

2003 – a colony of 200-250 pairs is discovered in Pakistan.

2006 – Pakistan bans the use of diclofenac. The Nepalese government bans the import of diclofenac. Alternative drug Meloxicam is considered safe for vultures.

This species has recently been redefined after having been considered a subspecies of Long-billed Vulture *Gyps tenuirostris*.

Range & population
Indian Vulture breeds in south-east Pakistan where it is rare and peninsular India south of the Gangetic plain, north to Delhi, east through Madhya Pradesh, south to the Nilgiris,

and occasionally further south. It was common until very recently, but since the mid 1990s, it has suffered a catastrophic decline of over 95% throughout its range, in common with other vulture species of southern Asia. Just one tiny population in the Ramanagaram Hills of Karnataka remains in inland southern India, and it is rare elsewhere within its former range. Declines within the Indian subcontinent are ongoing at rates reported to be between 22 and 48 percent per year in recent years. There is some hope that southern Indian populations will have avoided the rapid declines that have occurred to the north, as the region where these occurr lies south of the 'cow belt' where livestock are eaten and therefore vultures are expected to feed largely on wild prey. It is found in cities, towns and villages near cultivated areas, and in open and wooded areas. This species feeds almost entirely on carrion, and often associates with White-rumped Vulture *G. bengalensis* when scavenging at rubbish dumps and slaughterhouses. It nests almost exclusively in small colonies on cliffs and ruins, although in one area, where cliffs are absent, it has been reported nesting in trees. Vultures also play a key role in the wider landscape as providers of ecosystem services. They were previously heavily relied upon to help dispose of animal and human remains in India.

Threats

Extensive research has identified the non-steroidal anti-inflammatory veterinary drug, diclofenac, to be the cause behind this rapid population collapse. This drug used to treat domestic livestock is ingested by vultures feeding on their carcasses leading to renal failure causing visceral gout. By mid-2000, *Gyps* vultures were being found dead and dying in Pakistan and throughout India, and major declines and local extirpations were being reported. Modelling has shown that to cause the observed rate of decline in *Gyps* vultures, just one in 250 livestock carcasses need contain diclofenac residues. Other likely contributory factors are changes in

human consumption and processing of dead livestock, and poison and pesticide use, but these are probably of minor significance.

Since the collapse of the vulture population the number of feral dogs in parts of India has increased by 20 times since the 1980s and rabies now poses an increased threat to human populations in the Indian Subcontinent.

Conservation actions to date

It has been reported from many protected areas across its range. The Indian government has now passed a bill banning the use of the veterinary drug diclofenac; their aim was to phase out its use by late 2005. Efforts to complete this process and replace diclofenac with a suitable alternative are ongoing in India, Pakistan and Nepal. Drug companies have now developed Meloxicam, a cheap alternative to diclofenac prompting the Nepalese government to adopt this and ban the import of diclofenac with immediate effect in 2006. 'Vulture restaurants' are being established in an attempt to provide safe food sources for remaining birds and also enable research into vulture life histories and movements. Captive breeding efforts are ongoing and successes are hoped for. A website, *www.vulturerescue.org*, has been set up to allow researchers to contribute data on known colonies to assist the identification of founder individuals for captive breeding efforts that represent the full geographical spread of the species

Conservation actions required

- Identify the location and number of remaining individuals and identify action required to prevent extinction.
- Measure the frequency of diclofenac treated carcasses available to vultures.
- Support the ban on the veterinary use of diclofenac, and support species management or restoration, as needed.
- Initiate public awareness and public support programmes.
- Monitor remaining populations, in particular, survey southern India where it is hoped vulture populations may not have crashed to the same extent that they have in the rest of the Indian Subcontinent.
- Support captive breeding efforts at a number of seperate centres.
- Promote the immediate adoption of Melixocam as an alternative to diclofenac.

Rajasthan, April 2006

Photo: © Devki Nanda

Near Ramanagar in Karnataka, India, 2007

Photo: © Ganesh H Shankar

Near Ramanagar in Karnataka, India, 2007

Photo: © Ganesh H Shankar

Slender-billed Vulture

Gyps tenuirostris

Bharathpur, 2004

Photo: © Amano Samarpan

Population: 2,500-9,999 ↓

History

1844 – George Robert Gray (1808-1872) describes the species.

2001 – Long-billed Vulture *Gyps tenuirostris*, is renamed Slender-billed Vulture and Indian Vulture *Gyps indicus* receives specific status.

2002 – classified as Critically Endangered.

2006 – Pakistan bans the use of diclofenac. The Nepalese government bans the import of diclofenac. Alternative drug Meloxicam is considered safe for vultures.

2007 – a colony is discovered in Cambodia in January. In August, the Haryana breeding centre is affected by floods but the vultures kept there are safe.

Long-billed Vulture *Gyps tenuriostris* was recently split into this species and Indian Vulture *Gyps indicus*.

Range & population

Slender-billed Vulture is found in India north of, and including, the Gangetic plain, west to at least Himachal Pradesh and Haryana, south to southern West Bengal (and possibly northern Orissa), east through the plains of Assam, and through southern Nepal, north and central Bangladesh, and Myanmar (except the north). It once occurred in South-East Asia, but it is now thought to be extinct in Thailand and Malaysia, and the only recent records are from Cambodia where the first nests recorded in the country was recently found, and southern Laos. Considerable confusion over the taxonomy and identification of *Gyps* vultures has occurred, making it difficult to be sure of claims for this species. It was once common, but in South-East Asia populations declined through the latter half of the nineteenth century and the first half of the twentieth century, and are now probably very small and restricted in distribution. Small numbers were recorded during a recent survey in Shan State (Myanmar). In India and Nepal, the species was common until very recently, but since the mid 1990s, it has suffered a catastrophic decline

124

(up to 99%). Probably owing to the effects of diclofenac breeding success in parts of its Indian range is reportedly low; of 14 nests found in Assam just 4 had chicks. Diclofenac is apparently entirely absent in Cambodia, adding greater emphasis to that remaining small population.

It inhabits dry open country in the vicinity of human habitation, but also breeds in open country far from villages. In South-East Asia it was found in open and partly wooded country, generally in the lowlands. This species feeds almost entirely on carrion, scavenging at rubbish dumps and slaughterhouses. It has only been recorded nesting in trees, usually large ones (often *Ficus*), at a height of 7-14 m and often near villages. It is social and usually found in conspecific flocks, interacting with other vultures at carcasses. While feeding considerable aggregations can form, and regular communal roost sites are used.

Movements are poorly known. While it is essentially sedentary, wing-tagging and monitoring of birds at vulture restaurants has shown that they will forage over a vast range. The degree of connectivity of apparently separate populations is not known. Vultures also play a key role in the wider landscape as providers of ecosystem services. They were previously heavily relied upon to help dispose of animal and human remains in India. Furthermore, since the collapse of the vulture population the number of feral dogs in parts of India has increased by 20 times since the 1980s and rabies now poses an increased threat to human populations in the Indian Subcontinent.

Threats

By mid-2000, *Gyps* vultures were being found dead and dying throughout India, and major declines and local extirpations were being reported. The anti-inflammatory veterinary drug diclofenac used to treat domestic livestock has been identified as the cause of mortality from renal failure resulting from visceral gout in the vast majority of examined vultures. The vultures ingest the drug when feeding on livestock carcasses, especially so in areas where the human population does not consume livestock, and they are left when deceased. Modelling has shown that to cause the observed rate of decline in *Gyps* vultures, just one in 250 livestock carcasses need contain diclofenac residues.

Other likely contributory factors are changes in human consumption and processing of dead livestock, and poison and pesticide use, but these are probably of minor significance. East of India, the near-total disappearance of the species pre-dated the present crisis, and probably results from collapse of large wild mammal populations and improved animal husbandry of deceased livestock, but persecution is also thought to be a problem.

Conservation actions to date

It has been reported from many protected areas across its range. The Indian government has now passed a bill banning the use of the veterinary drug diclofenac that has caused the rapid population decline across the Indian Subcontinent; their aim was to phase out its use by late 2005. Efforts to complete this process and replace diclofenac with a suitable alternative are ongoing. Drug companies have now developed Meloxicam, a cheap alternative to diclofenac, prompting the Nepalese government to adopt these and ban the import of diclofenac with immediate effect in 2006. Given that residual diclofenac in just one carcass in 250 is enough to have caused the declines seen 'vulture restaurants' have been used in an attempt to provide safe food sources for remaining birds. Vulture restaurants are also used as ecotourism attractions in parts of the species range to raise awareness and fund supplementary feeding programmes and research. Birds have been satellite tagged in various parts of their range to improve understanding of their movements, foraging range, site fidelity etc. in order to develop suitable conservation strategies for the species. The Report of the International South Asian Vulture Recovery Plan Workshop in 2004 gave a comprehensive list of recommendations including establishing a minimum of three captive breeding centres each capable of holding 25 pairs. Captive breeding efforts began in 2006 when 18 Slender-billed vultures were captured for the captive-breeding facility in Pinjore, India. The centre is part of a captive breeding programme established by the RSPB and Bombay Natural History Society. A website, *www.vulturerescue.org*, has been set up to allow researchers to contribute data on known colonies to identify founder individuals for captive breeding efforts that represent the full geographical spread of the species.

Conservation actions required

- Identify the location and number of remaining individuals and identify action required to prevent extinction.
- Measure the frequency of diclofenac treated carcasses available to vultures.
- Support the ban on the veterinary use of diclofenac, and support species management or restoration, as needed.
- Initiate public awareness and public support programmes.
- Monitor remaining populations, in particular replicate conservation and research activities that have been implemented in Cambodia in Myanmar.
- Support captive breeding efforts at a number of separate centres.
- Promote the immediate adoption of Melixocam as an alternatives to diclofenac.

Photo: © Ron Hoff

Cambodia, 2007

Photo: © Andy & Gill Swash

Nepal, 1996

Red-headed Vulture
Sarcogyps calvus
Population: 2,500-9,999 ↓

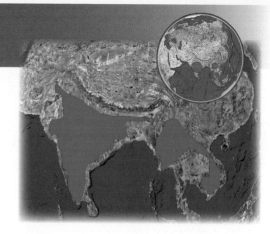

Cambodia, 2006

Photo: © Jonathan C Eames

History

1786 – first described by Austrian-Italian naturalist Giovani Antonio Scopoli (1723-1788).

1994 – considered Lower Risk/Near Threatened.

2006 – Pakistan bans the use of Diclofenac. The Nepalese government bans the import of diclofenac. Alternative drug Meloxicam is considered safe for vultures.

This species has also been called King Vulture.

Range & population

Red-headed Vulture occurs in Nepal, India, Bangladesh, Bhutan, Myanmar, Laos, Vietnam and Cambodia. It possibly occurs in south-east Tibet, China while it has not been recorded from Yunnan, China since the late 1960s. Historically, it was considered one of the most widespread vultures in India, albeit never forming large congregations such as the *Gyps* species. Formerly regular in Pakistan it is now considered a straggler there. It is absent from Malaysia and Singapore where it also occurred historically and is considered near extinct from Thailand.

Recent information indicates that in India the species started undergoing rapid decline (41% per year) in about 1999, and declined by 94% between 2000 and 2003. Given its rarity in South-East Asia, it is unlikely that more than a few hundred individuals remain there, while the total population seems unlikely to exceed 10,000 mature individuals given the patchiness of its distribution across India and the apparently catastrophic very recent declines.

It frequents open country (often near human habitation), well-wooded hills and dry deciduous forest with rivers, usually below 2,500 m. It occurs at lower density than *Gyps* vultures owing to its predominantly territorial behaviour and it is generally found in smaller flocks, and is more shy at carcasses. Red-headed Vulture also feeds on easy prey such as turtles and can pirate on eagles. It has a display flight that differs from other vultures in being more acrobatic.

Threats

The disappearance of vultures from Asia is linked to a suite of factors, amongst which can be listed the demise of wild ungulates, the intensification of agriculture, increased sophistication of waste disposal techniques, direct persecution and disease. However, rapid declines over the last eight years are believed to have been driven by the pharmaceutical drug diclofenac used to treat livestock, which has proven highly toxic to vultures. It seems plausible that this species previously had less exposure to the toxin owing to competitive exclusion from carcasses by *Gyps spp.* vultures.

Conservation actions to date

The use of the pharmaceutical drug diclofenac to treat livestock has recently been banned across the Indian Subcontinent. Monitoring of vultures has been conducted in a number of protected areas in India. Monitoring of vulture populations, combined with supplementary feeding, is underway in the northern and eastern plains of Cambodia.

Conservation actions required

- Continue monitoring the species throughout its range.
- Support the ban on diclofenac and ensure that it is effectively implemented.
- Continue trials of supplementary feeding in South-East Asia, where food supply may be a limiting factor to the species' populations.

Bharatpur, India, 1999

Photo: © Samuel Hansson

Philippine Eagle
Pithecophaga jefferyi

Population: 180-500 ↓

Cinchona, Philippines, 2007

Photo: © Rich Lindie

History

1896 – British explorer and naturalist John Whitehead (1860-1899) observes the first Philippine Eagle. A few weeks later, his servant Juan obtains the first specimen.

1897 – W. R. Ogilvie-Grant shows the eagle skin in a London restaurant. It gets its latin name two weeks later, commemorating Whitehead's father, Jeffery.

1965 – famous aviator Charles Lindbergh champions the cause of the Philippine Eagle together with Philippine scientist Dr. Dioscoro Rabor.

1969 – Monkey-eating Eagle Conservation Programme is initiated.

1976 – a captive Philippine Eagle in Rome zoo dies, it had been obtained as an adult in 1944.

1992 – first two captive-bred Philippine Eagles bred through artificial insemination and are raised by the Philippine Eagle Foundation.

1995 – Presidential Proclamation declaring the Philippine Eagle as the country's national bird.

1999 – first successful hatching of an eaglet from an eagle couple naturally paired in captivity.

2004 – first release of a captive-bred bird, called "Kabayan" on Earth Day April 22nd into the forest of Mount Apo, Mindanao.

2005 – the released male "Kabayan" gets electrocuted accidentally in early January.

Range & population

Endemic to the Philippines, where it is known from eastern Luzon, Samar, Leyte and Mindanao. Mindanao supports the bulk of the population, with recent research estimating 82-233 breeding pairs. However, information on breeding rates and success, and mortality suggests that recruitment to the breeding population may be slim to none. Estimates from other islands are six pairs on Samar and perhaps two on Leyte. Luzon may have very few left; but these calculations should be considered precautionary.

It inhabits primary dipterocarp forest, particularly in steep terrain, sometimes frequenting secondary growth and gallery forest, from lowlands to at least 1,800 m. On Mindanao eagles begin nesting from September to December in primary and disturbed forest, laying their nest c. 30 metres above the ground. A complete breeding cycle lasts two years with successful pairs raising one offspring. Upon discovery it was known as monkey-eating eagle as natives considered it preyed exclusively on these. Later studies in Mindanao have revealed that eagles there primarily feed on flying lemurs and other small mammals and occasionally on reptiles and birds as well. In contrast, little is known of what eagles eat in Luzon where flying lemurs are absent.

Threats

Forest destruction and fragmentation, through commercial logging, timber poaching and shifting cultivation, is the principal threat. Old-growth forest continues to be lost rapidly; such that as little as 9,220 km² may remain within the eagle's range. Moreover, most remaining lowland forest is leased to logging concessions. Mining applications pose an additional threat. Owing to its repeated use and high breeding site fidelity, nesting sites are more vulnerable to these threats. Uncontrolled hunting (for food and, at least formerly, zoo exhibits and trade), including accidental captures in traps intended for deer and wild pig, is highly significant and evidence suggests it may be limiting recruitment to the breeding population to zero. Electrocution may pose a future threat as electrification programs spread.

Conservation actions to date

Since 1970, various initiatives have been launched, including the passing of legislation prohibiting persecution and protecting nests, survey work, public awareness campaigns, captive breeding and a socio-economic project to alleviate pressure on an eagle territory whilst increasing local economic prosperity. It occurs in several protected areas including the Northern Sierra Madre Natural Park on Luzon, and Mt Kitanglad and Mt Apo Natural Parks on Mindanao. A Philippine Eagle Foundation, *www.philippineeagle.org*, exists which runs the Philippine Eagle Centre in Davao City, Mindanao and oversees captive-breeding efforts and monitoring and conservation of wild populations. Further experimental releases are planned, preceding a full-scale reintroduction programme to supplement wild populations.

Conservation actions required

- Conduct further research into distribution, numbers, ecological needs and threats, particularly in Luzon, Leyte and Samar Islands where no nest has ever been studied.
- Declare and manage important nesting sites as critical habitats free from logging and mining activities.
- Extend the protected-areas system to embrace known eagle nests and habitat.
- Implement habitat management schemes, including forms of 'Payments for Environmental Services', for the benefit of wildlife and local people.
- Integrate eagle-friendly practices into forestry and mining policies.
- Launch a campaign to engender national pride and respect for the eagle.

Ridgway's Hawk
Buteo ridgwayi

Dominican Republic

Photo: © J William S Clark

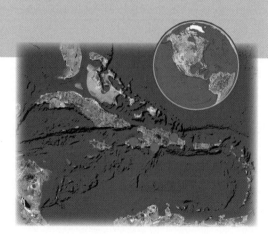

Population: 250 ↓

History

1883 – American ornithologist Charles B. Cory (1857-1921) describes the species.

2003 – 93 individuals are recorded in Los Haitises National Park, north-east Dominican Republic, including 37 pairs, 30 of which attempted nesting with eight successful pairs fledging 10 chicks.

2005 – 83 fledglings are produced from 45 successful (out of 66) attempts in Los Haitises NP.

2006 - 114 pairs recorded, and a total of 241 birds documented.

Range & population

Ridgway's Hawk occurs in the Dominican Republic and the Dominic island of Beata. Historically it was found in Haiti and the adjacent Haitan islands of Gonâve, Grande Cayamite (where it was reported as common in 1962) but is apparently extinct from Haiti now. There is a single record from the island of Culebra off Puerto Rico (to USA). It was formerly widespread, but has declined steeply and is now extremely rare, and the population stronghold is Los Haitises National Park, north-east Dominican Republic, with very few recent records outside of it. Individuals and even a nest reported found in the Sierra de Bahoruco, a National Park in the Dominican Republic, in 1997 may relate to other hawk species. There may be a few birds persisting in this area but

no individuals were found there in 2002. It was also recorded in human-modified habitat on the Samaná Peninsula in 2003. It occurs up to 2,000 m in a variety of undisturbed forest-types including rainforest, subtropical dry and moist forests, pine forest and limestone karst forest and marshland and is occasionally seen in secondary and agricultural habitats. Prey includes predominantly lizards and snakes, and some small mammals. Nests have been found in mature tall trees (sometimes palms), with nest-building in February-March and eggs laid in March-April. It lays 1-3 eggs and pairs have successfully fledged three chicks, but more typically one or two. Males are known to participate in incubation. Hispaniola Royal Palms *Roystonea hispaniolana* are commonly used as nesting trees in human-modified habitat where no mature

lake. However, this population has begun to decline rapidly owing to rapid habitat conversion. This rate of decline will equate to over 80% during a three generation period unless it is halted. Were this decline to continue unchecked, it is conceivable that the species may be extinct in the country by 2012. It inhabits lowland dry, or seasonally inundated, natural and semi-natural grasslands, often interspersed with scattered scrub or patchy open forest. Most Indian populations appear to be resident. In Cambodia it is known to make relatively local seasonal movements in response to the flooding regime of the Tonle Sap lake, in the dry season, the species breeds in grasslands in the inundation zone of the lake; it then moves to nearby open forest areas during the wet season. It breeds in March to June, lays 1-2 eggs and is polygamous. Food consists of vegetable matters such as shoots, seeds and berries mainly in winter and spring, while vertebrates such as small snakes, lizards, locusts and beetles are consumed during the rest of the year.

Threats
The key threat is extensive loss and modification of grasslands through drainage, conversion to agriculture, overgrazing, inappropriate cutting and burning regimes and heavy flooding. In particular, the spread of dry season rice cultivation in Cambodia is rapidly converting existing grassland habitat. Excessive hunting for sport and food may have triggered its decline, and continues to be a serious threat, especially in Cambodia. Other threats include human disturbance and trampling of nests by livestock. In South Asia, most populations are small, isolated and vulnerable to local extirpation.

Conservation actions to date
Several populations occur within protected areas, the most important being Chitwan National Park, Royal Bardia National Park and Sukla Phanta Wildlife Reserve in Nepal and Kaziranga, Dibru-Saikhowa and Dudwa National Parks in India. In South-East Asia a tiny population may still remain at Tram Chim National Park in Vietnam, and another at Ang Trapeang Thmor Sarus Crane Conservation Area in Cambodia. The Wildlife Conservation Society, BirdLife International and their government partners are currently engaged in a programme of conservation activities in the Tonle Sap floodplain of Cambodia, aimed at reducing habitat loss and hunting pressure on the species. Recent achievements include the designation of over 350 km² of Bengal Florican habitat as 'Integrated Farming and Biodiversity Areas' (IFBA). Work is on-going to establish effective management structures for these areas and build constituencies of support for their conservation among local stakeholders. These activities appear to be having some early success in arresting the rapid decline of the species in Cambodia, but their long-term outcome remains to be seen.

Conservation actions required
- Research on understanding Bengal Florican breeding productivity.
- Development of monitoring protocols for Bengal Florican densities, habitat extent and human use in the proposed Integrated Farming and Biodiversity Areas (IFBAs).
- IFBA and Protected Area management regime design and management planning including appropriate rotational burning, grazing and cutting.
- Advocating support for IFBA conservation and promote grassland conservation awareness initiatives in all range countries.
- Continue surveys for populations, particularly in Banteay Meanchey, Battambang and Pursat provinces, Cambodia.
- Monitor known populations.
- Extend, upgrade and link protected areas in India and Nepal, and establish new ones.
- Encourage grassland regeneration.
- Devise and promote a conservation strategy for all bustards in India.

BirdLife Species Guardian **Seng Kim Hout**

Photo: © Amano Samarpan

Kaziranga, India, 1994

Photo: © Per Smitterberg

Suklaphanta Wildlife Reserve, 2006

Photo: © Laxman P Poudyal & Paras B Singh

Siberian Crane
Grus leucogeranus
Population: 3,200 ↓

Photo: © Park Jong-Gil

Heukans Island, South-Korea, November 2004

History
1773 – German-born zoologist Peter Simon Pallas (1741-1811) describes the species.

1977 & 1978 – Russian eggs are flown to the International Crane Foundation in the USA for incubation and hatching.

2006 – only two Siberian Cranes (both males) return to the wintering site in northern Iran in October, one disappears later.

2007 – the countries of west and central Asia meet in Almaty, Kazakhstan to form an international network to save the Siberian Crane.

Range & population
Three regional populations are recognised. The eastern population, holding 95% of the total, breeds between the rivers Kolyma and Yana and south to the Morma mountains. The main wintering sites are in the middle to lower reaches of the Yangtze river, especially Poyang Hu lake, China. The central population breeds in the basin of the Kunovat river, Russia and winters at Keoladeo National Park, India. This population is biologically extinct. Passage birds have been recorded in Turkmenistan, and Kazakhstan. The western population breeds in the Tyumen District, Russia, and winters on the Caspian shore of Iran. Birds pass through Azerbaijan on passage and use the Volga river delta as a staging post. This population consists of single individuals. It is the most aquatic member of its family, breeding and wintering in wetlands and preferring wide expanses of shallow (up to 30 cm) fresh water with good visibility, where it feeds primarily on the shoots, roots, seeds and tubers of aquatic plants, but also insects, fish and some rodents. It typically lays two eggs in late May to mid-June but generally does not fledge more than one chick.

Threats
The key threat is wetland loss and degradation at staging areas and wintering sites through agricultural development, the development of oilfields and increased human utilisation. Severe drought caused Poyang Lake, the main wintering site, to shrink dramatically in the winter of 2003-2004. Construction of the Three Gorges Dam will change the hydrological pattern of the lower Yangtze river and may have a major impact on the wintering population. Increasing levels of human disturbance are also a problem, particularly at Poyang Hu. Hunting on passage is the key threat to the central and western populations, and inhibits recovery. Also poisoning targeting waterbirds in China e.g. Huanzidong

Reservoir, Shenyang Region, appears to affect this species too. Pesticide use and pollution is a threat in India.

Conservation actions to date
It is legally protected in all range states. Range states have signed a Memorandum of Understanding to help protect key wetland sites and the United Nations Environment Programme and the International Crane Foundation launched the Siberian Crane GEF Project in 2003 to promote, develop and implement the conservation of key flyway wetlands across Asia for this species. The North East Asian Crane Site Network has been established and efforts to manage water levels at migration staging posts are underway in China. Several hundred captive birds exist in facilities in Belgium, China, Russia and the USA and captive-raised birds are being released in an effort to maintain the central population.

Conservation actions required
- Identify breeding sites in the Kunovat basin and possibly other areas in north-west Russia.
- Enforce conservation measures to minimise threats from the Three Gorges Dam to wetlands in the lower Yangtze.
- Expand the Kytalyk and Chaygurgino Resources Reserves (Russia).
- Expand the area of Poyang Hu Nature Reserve or establish additional reserves to cover all important wintering areas and manage water-levels.
- Reduce hunting pressure on the central population.
- Replicate the methodologies that have successfully helped to boost Whooping Crane populations in North America.

Photo: © Martin Hale

Mai Po Marshes Nature Reserve, Hong Kong, December 2002

132

Samoan Moorhen
Gallinula pacifica
Population: < 50, trend unknown

Painting: © Lyn Wells / BirdLife International

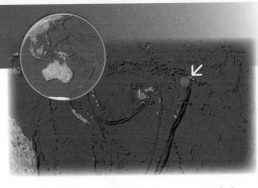

Range & population
This moorhen is endemic to Savai`i, Samoa, where it was last recorded in 1873. Possible records were made in 1987 in upland forest west of Mt Elietoga, and in 2003 on Mount Sili Sili by a bird tour group. It is restricted to primary montane forest and most probably feeds on invertebrates, including insects. One nest is described: it was found on the ground, constructed of a few twigs and some grass, and contained two eggs. It has exceptionally large eyes and may thus be nocturnal.

Threats
Cats, rats, pigs and dogs have no doubt contributed to its disappearance, and hunting may also have been a factor as it was formerly a favoured food of the human population. Slash-and-burn cultivation threatens remaining areas of upland forest on Savai`i, as farmers use forestry roads from heavily logged lowland forests to gain access to formerly inaccessible land. Wild cattle and pigs have browsed the understorey and ground-cover along the main range. In 2000, attempts were being made by sawmill operators to clear-fell the area south of Aopo village, the site where this species was last seen.

Conservation actions to date
A proposal is being developed to conduct surveys in Savai`i.

Conservation actions required
- Urgently conduct a survey to find this species and assess its status and conservation needs.
- Protect foothill and upland forest for this and other species in north-west Savai`i.
- Train local people to do bird surveys, generally involve the community and improve awareness of the species.

Makira Moorhen
Gallinula silvestri
Population: < 50, trend unknown

Painting: ©Hilary Burn/HBW3 (Lynx Edicions)

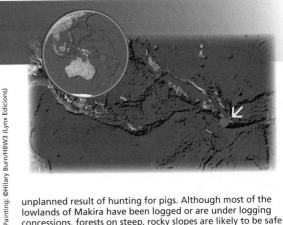

Range & population
The Makira Moorhen is known only from the type-specimen collected in 1929, and a subsequent observation of one in 1953 on Makira (San Cristobal), Solomon Islands. Unidentified calls heard in 2004 were reported to belong to this species by local people who claimed to see it rarely. The records are from rainforest on steep, rocky hills with many small rivers but no standing water. It has been suggested that it may also inhabit the largely unexplored swamps of north Makira, but no evidence of it was found there in a very brief survey in 1998.

Threats
It is likely to have declined from predation by introduced mammalian predators. Birds were also caught by village hunting-dogs but this was probably an uncommon and unplanned result of hunting for pigs. Although most of the lowlands of Makira have been logged or are under logging concessions, forests on steep, rocky slopes are likely to be safe from commercial logging.

Conservation actions to date
Surveys around Hauta in the central mountain ranges have failed to find evidence of this species. The forests of the Hauta region are presently protected under a community sustainable use programme.

Conservation actions required
- Circulate coloured paintings to hunters in inland Makira to gather any information on its survival.
- Survey uninhabited inland mountains.
- Encourage tighter controls of commercial logging.
- Support the continuation and extension of community-based sustainable use programmes in the mountains.

New Caledonian Rail
Gallirallus lafresnayanus
Population: < 50, trend unknown

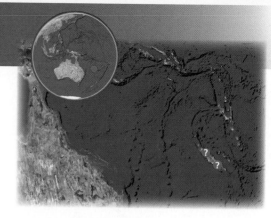

Painting: © Norman Arlott/HBW3 (Lynx Edicions)

Range & population
This rail is known from at least 17 specimens taken between 1860 and 1890 from New Caledonia (to France), apparently including the island des Pins. There are a scatter of later reports from near Mt Panié in the north and the headwaters of Rivière Blanche in the south in the 1960s and in 1984 (on Mt Panié) suggesting that it may yet survive in small numbers. Fieldwork and interviews in 1998 produced no sightings or credible reports from local hunters.

Threats
It is likely to have declined from predation by introduced species such as cats, pigs and rats which now occur throughout the island. Many historical records are of birds caught by hunting dogs and it is likely, therefore, that it remains at risk from village dogs on hunting trips and when straying.

Conservation actions to date
This species may be benefiting from the conservation action for Kagu *Rhynochetos jubatus*, particularly the control of introduced mammalian predators.

Conservation actions required
* Conduct further intensive surveys in remote forests.
* Survey the forested slopes of Mé Maoya which has a high population of Kagu.
* Include this species in the predator-control and public awareness programmes for Kagu.
* Extend these programmes to high-altitude areas.
* Publicise the search for this species amongst forest workers and villagers.

Javan Lapwing
Vanellus macropterus
Population: < 50, trend unknown

Painting: © Etel Vilaró/HBW3 (Lynx Edicions)

Threats
Its decline has been attributed to 'merciless' hunting and trapping. However, it seems far more likely that high levels of human disturbance and conversion of its habitat to aquaculture and agricultural land were the principal agents. The fact that it may have been a naturally low-density species could have exacerbated its susceptibility to extinction in the face of large-scale habitat loss and disturbance

Conservation actions to date
The species has been protected under Indonesian law since 1978. Several recent searches of historic and potential sites for this species have all drawn a blank.

Conservation actions required
* Tanjung Air needs surveying urgently, and other coastal wetlands and grasslands should be searched on Java and elsewhere in the Greater Sundas.
* Initiate immediate habitat protection in the event of its rediscovery.

Range & population
Javan Lapwing is known with certainty only from the island of Java, Indonesia, where it inhabited marshes, pastures and river deltas in the west (on the north coast) and the east (on the south coast). There are unsubstantiated claims from Timor and Sumatra. It was described as local and uncommon, apparently only ever encountered in scattered pairs, and has not been recorded since 1940. It inhabited "wide, steppe-like marshes" in river deltas, keeping to the least flooded areas during the rainy season. It occurred in isolated pairs, often in rather large areas, suggesting that it must have been a naturally low-density species. It was probably resident.

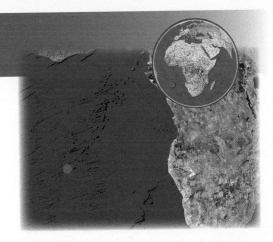

St Helena, 2005

History

1638 – first official mention of the species.

1656 – British traveller Peter Mundy visits the island in 1634, 1638 and this year. He describes a small landbird, "somewhat like a lark in colour, shape and note that runs off like a lapwing".

1873 – British conservationist James Edmund Harting (1841 – 1928) describes the species.

1988/89 – a census tallies 450 birds.

1998 – 340 individuals are counted.

2007 – the species is uplisted to Critically Endangered.

Range & population

This plover is the only surviving endemic landbird on St Helena (to UK) and declined sharply in the 1970s. Surveys in 1988-1989 (giving a total of c. 450 individuals) were repeated ten years later and revealed large declines at all important pastureland sites which were not offset by increases in lower density populations at semi-desert sites. Fieldwork in 1999-2000 and 2000-2001 suggested populations have stabilised at c.350 adults. However, recent survey data from 2005 and 2006 suggest the population has continued to decline.

Some 80% of its population occurs in pastureland, with highest densities in relatively dry, flat, short-sward pastures. Extended wet seasons resulting in extensive vegetation growth can delay or prevent breeding. It feeds on a wide range of invertebrates. More than one clutch (of two eggs) may be laid each year and replaced if eggs or chicks are lost. The proportion of a clutch that survives to independence is probably less than 20%, although adult survival is most likely high. Juveniles disperse widely in small flocks.

Threats

Livestock grazing has become unprofitable over much of St Helena, leading to major alterations to its preferred short-sward grassland habitat. Sward growth, due to lowered sheep densities, and reductions in arable land may have resulted in a decline in the quality of feeding habitat at some sites. For the same reason, scrub encroachment has resulted in a major population decline at one site. These factors probably resulted in the significant declines of the early 1990s. In addition, invertebrate prey populations may be subject to large-scale, short-term fluctuations. Cats and Common Myna *Acridotheres tristis* are probably significant predators of chicks and nests respectively. Evidence suggests feral cat populations may be increasing. Less effort has gone into trapping feral cats or neutering domestic pets in recent years. Increasing recreational use of off-road vehicles in semi-desert areas may result in disturbance and nest-destruction. Housing development has recently encroached on a number of minor breeding locations. Two major breeding areas were proposed as sites for an airport, but the airport plans are now stalled and the most important breeding site is an unlikely choice for this development.

Conservation actions to date

All bird species on St Helena have been protected by law since 1894. There are plans to form a National Trust to coordinate the work of environmental NGOs, including population monitoring, ecological research, habitat restoration and raising public awareness. A programme of trapping appears to have reduced feral cat populations in some areas. The Royal Society for the Protection of Birds has submitted a proposal to the Overseas Territories Environment Program to help conserve St Helena Plovers through a project titled "Enabling the people of St Helena to conserve the St Helena Wirebird".

Conservation actions required

- Monitor populations regularly, increase research into causes of nest-failure, and effects of pasture management and introduced species.
- Maintain pastures as grazing land and manage appropriately.
- Monitor changes in habitat quality closely.
- Restrict vehicle access to significant semi-desert site.
- Ensure that alternative plans are made for the proposed airport at Prosperous Bay Plain.
- Intensify trapping of feral cats around known sites.

St Helena, 2005

Sociable Lapwing
Vanellus gregarius

Photo: © Soner Bekir

Ceylanpinar, Sanliurfa, Turkey, 2007

Population: 2,500-3,000 ↓

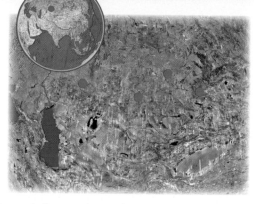

History

1771 – German-born Zoologist Peter Simon Pallas (1741-1811) describes the species.

2004 – an intensive research project at the breeding sites in central Kazakhstan is initiated.

2005 – a survey of historical breeding sites in the South Urals is conducted.

2006 – funding for three years is awarded the Kazakhstan research project.

2007 – surveys in northern Syria and south-eastern Turkey in March records over 1,500 and 1,000 individuals respectively, raising the possibility that these countries may form part of the regular wintering area. A flock of 189 is recorded near Bulanik, eastern Turkey on 25th September.

Range & population

Sociable Lapwing breeds in northern and central Kazakhstan and south-central Russia, dispersing through Kyrgyzstan, Tajikistan, Uzbekistan, Turkmenistan, Afghanistan, Armenia, Iran, Iraq, Saudi Arabia, Syria and Turkey, to key wintering sites in Israel, Eritrea, Sudan and north-west India. Birds winter occasionally in Pakistan, Sri Lanka and Oman. Despite its Middle Eastern wintering grounds, single Sociable Plovers turn up in the central parts of Western Europe rather frequently in late autumn. It is believed that these birds join flocks of Lapwings *Vanellus vanellus* which migrate in an east-westerly direction from Central Asia. It has suffered a very rapid decline and range contraction. In eastern Ukraine, the last breeding took place in the early 20th century. In northern Kazakhstan, a decline of 40% during 1930-1960, was followed by a further halving of numbers during 1960-1987. These declines have continued, or even accelerated.

It has a sporadic and irruptive pattern of semi-colonial breeding, mainly in the transition zones between Stipa and Artemisia grassland steppes where bare saline areas occur near water-bodies. It has been postulated that it evolved to nest in habitats created by nomadic or migratory herbivores, such as migratory Saiga *Saiga tatarica* or the horse and cattle of nomadic herders. Exact breeding habitat requirements are poorly known, although recent studies have shown a preference for nesting in areas of *Artemisia* where there is a greater abundance of dung and shorter vegetation. Nest survival during the egg stage is very low, particularly in areas with high numbers of cattle. The wintering grounds are dry plains, sandy wastes and short grass areas, often adjacent to water.

Threats

Key factors explaining the magnitude of recent declines remain unknown. On the breeding grounds, it may formerly have been threatened by the conversion of steppe to arable cultivation, but large areas of apparently suitable breeding habitat are unoccupied. The species' habitat may however have been altered by a reduction in grazing by large herds of native ungulates and, latterly, by the loss of the enormous herds of domestic grazing animals from state-sponsored collective farms. Breeding may now only occur in heavily-grazed areas in the vicinity of villages, where nesting birds are exposed to numerous threats, such as human disturbance and trampling by sheep or goats. Illegal hunting may also occur, particularly during migration and on the wintering grounds. It may also have been adversely affected by the increasingly dry climate in its breeding and wintering range.

Conservation actions to date

An international species action plan was published in 2004. It is legally protected in Armenia, Kazakhstan, Russia, Turkmenistan, Ukraine and Uzbekistan, but this is generally not enforced.

Conservation actions required

- Survey key wintering and passage sites and breeding range in Kazakhstan.
- Identify and evaluate key threats.
- Protect grassland steppe from conversion to agriculture.
- Protect and monitor nesting colonies.
- Manage livestock numbers to create appropriate sward conditions and minimise disturbance during the nesting period.
- Develop and implement national species action plans.
- Recreate areas of pristine steppe with natural herbivores such as saiga antelope.

Ceylanpinar, Sanliurfa, Turkey, 2007

Photo: © Soner Bekir

Near Korgaldzhino, N Kazakhstan, 2006

Photo: © Sergey Dereliev

Near Korgaldzhino, N Kazakhstan, 2006

Photo: © Sergey Dereliev

Korgalzhyn, Kazakhstan, 2006

Photo: © Inger Andersen

Black Stilt
Himantopus novaezelandiae
Population: 151 ↑

Near Twizel, South Island, New Zealand, 2006

Photo: © Chris Collins

History

1841 – British ornithologist John Gould (1804 -1881) describes the species.

1940s – the species has retracted to a remnant population in the Mackenzie Basin and may have numbered fewer than 500-1,000 birds from this decade onwards.

1979 – 8 eggs which are taken in October are successfully reared and result in 5 males and 3 females.

1981 – just 23 birds are known and intensive management begins.

2000 – 88 birds (39 adults) occur in the wild. 11 males and 9 females are held in captivity.

2001 – the wild breeding population consists of just seven productive pairs.

2002 – 125 birds are recorded in the wild. The captive population consists of 25 adults.

2004/5 – 11 productive pairs breed.

2005/6 – 14 productive breeding pairs in the wild and 7 breeding pairs in captivity.

2006/07 – 17 productive breeding pairs in the wild.

Range & population

The Black Stilt (Kakī) was formerly widespread, breeding and wintering across the North and South Islands of New Zealand, but following a long-term decline it is now restricted during the breeding season to the upper Waitaki Valley in the South Island. Approximately 95% of the population are sedentary, but small numbers still over-winter in the North Island. Numbers have fluctuated rather than climbed steadily and 12 dark hybrids (with Pied (Black-winged) Stilt *Himantopus himantopus*) are known. The partial recovery of its population is primarily thanks to the annual release of up to 80 captive-reared juvenile and sub-adults. The species' survival remains dependent on captive-breeding efforts replacing losses of wild adults, until predator-free breeding habitat can be maintained.

It breeds on braided riverbeds, but also occurs in wetlands and swamplands, and some of the population winters along the coastline in inter-tidal habitats. It feeds primarily on insects, but also takes small fish. It lays four eggs and will usually re-nest if the first clutch is lost early in the season. Most breed for the first time at 2-3 years of age. The average age of mortality is c. 7 years, and only 2 birds are older than 10 years.

Threats

Predators, in particular introduced mammals such as cats, ferrets, stoats, hedgehogs and brown rat, and the native Australasian Harrier *Circus approximans* and Kelp Gull *Larus dominicanus* are today the primary threat, but the combined impact of habitat loss has exacerbated declines. Nests are destroyed, and predation is potentially increased, by drainage and hydroelectric development, weed growth and flood-control programmes, and nesting birds are disturbed by recreational use of riverbeds. Adverse weather and natural flooding are additional, unpredictable threats. Hybridisation with Pied (Black-winged) Stilts or first-generation hybrids continues because of the low population size, but hybrids have much reduced fitness. Adult mortality in the wild remains very high (10-35%).

Conservation actions to date

Recent advances in release methods appear to have enhanced the initial survival of released birds from 20-45% to 80-100%, but recruitment to the adult population of released birds remains low (usually less than 30%), and causes of loss of released young require further testing. Active management involves collecting 1-4 clutches of 4 eggs. Parents readily re-lay, and up to 16 fertile eggs (usually 4-8) can be collected from a pair in a season. The collected eggs are reared in captivity. Playback calls are broadcast to chicks during captive-rearing to equip them with the behavioural and auditory recognition skills necessary for survival, and reduce their imprinting on humans. Trapping for predators around wild nests has been ongoing in most years from 1981 to 1999, and have improved fledgling survival rates where hatching eggs were returned to wild nests for parent-raising. Results were not clear-cut, and trapping was seasonal and small-scale. Year-round predator control on a large scale (23,000 ha) was initiated in 2005 in one site to test the effectiveness of predator control at this greater level of spatial and temporal intensity. Water-levels are manipulated in managed wetlands to attract birds to feed, and possibly breed, in areas where predators are controlled. Habitat restoration is ongoing, involving the removal of exotic weeds from riverbeds. The introduction of a second population on a suitable predator-free island is unlikely to occur as no New Zealand islands that have large wetlands are free from predation risk.

Conservation actions required

- Maintain and improve productivity of the captive population.
- Refine reintroduction programme to increase recruitment rates.
- Encourage public interest and support.
- Develop and maintain predator-free habitat in three or more large sites within the current range.

Slender-billed Curlew
Numenius tenuirostris
Population: < 50 ↓

Photo: © Chris Gomersall

Morocco, 1995

History

1817 – French ornithologist Louis Jean Pierre Vieillot (1748-1831) describes the species.

1924 – a nest is found near Tara, Omsk, Siberia.

1994 – a Memorandum of Understanding between 30 States in Europe, North Africa and the Middle East on the species comes into effect.

1995 – a flock of 19 birds is discovered in Italy in winter.

1996 – an international Action Plan is published.

1998 – a Slender-billed Curlew Working Group is established. In May a Slender-billed Curlew turns up in Northumberland, United Kingdom, and draws crowds of birdwatchers.

2002 – stable isotope analysis of museum skins indicates that breeding areas lie in Kazakhstan.

2007 – an unverified record is reported from Albania in May.

Range & population
There are only two confirmed cases of breeding Slender-billed Curlew, both near Tara, north of Omsk in Siberia, Russia, in the early 19th century. It migrates west-south-west from its presumed breeding grounds in Siberia through central and eastern Europe, predominantly Russia, Kazakhstan, Ukraine, Bulgaria, Hungary, Romania and the former Yugoslavia to southern Europe, Greece, Italy, Turkey, Algeria, Morocco and Tunisia. It has also been reported from Slovenia, Uzbekistan and Turkmenistan. Reports of birds wintering in Iran persist but require confirmation. Regarded as very common in the 19th century, it declined dramatically during the 20th century. Flocks of over 100 birds were recorded from Morocco as late as the 1960s and 1970s. However, between 1980 and 1990, there were only 103 records involving 316-326 birds, and from 1990-1999, this dropped to 74 records involving 148-152 birds, including a flock of 19 in Italy in 1995. Although there have

been reports from Bulgaria, Ukraine and Uzbekistan of larger groups, most recent verified records have been of one to three birds. In 1994, the population was estimated at only 50-270 individuals, but the paucity of recent confirmed records suggests it may now be lower than 50 birds. The only known nests were recorded on the northern limit of the forest-steppe zone in habitat more typical of taiga marsh. On migration and in winter, a wide variety of habitats are used, including saltmarsh, steppe grassland, fishponds, saltpans, brackish lagoons, tidal mudflats, semi-desert, brackish wetlands and sandy farmland next to lagoons.

Threats
Threats on the breeding grounds are unknown. Within its potential breeding range, the taiga has been little modified, the forest-steppe partially cultivated and much of the steppe modified by agriculture. Habitat loss in the wintering grounds is of unknown importance. There has been extensive drainage of wetlands in the Mediterranean and North Africa and potentially important areas in Iraq. Historically hunting was high, and may have been the key factor in its decline.

Conservation actions to date
A national action plan is in place in Italy. There have been several international initiatives to survey passage and wintering sites and potential breeding areas, collate records, protect key sites, raise public awareness and educate hunters. Several of the sites within the EU where the species has been recorded are designated as Special Protection Areas.

Conservation actions required
- Continue to monitor key wintering and passage sites.
- Search for breeding grounds (taking into account results of stable isotope analysis).
- Attach satellite transmitters to captured birds.
- Provide training in species identification along the migration route.
- Promote protection of habitat.
- Provide legal protection for this and similar species.
- Increase public awareness.

Photo: © Richard Porter

Hodeidah, Yemen, 1984

Eskimo Curlew
Numenius borealis
Population: < 50, trend unknown

Painting: © Francesc Jutglar/HBW3 (Lynx Edicions)

Range & population
Eskimo Curlew bred in north-western Canada and migrated via Labrador and New England, USA and the Caribbean to Argentina (especially the Pampas), and possibly Uruguay, Paraguay, southernmost Brazil and Chile south to Patagonia. It declined rapidly in the 1870s-1890s to become very rare in the 20th century. The last accepted records were in Barbados in 1963 (collected) and a flock of 23 in Texas in 1981. There have been some unconfirmed reports during 1987-2006. It bred (May–August) in treeless arctic tundra at 180–335 m, comprising grassy meadows with birch and sedge.

Threats
Spring hunting in North America partially explains the species'

near-extinction, but there was no recovery after hunting was outlawed and abandoned in c. 1916. The main cause is almost certainly the near total loss of prairies to agriculture, compounded by the suppression of prairie wildfires and the extinction of Rocky Mountain Grasshopper, a food source.

Conservation actions to date
It is protected in the USA, Canada, Argentina and Mexico. Its status has been fully documented, and identification details publicised. Breeding and wintering areas have been surveyed, and reported breeding sites investigated.

Conservation actions required
- Continue cooperative international assessments of historical sites.
- Survey possible breeding grounds.
- Investigate any credible sightings.
- Expand prairie habitat, and employ prescribed burnings.

Jerdon´s Courser
Rhinoptilus bitorquatus
Population: 50-249 ↓

Sri Lankamaleswara Wildlife Sanctuary, September 2005

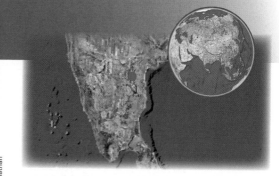

Photo: © P. Jeganathan

Range & population
Jerdon's Courser is a rare and local endemic to the Eastern Ghats of Andhra Pradesh and extreme southern Madhya Pradesh, India. It was assumed to be extinct until its rediscovery around Lankamalai in 1986. It inhabits sparse, thorny and non-thorny scrub-forest and bushes, interspersed with patches of bare ground, in gently undulating, rocky foothills. It is active mainly at night.

Threats
Specific threats are difficult to identify. The dependence of the local human population for resources may pose a serious threat to habitat through fuel wood-collection and livestock-grazing. In addition, extensive quarrying is destroying habitat.

Conservation actions to date
The Lankamalleswara Wildlife Sanctuary and Sri Venkateswara National Park have been declared as a direct result of its rediscovery. In 2006, India's Central Empowerment Committee ruled in favour of a precise route for the Telagu-Ganga canal that will entirely avoid courser habitat. Survey methods have been developed to conduct night-time listening surveys for identifying new populations and studying existing ones.

Conservation actions required
- Identify areas of suitable habitat within its putative range.
- Carry out a radio-telemetry study to determine the ecological requirements.
- Make recommendations for its conservation based on survey findings.
- Lobby against quarrying and proposed mining activities that threaten existing habitat.
- Initiate conservation awareness programmes.

Kittlitz´s Murrelet
Brachyramphus brevirostris
Population: 13,000-35,000 ↓

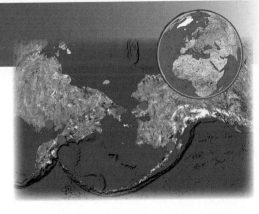

Photo: © Glen Tepke

Aialik Bay, Kenai Fjords National Park, Alaska, 2007

History
1829 – Irish zoologist Nicholas Aylward Vigors (1785-1840) describes the species.

1972 – a flock of 10,000 Kittlitz's Murrelets is reported in the Unakwik Inlet, Alaska.

1989 – 7-15% of the Prince William Sound population dies as result of the Exxon Valdez oil spill.

2002 – the Alaskan population is estimated to number 9,000-25,000 birds.

Range & population
Kittlitz's Murrelet has a distribution centred on the Bering Sea where it is rare and patchily distributed in both Russia and the USA. In Alaska, where c. 70% of the total population occurs, it is found from just east of Cape Lisburne south to the Aleutian chain and east to Glacier Bay and Stileime River. In Russia it is limited to the East Chukotskiy Peninsula in the Chukchi Sea west to Cape Schmidt and south to Anadyr Gulf, as well as Shelekov Bay in the north Sea of Okhotsk. Surveys in much of the Alaskan range indicate that populations have declined by >80-90% during the past 15 years. In Prince William Sound the population declined by 84% between 1989 (6,436 birds) and 2000 (1,033 birds) following a longer term decline since 1972 when the population numbered 63,000 individuals. In Malaspina Forelands, numbers declined by 38-75% in 1992-2002. In Glacier Bay, density estimates declined by 89% between 1991 and 2000, with c. 2,200 birds estimated there in 1999-2000. Total abundance in Icy Bay, Alaska was estimated to be 1,725-2,372 birds in 2002, suggesting a decline of 59% here over a three year period. There are no trend data from other parts of the species' range, but anecdotal information suggests population declines are occurring in at least some of these other areas. Wintering distribution is largely unknown, although there are records from coastal Kamchatka, the Kuril Islands and Hokkaido (Japan).
Only 20 nests have ever been found. It lays a single egg on the ground amongst unvegetated scree or on cliff faces at, or near, the tops of mountains in glaciated regions. It generally forages in different water types than the closely related Marbled Murrelet *Brachyramphus marmoratus*, preferring to feed during the breeding season in turbid waters of glacial origin. It feeds on fish and macro-zooplankton. The wintering distribution and habitat choice are poorly documented but populations are presumed to winter in ice-free areas to the south of the breeding range.

Threats
There have been strong links made between this species' decline and areas of glacial recession (possibly as a result of global warming). Other threats include habitat degradation and repeated disturbance of birds owing to recreational and commercial tour boat traffic, mortality in gillnet fisheries (documented in Prince William Sound, anecdotal accounts from elsewhere) and mortality from petroleum contamination. The near zero productivity in 1996-1998 for unknown reasons may lead to further future declines

Conservation actions to date
In the USA the species is recognised as a 'Species of Conservation Concern' on the Endangered Species Act; and it is listed in the Red Book of the USSR. Guidelines have been drawn up in the USA to avoid disturbance of nesting birds.

Conservation actions required
● Monitor population and trends in Alaska and Russia.
● Assess the impact of gill-net fisheries.
● Assess the impact of boat traffic on use of foraging areas.

Photo: © Glen Tepke

Aialik Bay, Kenai Fjords National Park, Alaska, 2007

Photo: © Edwin Winkel

Prince William Sound, Alaska, 2006

Chinese Crested Tern
Sterna bernsteini

Changle, Fujian Province, China, 2007

Population: < 50, unknown trend

History

1863 – described by Hermann Schlegel (1804-1884) as *Sterna bernsteini* from a specimen collected on Halmahera, Indonesia in November.

1903 – described as *Sterna zimmermanni* by Anton Reichenow (1847-1941).

1937 – 21 specimens, some in breeding condition, are collected on Muguan Dao islands, off Qingdao, China. This constitutes the first breeding occurrence of the species.

1978 – a sight record of three is made in June in Hebei province, China and is the first record since 40 years.

2000 – four adults and four chicks are found on Mazu archipelago which are administered by Taiwan but situated off Fuzhou on the east coast of mainland China. After that, 1-12 adults are recorded there and breeding attempts occurs almost every year except 2001 and 2003.

2004 – ten pairs are found nesting in Jiushan islands, Zhejiang while there are six breeding pairs with three chicks in the Mazu archipelago, and one pair at the Min Jiang river estuary, Fujian, China. The first record for Shanghai is made: an adult 5th September at Yangtze River estuary.

2006 – two pairs with three chicks and one first summer bird are recorded in the Matsu archipelago. A survey on islands off Shandong coast, including Muguan Dao reveals no sign of breeding.

2007 – up to eight birds are sighted at Min Jiang river estuary, in late June by a local birdwatcher and three nests are found in the Mazu archipelago.

Range & Population

The breeding grounds of this large tern are poorly known. Recent breeding records have been confirmed off the eastern coast of mainland China and Taiwan on uninhabited offshore islets harbouring colonies of other tern species (such as Greater Crested *Sterna bergii* and Bridled terns *Sterna anaethetus*). Migrant birds are seen in estuaries and river mouths. The wintering grounds and movements are poorly known, with only a few unconfirmed post-breeding records along the China coast, Thailand and Indonesia. A recent record from Xisha Archipelago, in April, 2004 indicates that it probably winters on islands of the south China Sea.

Threats

The disappearance of breeding colonies on islands off Shandong coast, Northern China is probably due to habitat loss caused by human settlement. Foraging and stop-over sites at coastal wetlands in southeast China are facing threats like reclamation, habitat degradation, pollution and other problems resulting from development. Egg-collecting by fishermen for food is regarded as the most serious threats to breeding colonies, while breeding sites as such are of less economical importance and therefore not subjected to, for example, exploition. Introduction of rats or other feral animals to breeding islands is a potential threat and habitat destruction and/or overfishing in feeding areas presumably as a big threat as for other seabirds. The Mazu Archipelago breeding sites are relatively undisturbed, due to their strategical importance although fishermen and tourists occasionally visit the islands. One breeding colony in Zhejiang was destroyed by a typhoon.

Conservation actions to date
The newly discovered colony and surrounding islands (71 ha) in Taiwan were declared a national nature reserve in 2000. There are several other protected areas along the Chinese coast where it could potentially occur, at least on passage. In Thailand, it is nationally protected, and the locality where it was historically recorded is protected as the Laem

Talumphuk Non-Hunting Area. In China, it has been listed as a Nationally Protected Species (Class II) since 1989, although a higher protection level is needed. A county-level waterbirds reserve was established at the Min Jiang river estuary, Fujian province in 2003. A protected area on marine ecosystem was established at Jiushan Islands, Zhejiang in 2003.Both sites are proposed for upgrading to a national level. Further surveys for both breeding and wintering grounds and education for fishery communities are highly required.

Conservation actions required
- Conduct surveys at its former localities, both in the presumed breeding and non-breeding ranges, and at other potentially suitable breeding sites in China.
- Take immediate conservation measures to safeguard any sites found, especially nesting colonies.
- Upgrade Huanghe Sanjiaozhou Nature Reserve to national reserve status and strengthen protection there.

Photo: © Jiang Hang-Dong

Changle, Fujian Province, China, June 2006

Photo: © Hao Zhang

Fuzhou, Fujian, China, 2006

Photo: © Martin Hale

Silvery Wood-pigeon
Columba argentina
Population: < 50, trend unknown

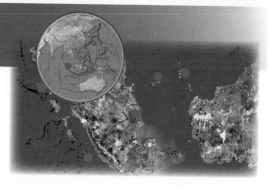

Painting: © Jan Wilczur/HBW4 (Lynx Edicions)

Range & population
This pigeon appears to have a highly restricted range, principally confined to islands off Sumatra, Indonesia, and off the west coast of Sarawak, Malaysia and Kalimantan, Indonesia. There is one confirmed record each from mainland Sumatra and Kalimantan and a provisional record in the Talang Talang Islands off western Borneo in 2001. It inhabits mangroves, woodland and coconut groves in the lowlands and hills of offshore islands, occasionally being found in similar habitats below 100 m on mainland Sumatra and Borneo. Although poorly known, available evidence suggests it wanders seasonally or disperses between islands in response to food supply.

Threats
Too little is known about the species to identify threats, although it may be speculated that settlement, deforestation, disturbance, hunting on small islands and the introduction of mammalian predators may have caused widespread declines as is the case for a number of other declining *Columbiformes*.

Conservation actions to date
No measures are known.

Conservation actions required
- Conduct surveys on islands within its historical range (and mangroves and swamp-forest of South Sumatra province) to clarify its current distribution, population status, movements and attendant threats.
- Formulate a conservation strategy involving protection of key islands, especially those supporting breeding populations.

Blue-eyed Ground-dove
Columbina cyanopis
Population: 50-249 ↓

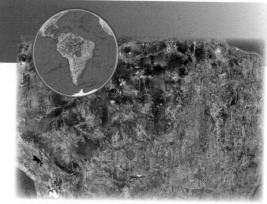

Painting: © Martin Elliott/HBW4 (Lynx Edicions)

Range & population
The Blue-eyed Ground Dove is known from very few records over a wide range in the interior of Brazil. There is a small population in the Serra das Araras, Mato Grosso, but the only other recent records are from near Cuiabá (also in Mato Grosso) in the 1980s, and one individual at Campo Grande, Mato Grosso do Sul, in 1992. Historical records are also scarce. It has been erroneously listed for Minas Gerais, but could conceivably occur in the extreme west of the state.
It occurs in campo cerrado grasslands, and was once observed in a rice-field after harvest. It is terrestrial and occurs singly or in pairs.

Threats
The reasons for this species' historical rarity are unknown because, until recently, large areas of potentially suitable habitat remained. It is now severely threatened by the massive destruction of the Brazilian Cerrado.

Conservation actions to date
It is protected under Brazilian law, and occurs in Serra das Araras Ecological Station. National parks encompass relatively large areas of potentially suitable cerrado grassland habitat.

Conservation actions required
- Survey the Serra das Araras to determine the size of the population and propose measures for its protection.
- Survey near Cuiabá and at Campo Grande to determine its status and protect these areas if appropriate.
- Survey any area with apparently suitable habitat, especially Emas National Park and Iquê-Juruena Ecological Station, taking care to avoid overlooking the species by confusing it with other sympatric species.
- Study its ecology to assess reasons for its historical rarity.

Purple-winged Ground-dove
Claravis godefrida
Population: 50-249 ↓

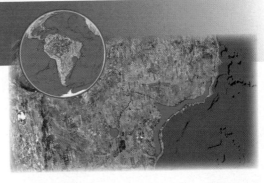

Photo: © Luiz Claudio Marigo

Range & population
In the beginning of the 20th century this ground-dove occurred from Bahia in Brazil, south through eastern Brazil to northern Argentina and eastern Paraguay, from sea-level to 2,300 m. The paucity of recent records, and the fact that none describe groups of more than five birds, suggests that extremely severe declines have occurred. It inhabits humid Atlantic forest, apparently with a preference for edge habitats in hilly, broken terrain. Records range from near sea-level to 2,300 m.

Threats
The clearance and fragmentation of Atlantic forest is the main threat. It is uncommon in trade, but the taking of additional birds from the wild must have a considerable impact on such a small population.

Conservation actions to date
It is protected by Brazilian law, and has been recorded in a number of protected areas in Brazil. It is also reported from Iguazú National Park, Argentina. However, numbers observed are small and no population is known to be adequately protected. The small captive population held by a few Brazilian aviculturists has apparently died out.

Conservation actions required
- Urgently survey to locate additional populations, using tape-playback.
- Monitor known populations.
- Study the species' dependence on bamboo flowerings.
- Record and document its vocalisations.
- Develop a CMS agreement for this and other bamboo specialists.

Grenada Dove
Leptotila wellsi
Population: 66-120 ↓

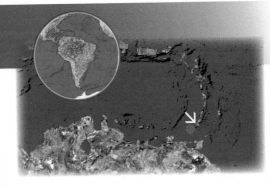

Mt. Hartman, Grenada, 2004

Photo: © Bonnie Rusk / BirdLife

Range & population
Grenada Dove is endemic to Grenada in the Lesser Antilles of which it is the national bird. It may have been always confined to xeric, coastal areas where climax vegetation was deciduous, seasonal forest and thorn woodland. Breeding is limited to the rainy season in the south-west, but is more extended on the less xeric west coast.

Threats
Chronic and continuing habitat loss for plantations and construction has possibly been compounded by introduced mongooses, cats and rats predating fledglings. At Mt Hartman, a golf course and road are under construction adjacent to, and between, occupied habitat. Hurricanes pose a pertinent threat now that the remaining population is so small.

Conservation actions to date
In 1996, parts of Mt Hartman and Perseverance, where it occurs, were declared a national park and a protected area, respectively; however, the Grenada government has recently sold off this park to Four Seasons for a resort development. A recovery plan was drafted in 1997. Grenada Dove is the national bird of Grenada and has been a focus of environmental education in schools, ecotourism and it features on stamps.

Conservation actions required
- Campaign against the imminent destruction of Mt Hartman National Park.
- Implement the recovery plan.
- Ensure that the Mt Hartman and Perseverance reserves are effectively protected.
- Restore habitat at existing and new sites.
- Establish two new subpopulations.

Negros Bleeding-heart
Gallicolumba keayi
Population: 50-249 ⬇

Photo: ©Stefan Luft / PESCP

NW Panay, 1999

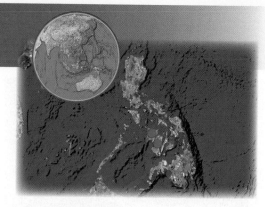

History
1877 – the species is discovered by W. A. Keay, a sugar estate owner in Negros.

1900 – W. E. Clarke describes the species in Ibis.

1997 – a population is discovered on the Philippine island of Panay.

Range & population
Negros Bleeding-heart is endemic to the Philippines, where it occurs on Panay and Negros. On Panay, it was recorded in 1997 at two sites on the north-west peninsula, having been reported by locals at five sites earlier in the decade. Since then, birds have been recorded nesting in the same area and further observations of the species have been made. On Negros, it was fairly common in the 19th century, but had become extremely rare by the 1930s. Since 1980, it has been recorded at just one locality (above Mambucal), despite several weeks of surveys, with unconfirmed local reports from six additional localities. Recent research identified a few small populations in southern Negros. It seems unlikely that more than a few hundred individuals remain on each island, although its status on Panay cannot be assessed with confidence, given its recent discovery there.

This predominantly terrestrial species appears to prefer dense closed-canopy forests from 300-1,000 m, exceptionally to 1,200 m. It is not clear whether it tolerates secondary forest. Records on Panay from selectively logged forest on limestone, and from open and severely degraded forest with few large trees, suggest that it may do. It seems unlikely that it undertakes more than very local movements in response to food patchiness. It has been recorded nesting in May and June with chicks fledging after only 12 days, apparently as an adaptation to the vulnerability of their open and low nests in epiphytic ferns. Nests appear to be regularly predated.

Threats
Primary forests have been almost totally destroyed on Negros (where just 4% of any type of forest cover remained in 1988) and Panay (where 8% remained). Habitat degradation, through clearance for agriculture, timber and charcoal-burning, continues to pose a serious threat to remaining fragments. This is exacerbated by trapping and hunting for food and, presumably, for the cage-bird trade. In 2005, five birds were killed by poachers in Negros. A number of nests have been depredated, though whether this is by native or introduced predators is unknown.

Conservation actions to date
The only recent records are from a protected area, Mt Canlaon Natural Park on Negros. Local reports also derive from the North Negros Forest Reserve, and another area where it was formerly recorded (Mt Talinis/Twin Lakes on Negros) has been proposed for conservation-related funding. In the mid-1990s, the species featured on a bilingual environmental awareness poster as part of the 'Only in the Philippines' series. It has been studied as part of the Philippine Endemic Species Project (PESCP). The North Negros Forest Natural Park was declared by Presidential Decree in 2006. Efforts are ongoing to strengthen protected area management and involve Negros Forests and Ecological Foundation, Inc. (NFEFI) and Siliman University - Angelo King Center for Research and Environmental Management (SUAKCREM) in the protection of the species.

Conservation actions required
- Conduct fieldwork in all areas from which the species has been locally reported and all other sites where suitable habitat remains, including Bulabong Puti-an National Park.
- Establish the proposed 100 km² North-west Panay Peninsula National Park, where the species has recently been discovered.
- Provide immediate effective protection for the North Negros Forest Reserve.
- Encourage careful reforestation activities around remaining forests.

Photo: ©Stefan Luft / PESCP

NW Panay, 1999

Mindoro Bleeding-heart
Gallicolumba platenae
Population: 50-249 ↓

Mindoro, 1998

Photo: © Pete Morris / Birdquest

History
1891 – Italian zoologist Tommaso Salvadori (1835-1923) describes the species.

1935 – the first special reserve is created on Mindoro.

1954 – considered locally common.

Range & population
This bleeding-heart is endemic to the island of Mindoro in the Philippines, where it is known from 15 localities. Since 1980, there have been records from just four localities (Puerto Galera, MUFRC Experimental Forest, Siburan and Mt Iglit-Baco National Park), with unconfirmed local reports from eight other sites, suggesting that remnant populations conceivably exist elsewhere. It was common in the early 20th century and apparently locally common as recently as 1954. Subsequently, unconfirmed reports suggested it was common in the recent past in the extreme south of the island. However, the paucity of reports from hunters and very low encounter rate by fieldworkers suggests that numbers have become very low. It is predominantly a terrestrial pigeon, sensitive to human disturbance, which inhabits closed-canopy primary and secondary lowland forest, preferring dry forest substrates on gentle slopes up to 750 m. Most of its time is spent on the ground, only using low branches of trees for roosting or breeding or when it is disturbed. Its diet consists of fallen seeds, berries, grains and invertebrates and fruit. The nest is usually situated below two metres. It is not known whether or not it undertakes altitudinal, seasonal or nomadic movements and breeding has been recorded between February and May.

Threats
Lowland forest destruction has almost eradicated this bird's entire habitat. In 1988, just 120 km^2 of forest remained on Mindoro, only 25% of which was closed-canopy. At current rates of loss, the island may lose all primary forest below 900 m within a few years. The forests at Siburan and Mt Iglit-Baco National Park are threatened by encroaching shifting cultivation and occasional selective logging. Rattan collection further disturbs the forest undergrowth. Dynamite-blasting for marble is a threat to forest at Puerto Galera. Hunting (using snares) for food and collection for the pet trade are additional threats, particularly during the dry season (February-May).

Conservation actions to date
It occurs in Mt Iglit-Baco National Park, where only tiny forest tracts remain. This is the largest protected area on Mindoro and is one of two ASEAN Natural Heritage Sites in the Philippines. The park is inhabited by tribal people, and much of the reserve consists of fire-maintained grassland which has modified the habitat. The forest at Siburan is effectively part of the Sablayan Penal Colony, although it is uncertain how much protection is afforded by this, or its inclusion in the F. B. Harrison Game Reserve. The Haribon Foundation, www.haribon.org.ph, have been working at the site for over five years and have established a site support group. Funding has been provided for faunal inventories and environmental education initiatives at Puerto Galera, where hunting has been locally prohibited. In the mid-1990s, the species featured on a bilingual environmental awareness poster in the "Only in the Philippines" series.

Conservation actions required
- Urgently produce a detailed map of remaining forests on Mindoro, and survey these systematically to clarify its current distribution and population status.
- Follow up any anecdotal reports of the species.
- Conduct ecological studies to assess its requirements for breeding and foraging.
- Produce a management plan for the forest at Siburan that reconciles biodiversity conservation with its role as a prison.
- Strengthen and support forest management by the Site Support Group at Siburan.

BirdLife Species Guardian **Haribon Foundation**

Mindoro, 2005

Photo: © Don Roberson

Sulu Bleeding-heart
Gallicolumba menagei
Population: < 50 ↓

Painting: © John Cox/HBW4 (Lynx Edicions)

Range & population
This species is endemic to the Sulu archipelago in the Philippines. It is known from two specimens taken on Tawitawi in 1891. The only evidence of its continued existence derives from unconfirmed local reports in 1995 from Tawitawi and the islands of Siasi, Tandubatu, Dundangan, Baliungan and Simunul. The species may survive in logged forest.

Threats
The remaining primary forest on Tawitawi has been cleared and areas of forest left were highly degraded and recently logged. In 2006 some forest tracts reportedly remained. Logging of the few remaining tracts, now confined to rugged, mountainous areas, is likely to be followed by uncontrolled settlement and conversion to agriculture. Small-scale logging

operations occur on Tandubatu, Dundangan and Baliungan. Hunting and trapping may have caused a substantial decrease during martial law in the 1970s.

Conservation actions to date
Military activity and insurgency continue to present a serious obstacle to general conservation activity in the Sulus. There are no protected areas in the archipelago. In 1997, a public awareness campaign focusing on the conservation of terrestrial biodiversity on Tawitawi was initiated.

Conservation actions required
- Conduct intensive surveys of all remaining forest tracts on Tawitawi and nearby islands to establish whether the species is still extant.
- Urgently propose any sites found to support the species for strict protection.
- Incorporate protective measures relevant to this species within conservation funding proposals for the Tawitawi/ Sulu Coastal Area.

Polynesian Ground-dove
Gallicolumba erythroptera
Population: 50-249 ↓

French Polynesia, 2006

Photo: © Pete Morris / Birdquest

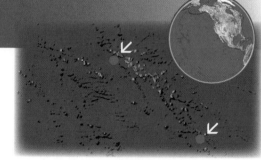

Range & population
This ground-dove formerly occurred in the Society Islands and throughout the Tuamotu Archipelago, French Polynesia. Recent records include on islets in Rangiroa Atoll and a new population discovered on Morane, Tuamotu in 2003. It favours primary forest on atolls with herbs, shrubs and ferns or dense shrubs. It has a varied diet, including caterpillars and other insects, seeds, green leaves, buds and fruit.

Threats
It was formerly caught by local people for food but it is more likely that the introduction of cats and rats are the real

reasons for its decline. Habitat loss is also likely to have been a factor as the largest atolls with the richest vegetation have been cleared for coconut plantations.

Conservation actions to date
Successful rat eradication programmes have been completed on one island of Rangiroa atoll. In 2005 a successful rat eradication was conducted on one of Rangiroa's motus (small islands) and follow up surveys in 2006 found 9 doves in the atoll.

Conservation actions required
- Conduct further surveys of existing and new populations.
- Protect Tenararo from introduction of predators and human disturbance.
- Identify suitable islands in the Acteon group for translocation.
- Increase public awareness through the local press and school conferences.
- Develop a Recovery Plan.

Negros Fruit-dove
Ptilinopus arcanus
Population: < 50 ↓

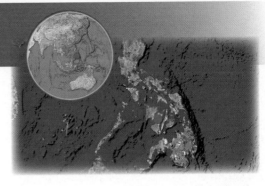

Painting: © John Cox/HBW4 (Lynx Edicions)

Range & population
Negros Fruit-dove is endemic to the Philippines, where it is known only by a single specimen collected on the island of Negros in 1953. The specimen was shot in a tall fruiting tree in primary forest at c. 1,100 m. It is possible that it is a lowland specialist. The recent discovery on Panay of other threatened species occurring on Negros, suggests that this enigmatic and surely very rare bird may be extant.

Threats
A combination of hunting, which affects all pigeons and fruit-doves on Negros, and habitat destruction are presumably the major threats. Just 4% of Negros remained forested in 1988,

and remnant tracts are small, heavily fragmented and under incessant pressure from clearance for agriculture, timber and charcoal-burning.

Conservation actions to date
The only record derives from Mt Canlaon Natural Park, which supports 115 km² of mainly montane forest. No other conservation measures are known to have been taken other than its depiction in the mid-1990s on a bilingual environmental education poster in the 'Only in the Philippines' series.

Conservation actions required
- Comprehensively survey all suitable lowland to mid-montane forested habitat on Negros to determine whether the species is extant.
- Conduct surveys for fruit-doves on Panay.
- Carry out, if possible, biochemical analyses on the type-specimen to confirm its taxonomic validity.

Marquesan Imperial-pigeon
Ducula galeata
Population: 202-282 ↓

French Polynesia, 2006

Photo: © Pete Morris / Birdquest

Range & population
This pigeon is endemic to Nuku Hiva in the Marquesas Islands, French Polynesia where recent surveys found the population was apparently stable. A translocated population on Ua Huka Island is anticipated to reach 50 individuals by 2008. It is found in remote wooded valleys from 250-1,300 m and is also seen in secondary forest and at the edge of banana and orange plantations. It feeds on fruit from trees and shrubs.

Threats
Illegal hunting is the main concern, though following an awareness raising campaign this appears to have

been reduced. Habitat has been modified and degraded by introduced vegetation and grazing by feral stock. However, cattle have been eradicated, and goats and pigs are decreasing. New roads and tunnels could result in anthropogenic threats. Introduced cats and rats are likely to constitute a threat.

Conservation actions to date
The bird is revered in local culture and hunting is forbidden (although it continues). Monitoring of the translocated Ua Huka population is continuing and further translocation may occur to increase the genetic base. Awareness raising campaigns have been met with success.

Conservation actions required
- Research predation by cats and rats.
- Promote public awareness.
- Establish the absence of avian diseases.
- Consider captive breeding.

Kakapo
Strigops habroptilus

Codfish Island 2007

Photo: © Simon Fordham

Population: 86 ↓

History

1845 – the first Kakapo is found by a European.

1894 – the first conservation attempt takes place when Richard Henry shifts several hundred birds from Fiordland to offshore islands. Stoats arrive and the effort fails.

1903 – three birds are transferred to Little Barrier Island, but disappear.

1912 – three birds are transferred to Kapiti Island.

1934 – the skin of a Kakapo is priced at 37 pence in the skin trade.

1936 – last sighting of a transferred bird on Kapiti Island.

1952 – New Zealand Deaprtment for Internal Affairs appeals for assistance in locating Kakapos.

1974 – helicopters are sent in to locate Kakapo, only eight birds are found.

1976 – the known population stands at 18 birds, all males, all in Fiordland.

1977 – a rapidly declining population of c.150 birds is discovered on Stewart Island including the first females seen in living memory.

1982-1992 – a total of 60 birds, 22 females and 38 males, survived to be transferred from Stewart Island to offshore island refuges.

1997 – the population begins to increase for the first time in recorded history.

2002 – the population increases by 39% from 62 to 86.

2007 – the Kakapo population stands at 55 adults (21 females and 34 males) and 31 juveniles (20 females and 11 males).

Range & population

This species formerly occurred throughout most of the North, South and Stewart Islands, New Zealand. Although it disappeared from most of its original range in the wake of human colonization, the species remained abundant in Fiordland and some other sparsely inhabited parts of South Island until the early twentieth century. Between 1980 and 1992, 61 remaining Stewart Island birds were transferred to cat and mustelid-free offshore islands, and are presently located on Codfish and Anchor Islands, both of which are now free of all introduced mammals including rats. The population has increased to 86 birds following the implementation of intensive nest management techniques in 1995.

Kakapo is the heaviest species of parrot. It is entirely herbivorous feeding on leaves, stems, roots, rhizomes fruit, nectar and seeds. It is unique among parrots in having a lek system for mating. The breeding season takes place between December and April and males gather on display grounds where they dig shallow bowl depressions in the ground. As they have inflatable throat sacs, the booming call the male produces may be heard for distances up to 5 km. It has been described as follows by British author Douglas Adams: "(The kakapo boom) was like a heartbeat: a deep powerful throb that echoed through the dark ravines. It was so deep that some people will tell you that they felt it stirring in their gut before they could discern the actual sound, a sort of wump, a heavy wobble of air."

Males compete against each other and can release thousands of booms a night. It breeds only every two to five years and times breeding to coincide with infrequent superabundant fruit crops of certain podocarp tree species. It lays 1-4 eggs and the female incubates these alone for around 30 days. Eggs and chicks are frequently left unattended for several hours each night when the female feeds. Female Kakapo take eight to 11 years to reach breeding age, while males are sexually mature at five years of age. Kakapo have the lowest metabolic rate of any bird so far measured and may be the longest lived of all birds; average longevity is currently estimated at 90 years with 95% confidence limits of 50-120 years. One male captured as an adult in Fiordland in 1975 is probably at least 70 or 80 years old. Adult survival is now more than 99% per year.

Codfish Island 2007

Photo: © Tristan Rawlence

Threats
This parrot lives most of its life on the ground and birds in all ages are susceptible to predators as they cannot fly to safety and many birds also are tame. The longevity and slow reproduction rate contribute their vulnerability. The kakapos' skins were highly prized by the Maori people. Cloaks were made from kakapo feathers and the birds were also hunted with dogs for meat. Historically, Polynesian Rat (Kiore) introduced by Maoris caused a slow decline of the species but when other introduced animals such as cats, dogs and rats began to feed on kakapos about 150 years ago the rate of decline increased. In the 1930s the market was so flooded

with skins that they were only worth 37p each and the species was extinct from the North Island of New Zealand. On Stewart Island, 56% of radio-tagged adults were killed by feral cats. Poor hatching success and the low frequency of breeding slow efforts to increase the population size quickly. In 2004, three juvenile females died of septicaemia caused by the widespread bacterium *Erysipelas rhusiopathiae (erysipelas)* following their transfer from one island to another.

Conservation actions to date
The first recovery plan was drawn up in 1989 and in 1991 the Kakapo Recovery Programme was set up to conserve the species. The Programme is a partnership between the New Zealand Department of Conservation, Forest and Bird, and New Zealand Aluminium Smelters (NZAS).

The project got a poor start in the 1991-92 season when three females produced six chicks on Codfish Island but fruits failed to ripen. A combination of starvation and predation made only one chick survive, which became the first hand-reared kakapo, named Hoki, and is now transferred to Maud Island. Supplementary feeding has increased clutch size and nestling survival but not breeding frequency or hatching success. All individuals are radio-tagged, and their location and survival monitored throughout the year. Each nest is monitored continuously using infra-red video cameras, and heat pads are placed over eggs and nestlings while females forage. In 1998, the Polynesian rat (*Rattus exulans*) (a predator of eggs and nestlings) was eradicated from Codfish Island. Research on genetics, artificial insemination and nutrition is ongoing. Methods for hand-rearing chicks that fail to thrive in the wild have been developed; 73% of hand-reared chicks now survive to fledging and hand-reared chicks currently comprise 40% of all chicks fledged. Providing ad lib quantities of supplementary food to females was found to cause them to produce more male chicks; reducing the amount of supplementary food returned the sex ratio at hatching to unity. Efforts to quantify and manage the population's genetics have been undertaken in order to improve the currently low genetic diversity hatching rate. Translocations are regularly carried out to take advantage of locally abundant fruit crops and thereby increase the frequency of breeding. In 2006, a search of Fiordland failed to find any evidence of the continued survival of Kakapo there.

Conservation actions required
- Continue research to identify the factors that limit breeding frequency and productivity and address these urgently.
- Maintain existing management practices responsible for reversing the population's decline, including the Kakapo Recovery Programme.

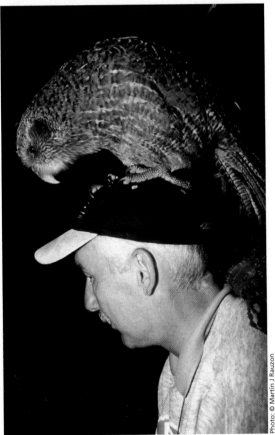

Maud Island, 2002

Photo: © Martin J Rauzon

151

Yellow-crested Cockatoo
Cacatua sulphurea
Population: 2,500-9,999 ↓

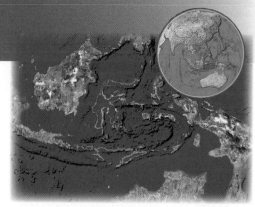

Komodo, Indonesia, 1997

Photo: © Stefan Behrens

History

1788 – the species is described by German zoologist Johann Friedrich Gmelin (1748-1804).

1981-1992 – CITES record 96,785 birds exported from Indonesia.

1989 – EU bans imports.

1992 – the US bans imports.

1993 – trade is stopped, before this in average 1600 birds a year were taken from Sumba.

1994 – a zero-quota for wild birds caught in Indonesia is established.

Range & population

This cockatoo is endemic to Timor-Leste and Indonesia, where it was formerly common throughout Nusa Tenggara (from Bali to Timor), on Sulawesi and its satellite islands, and the Masalembu Islands (in the Java Sea). It has undergone a dramatic decline, particularly in the last quarter of the 20th century, such that it is now extinct from many islands and close to extinction on most others. Sumba appears to support the largest remaining population, tentatively estimated (in 1992) at c. 3,200 birds (but declining, perhaps by 500 birds annually with just 10% of the island still forested in 34 fragments), with other significant (but considerably smaller) populations on Komodo, Sulawesi, Buton, Moyo and Timor-Leste. Its current status on several small islands is unclear. It inhabits forest (including evergreen, moist deciduous, monsoon and semi-evergreen), forest edge, scrub and agriculture up to 500 m on Sulawesi, and 800 m (sometimes 1,500 m) in Nusa Tenggara. On at least some islands (e.g. Sumba), it appears heavily dependent on closed-canopy primary forest. On others, it survives despite the total clearance of original vegetation, indicating that its habitat requirements are somewhat flexible. Breeding takes place from September to May on Sumba and the pairs bond for life. It nests in tree cavities.

Threats

Its precipitous decline is almost entirely attributable to unsustainable exploitation for internal and international trade. Large-scale logging and conversion of forest to agriculture across its range has exacerbated the decline, and the use of pesticides since around 1989 is a further potential threat. At least formerly, the species was regarded as a crop-pest, and consequently persecuted. High rainfall years appear to limit productivity considerably resulting in very low recruitment. Furthermore, competition for cavity nest sites with other parrots and owls leads to low productivity.

Conservation actions to date

A cooperative recovery plan has been developed and adopted. Populations occur in several protected areas, the most important being Rawa Aopa Watumohai and Caraente National Parks (on Sulawesi) which support up to 100 individuals, Suaka Margasatwa Nature Reserve on Pulau Moyo, Komodo National Park and two national parks on Sumba: Manupeu-Tanahdaru and Laiwangi-Wanggameti. The Noni Conis Santana proposed National Park in Timor holds 100 birds. Moratoria on international trade have been effective in allowing several subpopulations on Sumba to increase in number between 1992 and 2002, though densities remained below those typical of other cockatoo species.

Conservation actions required

- Conduct further surveys to identify the most appropriate areas for conservation action and to periodically monitor key populations.
- Conduct ecological research to clarify options for its management and conservation.
- Provide support for relevant protected areas and conservation initiatives within its range and protect nest-trees where possible.
- Strengthen control and monitoring of trade.
- Promote widespread community-based conservation initiatives.
- Recommendations made specifically for the protection of the species in Komodo National Park were to conduct annual monitoring, maintain regular patrols, raise awareness in local communities and study human activities and impacts within the park.

Komodo, Indonesia, 1997

Photo: © Stefan Behrens

Philippine Cockatoo
Cacatua haematuropygia
Population: 1,000-4,000 ↓

Palawan, 2005

Photo: © Simon Harrap

Range & population
This cockatoo is endemic to the Philippines where it is now confined to 8 islands. Most birds, 750-2,800, are found on Palawan and its satellite islands but it also occurs on Tawitawi, Mindanao and Masbate. It appears restricted to lowland primary and/or secondary forest, in or adjacent to riverine or coastal areas with mangroves. It depends on seasonally fluctuating food resources and is partially nomadic.

Threats
On Palawan, trapping is particularly serious. Lowland deforestation and mangrove destruction have been extensive throughout its range, and have contributed significantly to its decline. It is also persecuted as a crop-pest, hunted for food and captured for the bird-trade. The release of captive birds may introduce disease into the wild population. Introduced predators represent a threat at many potential release sites.

Conservation actions to date
It is known from five protected areas and awareness campaigns have been conducted nationwide. An international captive-breeding programme was initiated in 1992.

Conservation actions required
- Designate further protected areas.
- Support the proposed expansion of St Paul's Subterranean National Park.
- Regulate mangrove destruction.
- Promote economically viable alternatives to cockatoo-trapping.
- Enhance the education programme.
- Establish staffed posts at airports and ferry terminals.

Blue-fronted Lorikeet
Charmosyna toxopei
Population: 50-249 ↓

Painting: © Norman Arlott/HBW4 (Lynx Edicions)

Range & population
This lorikeet is endemic to the island of Buru, South Maluku, Indonesia, where it was known from seven specimens collected in the 1920s. It was recorded between 1979-1981 with unconfirmed reports until 2006. The lack of confirmed records makes it problematic to assess this species' population size, but it has been described as 'quite common', though only from one part of a very small range. Anecdotal information collected from interviews with local people suggests that it is probably a lower montane species, which in some years occurs down to the coastal lowlands.

Threats
Forest clearing, selective logging, degradation and fragmentation by shifting agriculture is a major threat. However, the island's extensive montane forests still remain largely undisturbed. The species is not kept as a pet, nor apparently is it traded.

Conservation actions to date
No measures have been taken, although an area of 1,450 km² on Gunung Kelapatmada in the west of the island is proposed as a reserve. It remains to be confirmed whether this site meets the conservation needs of all Buru's threatened landbirds.

Conservation actions required
- Conduct widespread surveys ranging out from the Teluk Bara/Lake Rana area, to establish its current status, distribution, habitat requirements and movements.
- If key sites for the species are identified, propose their establishment as strict protected areas.
- Support the establishment of a proposed reserve at Gunung Kelapatmada.

New Caledonian Lorikeet
Charmosyna diadema
Population: < 50 ↓

Painting: © Norman Arlott/HBW4 (Lynx Edicions)

disappeared from the island. Several *Charmosyna* lorikeets have undergone severe population declines or fluctuations of unknown cause. It is possible that introduced disease (such as avian malaria) or more likely mammals (notably rats) may have been a cause of decline.

Range & population
This lorikeet is known from three females collected in 1859 (two), and in 1913 on New Caledonia (to France). The earliest reports were that it inhabited forest and occasionally fed in *Erythrina* trees. 1953/4 and 1976 unconfirmed observations were from *Melaleuca* savanna/humid forest ecotone, while a 1920s report was from low scrubland. Most closely-related species are nomadic, occur primarily in montane forest, but range into lowland forests, for which they may have a seasonal dependence.

Threats
Montane humid forest is not under threat, but it is possible that this species has a requirement for other habitats, some of which, notably lowland semi-deciduous forests, have nearly

Conservation actions to date
The Mt Panié massif, one of the most likely sites where it may yet occur, is a floral reserve where the habitat is protected. Two recent conservation reviews have recommended that this reserve is upgraded to a special faunal and floral reserve and also extended to include Mts Colnett and Ignambi to the north as one contiguous forest block.

Conservation actions required
* Survey other suitable mountains.
* Publicise the search for this species among forest workers and villagers.
* Advocate upgrading and extension of Mt Panié floral reserve.

Red-throated Lorikeet
Charmosyna amabilis
Population: < 50 ↓

Photo: © William Beckon

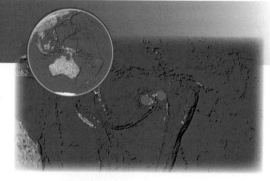

Range & population
This lorikeet occurs patchily distributed on the islands of Viti Levu, Vanua Levu, Taveuni and Ovalau in Fiji. The last reported sighting was in 2001. It is found in mature forests above 500 m but has also been recorded in mangroves. It is usually found in small flocks high in the canopy feeding on nectar and pollen from flowering trees. Its breeding ecology is unknown.

Threats
However, the rarity and assumed decline of this species is probably largely the result of predation by introduced mammals, such as Black Rat *Rattus rattus*. Ongoing increases in logging and the road network are likely to be increasing rat density.

Conservation actions to date
It is protected under Fijian law. On Viti Levu, it occurs within the Tomaniivi Nature Reserve, but this is not large enough to maintain a resident population. On Taveuni, the combination of the Ravilevu Nature Reserve and the Bouma National Heritage Park provides an area of adequate size for its conservation but the lorikeet remains very rare.

Conservation actions required
* On Viti Levu, repeat forest surveys and assess threats.
* Establish safe populations in captivity or on rat-free islands.
* Develop local expertise in survey methodology to enable monitoring.
* Identify further suitable areas for the conservation of this species.
* Survey other islands, notably montane Taveuni.
* Conduct surveys between between August and October.

Chatham Albatross. Photo: © Ron Hoff

Malherbe's Parakeet
Cyanoramphus malherbi
Population: < 50 ↓

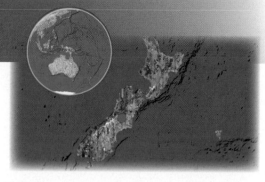

Maud Island, New Zealand, March 2007

Photo: © Jack van Hal

This species was previously considered a subspecies of Yellow-crowned Parakeet *Cyanoramphus auriceps*.

Range & population
This parakeet is only known with certainty from three valleys in the South Island of New Zealand. It was once present in the North, most of the South, and Stewart Islands. Surveys in December 2006 found that an earlier translocation to Chalky Island in Fiordland had been successful, with birds breeding and the population expanding to utilise all corners of the island. It requires mature trees with natural hollows or cavities for nesting and it feeds on seeds, fruits, leaves, flowers, buds and invertebrates.

Threats
The impact of introduced predators is likely to be the primary cause of decline. The species' hole-nesting behaviour leads to a reduced ratio of females in the population due to predation on the nest. Sufficient nest holes are unlikely in managed beech forest.

Conservation actions to date
The Hurunui population is subjected to integrated pest management and nest-monitoring. The Hawdon population received stoat control only during plague years. Work has been successful at establishing a captive population and reintroduction is planned for Maud Island.

Conservation actions required
- Complete surveys and monitoring techniques.
- Study breeding biology and ecology.
- Stabilise and increase numbers.
- Establish further populations on predator free offshore islands.

Orange-bellied Parrot
Neophema chrysogaster
Population: 150 ↓

Werribee, Victoria, 2007

Photo: © Chris Tzaros

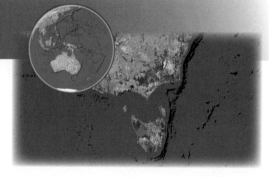

Range & population
This parrot breeds in a very small area in south-western Tasmania, Australia. Birds migrate and overwinter at sites scattered from south-east South Australia east to south-east New South Wales. It nests in hollows, feeding on the ground on grass and sedge seed from surrounding moorlands. After breeding, it disperses to saltmarshes, dunes, beaches, pastures and shrublands close to the coast.

Threats
The primary reason for the species' decline is thought to be fragmentation and degradation of overwintering habitat by grazing, agriculture and urban and industrial development. A captive population has been quarantined after individuals died of unknown causes.

Conservation actions to date
A recovery team was established in 1980. Habitat in Tasmania, Victoria and King Island has been reserved or is managed. Breeding, migration and winter counts are made annually. A captive-breeding programme has been established and c. 75 birds are released annually. Released birds have migrated successfully between their breeding and wintering grounds. Awareness-raising and education programmes are conducted.

Conservation actions required
- Survey all saltmarsh in wintering range.
- Model breeding and feeding habitat to assess availability.
- Control human disturbance and predators.
- Create new winter habitats and protect existing ones.
- Develop and implement a media strategy.

Lear's Macaw
Anodorhynchus leari
Population: 751 ↓

Photo: © Helmut Schumann

Jeremoabo-Canudos, 2007

History
1858 – Napoleon's nephew Charles Lucien Bonaparte (1775-1840) describes the species.

1950 – Olivierio Pinto finds a specimen in captivity, which has been trapped in Bahia state.

1965 – Karel H. Voous suggests the 'species' could be a hybrid.

1978 – a wild population is found at last.

1994 – the population is estimated at 140 birds.

2007 – 751 birds are counted by Fundação Biodiversitas staff in June flying out from a roost at the Canudus Biological Station.

Range & population
This species was known to science for 150 years from trade birds, before a wild population was found in 1978. It counted 246 birds in 2001 and formed two colonies at Toca Velha and Serra Branca, south of the Raso da Catarina plateau in north-east Bahia, Brazil. In 1995, a roosting site holding 22 birds was located at Sento Sé/Campo Formoso, 200 km to the east. Initially, this was thought to represent a distinct subpopulation, but is now considered to refer to birds from the Toca Velha/Serra Branca population following patches of fruiting licurí *Syagrus* palms. The severity of existing threats indicates that the species continues to decline. There is a small captive population but breeding is sporadic and uncoordinated.

It occurs in arid caatinga with sandstone cliffs (for colonial nesting and roosting) and stands of licurí palms. It forages in trees and on the ground, largely for licurí palm nuts (individuals eat up to 350 a day), but also *Melanoxylon*, *Atropha pohliana*, *Dioclea*, *Spondias tuberosa*, Agave flowers and maize. Breeding is in February–April. Two young often fledge.

Threats
In 1992–1995, c. 20 birds were caught and sold to smugglers from Toca Velha/Serra Branca and, in 1996, at least 19 individuals were taken. Licurí palm-stands formerly covered 250,000 km² but have been vastly reduced by livestock-grazing. A major fire could now eradicate most of the food supply for the Toca Velha/Serra Branca population. Hunting for food and wildlife products are potential threats.

Conservation actions to date
Protected by Brazilian law. Infiltration of trading networks and improved surveillance at breeding sites has resulted in arrests of poachers, smugglers and collectors. The Toca Velha/Serra Branca cliffs are guarded and receive partial (but largely inadequate) protection from the Raso da Catarina Ecological Station. However, a detailed plan for land acquisition has been developed and there are plans to grow, plant and fence 50,000 licurí palm seedlings. Management agreements with key landowners have been signed.

Conservation actions required
- Ensure the *de facto* protection of all known populations.
- Continue to liaise with local people to locate populations.
- Study the nesting ecology to estimate reproductive success, determine home ranges and consider double-clutching.
- Develop a long-term strategy of planting and protecting licurí palms.
- Enforce legal measures, especially through local patrolling to prevent trapping.

Photo: © Ciro Albano

Jeremoabo, state of Bahia, NE Brazil, 2006

Night Parrot
Pezoporus occidentalis
Population: < 50, trend unknown

Painting: © Richard Allen/HBW4 (Lynx Edicions)

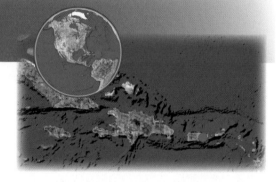

Range & population
This peculiar parrot is endemic to Australia, where historical records are spread throughout the arid and semi-arid zones. Three birds were reported in the Pilbara region of Western Australia in April 2005. A dead bird was found by Queensland Park and Wildlife Service Rangers in Diamantina National Park, Queensland in November 2006. Most specimens have been obtained from hummock grasslands or shrublands. The recent 2005 record involved birds drinking at a water hole.

Threats
Threats are extrapolated from their presumed effects on medium-sized, arid-zone mammals, and include predation by feral cats and foxes, altered fire regimes, competition for food, degradation of habitat near water by stock or rabbits, and reduced availability of water as a result of over-use by feral camels.

Conservation actions to date
Numerous searches have been carried out in an attempt to find birds. Appeals for information leading to the rediscovery of the species have received much publicity in arid Australia, especially in the Northern Territory and Western Australia.

Conservation actions required
* Develop alternative detection techniques.
* Conduct a thorough GIS analysis of recent and historic records against habitat to derive a population estimate for the species and identify priority areas to conduct searches.
* Develop captive-breeding and release techniques.
* Encourage individuals or voluntary organisations to follow up any plausible reports providing appropriate logistic support.
* Develop a contingency plan for any site where birds are found.

Puerto Rican Amazon
Amazona vittata
Population: 30-35 ◄►

Painting: © Norman Arlott / BirdLife

Hunting for food and pest control and the cage-bird trade have had crippling effects. The principal threats are now competition for nest-sites, loss of young to parasitic botflies, predation and natural disasters such as hurricanes. Predator-aversion training pre-release has improved the survival of captive-reared birds after release into the wild. Predation by alien invasive mammals has an impact.

Conservation actions to date
Since 1968, artificial nest-sites, control of nest predators and competitors and captive breeding and reintroduction has taken place. All remaining habitat is protected in the Caribbean National Forest.

Range & population
This species is endemic to Puerto Rico (to USA). There has been a drastic decline with an all-time low of 13 birds in 1975. In 2006 20 birds were released in the Rio Abajo State Forest marking the beginning of a second population in the wild. It is now restricted to forest at elevations of 200-600 m. The breeding season is late February-July, when it nests in large, deep tree-cavities and lays 3-4 eggs.

Threats
There has been an almost total loss of suitable forest habitat.

Conservation actions required
* Maintain the conservation management programme.
* Improve synchronisation of breeding of wild and captive birds.
* Integrate exotic predator trapping into the existing conservation management programme.

Glaucous Macaw
Anodorhynchus glaucus
Population: < 50, unknown trend

Painting: © Lluis Sanz/HBW4 (Lynx Edicions)

Range & population
This macaw was formerly widespread but clearly very local in north Argentina, south Paraguay, north-east Uruguay and Brazil. It became rare before or early in the second half of the 19th century and there were only two acceptable records in the 20th century; in Uruguay in 1951 and Brazil in the early 1960s. Persistent rumours of recent sightings, local reports and birds in trade indicate that a few birds may still survive.

It appears to have been adapted to consume palm nuts as its staple diet, and therefore presumably wandered into palm-savannas and potentially lightly wooded areas. It nested and roosted on cliffs.

Threats
Settlement of the major river basins within its range was presumably accompanied by the widespread loss of palm-groves, either through direct clearance for agriculture or the suppression of regeneration by colonists' cattle. It is likely it was a target for hunters. There is some evidence that it was traded.

Conservation actions to date
Protected under Brazilian law. There are ongoing funding proposals to attempt to finance a programme of work aimed at confirming this species presence in the wild.

Conservation actions required
- Repeat surveys, including video camera traps, to confirm whether an extant population remains.
- Conduct interviews with local people, especially former and active parrot trappers, to assess the likelihood that any populations remain.
- Prepare to follow-up on any positive data from these interviews.

Spix's Macaw
Cyanopsitta spixii
Population: < 50, unknown trend

Photo: © Luiz Claudio Marigo

Range & population
This macaw was known for 150 years until it was found in Bahia, Brazil in the 1980s. The three remaining birds in Brazil were captured for trade in 1987 and 1988. However, a single male, paired with a female Blue-winged Macaw *Propyrrhura maracana*, was discovered in July 1990 but had died by the end of 2000. It apparently requires gallery woodland. Breeding occurs during the austral summer. Two or three eggs are laid (up to four in captivity).

Threats
Trapping for trade is responsible for its current proximity to extinction. Human impact has resulted in clearance for crop cultivation, increased hunting for food and trapping for trade.

A hybrid strain of an invasive bee reportedly kills incubating parrots in the region. The captive population may suffer from inbreeding depression since all birds are closely related.

Conservation actions to date
Protected under Brazilian law. There are a variety of community conservation programmes that will pave the way for future reintroductions. A Working Group for the Recovery of Spix's Macaw, responsible for coordinating the captive breeding programme and establishing a blue macaw captive-breeding facility, has been established by Brazilian Institute for Environment and Natural Renewable Resources (IBAMA).

Conservation actions required
- Identify a suitable release site for the potential annual release of captive-bred birds.
- Protect and improve habitat at the identified release site.
- Establish a well-resourced Blue Macaw captive-breeding facility at Praia do Forte under IBAMA ownership.
- Introduce captive-bred fledglings to the wild and ensure protection from trappers.

Blue-throated Macaw
Ara glaucogularis
Population: 50-249 ↓

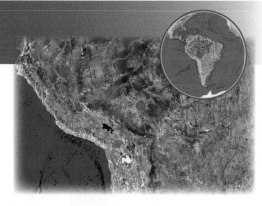

Llanos de Moxos, near Trinidad, Beni, Bolivia, 2005

Photo: © Charles Hesse

History
1921 – Roberto Dabbene describes the species.

1984 – live exports of the species are banned in Bolivia.

1992 – a wild population is discovered in Bolivia.

1993 – a survey estimates 54 individuals.

2006 – a new population with 100 individuals observed, is discovered in Bolivia

Range & population
This macaw is known from the Llanos de Mojos in north Bolivia, where it is concentrated east of the upper río Mamoré, Beni. Recent population and range estimates inferred c. 120 birds in a range of 8,600 km². A subsequent survey indicates that declines are probably still occurring. An estimated 1,200 or more wild-caught birds were exported from Bolivia during the 1980s, suggesting that the population was formerly much higher.

It inhabits a mosaic of seasonally inundated savanna, palm-groves, forest 'islands' and possibly gallery forest, in the Beni savannas. Motacú Palm *Attalea phalerata* comprises c. 60% of total vegetation cover and the macaw's presence is correlated with availability of its palm-fruit food. It nests in cavities within large trees between November and March, and 1-2 young are raised. The species does not appear to congregate in large flocks; instead it is most often found in pairs.

Threats
It is severely threatened by past and continuing illegal exploitation for the national and international cage-bird trade. All known sites are on private cattle-ranches, where burning and clearing for pasture, and tree-felling for fuel have reduced the number of suitable nest trees and inhibited palm regeneration. However, cattle-rearing has occurred in the region since the 17th century, and nest-site availability is not currently thought to be limiting. Nevertheless, nest-site competition from other macaws, toucans and large woodpeckers could be significant. There are fears that inbreeding within an increasingly fragmented population is resulting in reduced fertility.

Conservation actions to date
Live export from Bolivia was banned in 1984, but illegal export continues. The population in captivity (some of which is held in captive-breeding facilities) is many times larger than the wild population. There are no mechanisms to control internal trade, although attempts are being made to change the situation. Agreement has been reached with some landowners to control access and deter potential trappers, and negotiations with other landowners continue. A local environmental awareness campaign is in progress, targeting landowners, ranch personnel and school children. A Species Recovery Plan is currently being drawn up. Based on field surveys recommendations have been made that the Paraparau region, Beni Department, be given greater conservation priority. Much of the remaining population occurs on private ranch-lands. Many landowners are reportedly sympathetic to conservation work on their lands and continued support will benefit the species recovery.

Conservation actions required
- Conduct searches for further populations.
- Study its ecology, especially natural nesting requirements.
- Develop a programme of protection by full-time guards.
- Stop illegal exports.
- Instigate mechanisms for controlling internal trade.
- Continue negotiations with, and involvement of, local landowners.
- Continue the awareness campaign.
- Investigate the application of private reserves for the conservation of this species.

Loreto, Beni, Bolivia, 2005

Photo: © Joe Tobias

Loreto, Beni, Bolivia, 2005

Photo: © Joe Tobias

Yellow-eared Parrot
Ognorhynchus icterotis
Population: 700-750 ↑

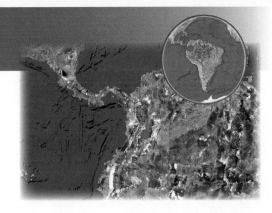

Roncesvalles, Tolima, Colombia, 2005

Photo: © Alonso Quevedo

History
1854 – French amateur ornithologist Francois Victor Massena (1799-1863) and his nephew Charles de Souancé (1823-1896) describe the species.

1999 – a population which numbers 81 individuals is discovered by Paul Salaman in Colombia. Fundacion ProAves initiates major conservation program for the species.

2002 – national awareness campaign to save wax palm and parrot at Palm Sunday starts.

2004 – forty nest-boxes for Yellow-eared parrots have been mounted.

2005 – the population is estimated to number about 600 birds.

2006 – Yellow-eared Parrot reserve established to protect core population in Antioquia.

2007 – a pair of Yellow-eared parrots successfully nest in a man-made nestbox. The species' population climbs to 750 individuals.

Range & population
This parrot formerly occurred in all three Andean ranges of Colombia, from Norte de Santander and Antioquia to Nariño and in north-west Ecuador, south to Cotopaxi. It was once common to abundant, but is now extinct in Ecuador and declined to a single breeding colony of 81 birds in 1999 in the Central Andes of Colombia. Intensive conservation efforts from 1999 to the present date by Fundacion ProAves has recovered the species to over 700 individuals in both the Western and Central Andes.

It inhabits humid montane forest, primarily between 2,200–3,100 m, favouring areas dominated by wax palms *Ceroxylon quindiuense*, Colombia's national tree which can reach up to 225 ft height and in which it roosts, nests and feeds. The species is resident at two sites, with young birds from recent years wandering across the Central and Western Andes in search of food (fruiting/seeding blooms of *Ceroxylon, Citharexylon, Podocarpus* and *Sapium spp.*). Two breeding cycles in April–November were noted at one colony. Breeding pairs enlist the help of 'brood-helpers' during the chick-rearing stage.

Threats
It has suffered considerable habitat loss and fragmentation (90–93% of montane forest in Colombia) throughout its range; however, several sizeable areas of habitat remain within its historic range, suggesting additional causes of decline. Wax palm mortality is accelerating and they suffer poor recruitment because cattle browse young trees, and logging in adjacent areas increases their susceptibility to disease. Wax palms are incredibly long-lived and slow-growing (mature individuals are over 100 years old). They are also harvested and used by Colombians for Palm Sunday processions commemorating the entry of Jesus into Jerusalem, where residents greeted him by waving palm branches. Peasants fell the wax palms to strip the highly prized emerging fronds for sale to worshippers. Furthermore, dead wax palms that are essential for nest sites are often cut down for fence posts. In Ecuador, hunting for food was prolific, and trapping has had some impact in Colombia, although the species is notoriously hard to keep in captivity.

Conservation actions to date
In 1999, Fundacion ProAves launched a conservation campaign with the support of Loro Parque Fundacion and others that has lead to the species recovery in Colombia. Principal actions included establishment of protected areas (including the Yellow-eared Parrot reserve and Colombia's first ecological easement), reforestation (especially with key food plants and wax palms), nest-boxes, education campaign and community involvement (including a Parrot Bus that has educated over 30,000 children and adults), and most importantly direct protection and monitoring

Conservation actions required
- Monitor the population.
- Search for additional subpopulations.
- Buy and protect further habitat.
- Install more nest-boxes.
- Sustain reforestation and land stewardship scheme.
- Strengthen community awareness and involvement programmes.

Roncesvalles, Tolima, Colombia, 2005

Photo: © Alonso Quevedo

Grey-breasted Parakeet
Pyrrhura griseipectus
Population: 50-249 ↓

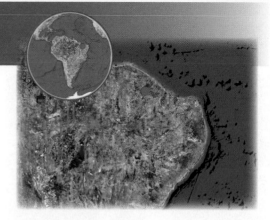

Serra de Baturitá, state of Ceará, NE Brazil, 2006

Photo: © Ciro Albano

History
1900 – Italian zoologist Tommasi Salvadori (1835-1923) describes the species.

2005 – the species recognized as valid by the international scientific community.

2006 – the species recognized as Critically Endangered by international conservation groups.

2007 – Conservation projects sponsored by the Brazilian 'Fundação O Boticário de Proteção à Natureza' and the Loro Parque Fundacion, are conducted by the Brazilian NGO Aquasis.

This species was previously considered to belong to the Maroon-faced Parakeet *Pyrrhura leucotis* group, but was given specific status in 2005.

Range & population
This parakeet is currently known from one area in north-east Brazil: the Serra do Baturité in Ceará. Here it seems to be very uncommon and to have been extirpated from several areas, but there are recent records of groups in the Serra do Baturité Environmental Protection Area. The forests of Serra do Baturité have been greatly reduced to make room for shade and sun coffee and only 13% of the forest remained in 1996. The species was formerly known from three other areas: the eastern slope of the Serra de Ibiapaba and the municipality of Quixadá, both in Ceará, and the tiny Serra Negra in Pernambuco where flocks of 4-6 individuals were regularly seen in the early 1980s, but from where there are no recent records. There are also unconfirmed reports from 1991 in Murici Ecological Station in Alagoas which possibly refer to released individuals as recent fieldwork there has failed to locate the species. The species has declined dramatically in the past, a trend which may be ongoing. In six months of the ongoing research initiated in January 2007 by the Brazilian NGO Aquasis in the Baturité Mountains, about half

of the remaining forested area has been investigated, and 80 individuals were observed.

It occurs in montane humid forest enclaves (above 500 m) in the otherwise semi-arid north-east Brazil. These wet 'sky islands' are known locally as 'brejos'. Humid forests grade into semi-deciduous forest and eventually dry, xeric caatingas in lower areas. The forests are restricted to upland granite or sandstone areas which receive up to 4 times the annual rainfall of lower altitudes. The humid forests atop the Baturité massif form a continuous canopy c. 20 m tall, with some emergent trees. Birds feed on fruit and seeds in the canopy of humid and semi-deciduous forest.

Threats
Habitat destruction has played a role in the species' decline with original forest cover now reduced to just 13%. Coffee plantations (especially sun coffee versus shade coffee) are impacting upon the species' habitat. Preliminary research results indicate that the lack of old-growth tree species suitable for nest building may be a limiting factor. The principal threat, however, comes from ongoing trapping for illegal local and national trade. The species also occurs in the international cage bird trade.

Conservation actions to date
It occurs within the Serra do Baturité Environmental Protection Area, but this area is designated for sustainable use and is not managed for conservation. Land management by a private landowner in the area has led to an increase in one small known population. Since 2007, the Brazilian NGO Aquasis has been conducting two research projects: one sponsored by the Brazilian 'Fundação O Boticário de Proteção à Natureza' aimed at surveying the Baturité Mountains in order to determine the conservation status of the species and aspects of its biology; and another sponsored by the Loro Parque Fundacion, where the team is assessing several sites in NE Brazil looking for other remaining populations.

Conservation actions required
- Survey similar areas as the Baturité Mountains in NE Brazil, to look for extant populations.
- Continue monitoring the known population in the Serra do Baturité.
- Provide incentives for landowners to establish a network of private reserves in the Baturité Mountains.
- Develop conservation tools and strategies to improve conservation management in the Serra do Baturité Environmental Protection Area (e.g. Management Plan, Zoning).
- Monitor and control trade at local, national and international levels.
- Investigate the feasibility of using artificial nests to increase reproductive success.
- Conduct awareness campaigns to promote the Grey-breasted Parakeet as a symbol for the conservation of the moist forests and associated biodiversity in the Baturité Mountains.

Indigo-winged Parrot
Hapalopsittaca fuertesi
Population: 50-249 ↓

RNA El Mirador, Near Genova, Quindio, Colombia, 2006

Photo: © Alonso Quevedo

History

1911 – the first specimens are obtained at Laguneta and Santa Isabel.

1912 – American ornithologist Frank M. Chapman (1864-1945) describes the species. It is named after the famous American ornithologist and painter Louis Agassiz Fuertes (1874-1929).

2002 – the first confirmed sighting is made in July at 3,000 m in the central Andes by Fundacion ProAves when 14 birds are located in a small area of forest.

2003 – the first active nest is found in February. Protection and management of the breeding population commences.

2004 – artificial nest-boxes result in tremendous success for the species and population recovery commences.

Range & population

This parrot has a highly restricted range on the west slope of the Central Andes of Colombia near the border of Quindío, Risaralda and Tolima. Until 2002 it was known with certainty only from the type-series from 1911. The species was rediscovered by Fundacion ProAves in montane forest in Génova municipality, Quindío Department, where the largest group observed consisted of 25 birds and the total population was approximately 60 individuals. The population increased to 160 individuals (in December 2006) thanks to intensive conservation efforts by ProAves, which have resulted in 87% hatching success and 95% fledging success amongst breeding birds in the Central Cordillera.

This is a poorly-known inhabitant of cloud-forest. It is restricted to mature montane cloud forest with a high occurrence of mistletoe as mistletoe berries are a key food source. Studies since 2003 have gathered extensive information on the species breeding and feeding ecology, with the nesting period from January to May.

Threats

Clearance of forest in the region of the type-locality was already extensive in 1911, and very little habitat now remains. The species is almost entirely unprotected. For example, only five of 25 breeding pairs are within the El Mirador municipality protected areas. The species is highly threatened by forest loss for cattle pasture and selective logging of mature trees, which are vital for nesting, for timber and firewood.

Conservation actions to date

Fundación ProAves with the support of Fundacion Loro Parque and American Bird Conservancy are providing protection at one stronghold for this species.

Conservation actions required

- Acquire private properties with core breeding population and protect the species from expanding pasturelands.
- Ensure the effective management of the El Mirador Muncipality Natural Reserve.
- Work with local community in raising awareness and avoid possible trade of the species.
- Provide more artificial nest-boxes.

Reserva Natural El Mirador, 2004

Photo: © Charles Hesse

Reserva Natural Colibri del Sol, 2006

Photo: © Alonso Quevedo

Sumatran Ground-cuckoo
Carpococcyx viridis
Population: 50-249 ↓

West-central Sumatra, May 2006

Photo: © Matthew Linkie

This species was previously treated as Bornean Ground-cuckoo *Carpococcyx radiceus* but is now split into a species of its own.

Range & population
Endemic to the island of Sumatra, Indonesia where it was unrecorded since 1916 until an individual was trapped in November 1997 at Bukit Barisan Selatan National Park. There were several field observation in 2007.
It occurs in primary or little-disturbed forest, though a recent camera-trap record originates from regenerating secondary growth.

Threats
Deforestation has been extensive on Sumatra and this is probably the main threat. At the type locality, Gunung Singgalang, forest had been cleared up to 1,800-1,900 m as early as 1917. In addition, being a ground-forager, it is possibly susceptible to hunting using snares.

Conservation actions to date
There are 20 protected areas in the Barisan Mountains, some of which lie within the current known range of this species. Survey effort is likely to increase following the recent recording of its call.

Conservation actions required
* Choose potential survey areas by identifying remaining habitat tracts in the Barisan Mountains.
* Conduct extensive surveys.
* Review whether key populations are adequately represented within the existing protected-areas network, and if not, advocate establishment of further strategic protected areas.
* Afford the species full protection under Indonesian Law.

Black-hooded Coucal
Centropus steerii
Population: 50-249 ↓

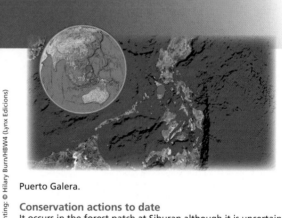

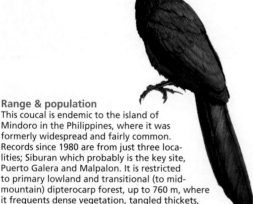

Painting: © Hilary Burn/HBW4 (Lynx Edicions)

Range & population
This coucal is endemic to the island of Mindoro in the Philippines, where it was formerly widespread and fairly common. Records since 1980 are from just three localities; Siburan which probably is the key site, Puerto Galera and Malpalon. It is restricted to primary lowland and transitional (to mid-mountain) dipterocarp forest, up to 760 m, where it frequents dense vegetation, tangled thickets, vine-covered shrubs and bamboo.

Threats
Extensive deforestation on Mindoro has reduced forest cover. Slash-and-burn cultivation, occasional selective logging and rattan collection threaten remaining forest fragments. Dynamite blasting for marble is an additional threat to forest at Puerto Galera.

Conservation actions to date
It occurs in the forest patch at Siburan although it is uncertain how much protection is afforded by its inclusion in the F. B. Harrison Game Reserve. Funds have been provided for faunal inventories and community-based environmental education initiatives at Puerto Galera. An education programme has also been started at Malpalon.

Conservation actions required
* Establish formal, managed protected areas to conserve remnant forest at Malpalon and Puerto Galera.
* Extend Mt Iglit-Baco National Park to encompass remaining lowland forest tracts.
* Devise and implement a management plan for the forest at Siburan that reconciles biodiversity with its role as a prison.
* Raise public awareness about the status and importance of this species.

Dwarf Olive Ibis. Photo: © Nik Borrow

Siau Scops-owl
Otus siaoensis
Population: < 50, trend unknown

Painting: © Friedhelm Weick

Range & population
This owl is only known from one specimen collected on the island of Siau, north of Sulawesi, Indonesia, in 1866. Given the small size of this island, and its generally unvegetated volcanic upper reaches, the original population was probably always modest in size, and any surviving population must be tiny, given that little forest remains. There is some suggestion that the species might survive on the basis of accounts given by local people, however, a recent survey of nocturnal birds in northern Sulawesi spent 32 days on Siau Island and failed to confirm that it still occurs on the island.

Threats
Siau is currently experiencing rapid deforestation. In 1995, there was some lowland forest around Lake Kepetta in the south of the island, but this had been felled by 1998. In August 1998, the island was judged to have been largely converted to mixed plantation and scrub, but small patches of low trees survived

Conservation actions to date
At present, the only measures taken have been brief unsuccessful searches for this species. In October 1998, a five-day survey determined that only 50 ha of forest remained, all above 800 m on Gunung Tamata, in the centre of the island.

Conservation actions required
* Survey the remaining forest on Siau and Tagulandang at different times of year, investigating any patch of trees, however remote the possibility of success may seem.
* In the event of its survival, initiate conservation measures at the site of rediscovery.

Anjouan Scops-owl
Otus capnodes
Population: 50-100 ↓

Photo: © Charles Marsh

Near Lingoni, Anjouan, Comoro Islands, 2005

Range & population
This scops owl was rediscovered on Anjouan (= Ndzuani) in the Comoro Islands in June 1992, after an absence of records dating back to 1886. It survives in remaining fragments of native upland forest, and appears to be dependent on large trees with cavities for nesting and roosting, usually on steep slopes. It was recently found as low as 300 m in highly degraded forest. It has been recorded perching in thick cover, 3-15 m from the ground. Insects are believed to form at least part of its diet.

Threats
Habitat clearance is accelerating for agriculture, timber extraction and charcoal manufacture. Remaining habitat is becoming increasingly degraded through human disturbance and invasion by exotic plants. Hunting for food by the increasing human population is also a threat. Severe cyclones are a regular threat to remaining forest fragments.

Conservation actions to date
Long-term, ongoing developments that will benefit wildlife in general include a family-planning programme, environmental education projects, and the formation of a non-governmental environmental organisation (Ulanga).

Conservation actions required
* Investigate if use of nest-boxes would help.
* Conduct research into the ecology of this species.
* Consider protecting the remaining fragments of primary forest.
* Consider establishing a captive population.
* Continue environmental education projects.

Moheli Scops-owl
Otus moheliensis
Population: 400 ⬇

Photo: © Claire Spottiswoode

Range & population
This species is endemic to Mohéli in the Comoro Islands. It is relatively abundant with a density estimated at one individual per 5 ha of near-primary forest and one individual per 10 ha of degraded forest. It is found in dense, humid forest, which remains only on the central mountain peak and its upper slopes. It is common in intact forest, but less so in forest underplanted for agriculture.

Threats
By 1995, intact, dense, humid forest remained on only 5% of the island, owing primarily to conversion for subsistence agriculture, underplanting, clear-felling and cultivation, and abandonment of sparsely vegetated land, which is highly susceptible to erosion and landslides. Invasive exotic plant species, such as jamrosa *Syzygium jambos*, *Lantana camara* and *Clidemia hirta*, are abundant in the forest and are degrading the native habitat. Hunting probably affects this species. Introduced species including rats, are common, and may compete for food or predate its nests.

Conservation actions to date
The highlands of the island are currently unprotected, but proposals have been made to protect them by extending the Réserve Marine de Nioumachoua.

Conservation actions required
- Research the ecology of the species to aid conservation plans.
- Create a reserve in the interior of the island to protect suitable habitat.
- Develop an environmental education programme to increase local awareness.

Grand Comoro Scops-owl
Otus pauliani
Population: 2,000 ⬇

North of M'Lima Manda, 1989

Photo: © Marc Herremans

Secondary forest in the agricultural belt on the mountain is dominated by exotic plants which could spread into and degrade remaining native forest. Commercial logging occurs on the south-west slopes. Grazing is increasing - even at high altitudes - and could prohibit forest regeneration. Introduced rats and Common Myna *Acridotheres tristis* may act as competitors or nest predators.

Range & population
This species is found only on Mt Karthala, an active volcano on Grand Comoro (= Ngazidja), in the Comoro Islands. C. 100 km² of suitable habitat exists. It is found from 650 m upwards to the tree line. It is territorial, occurring in primary, montane, evergreen forest, favouring areas with old hollow trees, but is also found in 'pioneer forest' (forest that grows on rocky soils). Its feeding and breeding ecology are unknown.

Threats
Agriculture has advanced steadily up the slopes of Mt Karthala toward the habitat of Grand Comoro Scops Owl.

Conservation actions to date
A protected area (national park, biosphere reserve or resource management area) on Mt Karthala has been suggested.

Conservation actions required
- Research the ecology of this species.
- Create a protected area on Mt Karthala to encompass the remaining native forest.
- Encourage locally-organised ecotourism as an alternative source of income for inhabitants of the Mt Karthala area.
- Develop an environmental education programme on the island.

Forest Owlet
Heteroglaux blewitti

Photo: © Mark Beaman / Birdquest

Melghat Sanctuary, Maharashtra, February 2007

Population: 50-249 ↓

History

1872 – William Turnbull Blewitt collects a specimen at current eastern Madhya Pradesh on 14th December.

1873 – A. O. Hume (1829-1912) describes it as *Hetereoglaux blewitti*.

1877 – Geologist V. Ball collects a specimen in western Orissa.

1884 – J. Davidson collects his last specimen which is also the last reliable record for 113 years.

1975 – searches for this species in Orissa are unfruitful.

1976 – searches for the species in Maharashtra are unsuccessful.

1997 – Pamela Rasmussen, Ben King and David Abbott rediscover the species in Maharashtra.

1998 – the calls of this species is recorded for the first time.

2000 – 25 Forest Owlets are reported from two new sites in Maharashtra and Madhya Pradesh.

2004 - 2007 – a search in the five states Chhattisgarh, Gujarat, Madhya Pradesh, Maharashtra and Orissa only produces records in Madhya Pradesh and Maharashtra. 45 adults and 7 juveniles are seen.

Range & population

This species is endemic to central India. Until its rediscovery in 1997, it was known from seven specimens collected during the 19th century at four localities in two widely separated areas, northern Maharashtra, and south-east Madhya Pradesh/western Orissa. In 2000, a survey of 14 forest areas across its former range located 25 birds at four sites in northern Maharashtra and south-western Madhya Pradesh, including three pairs at Taloda Forest Range and seven pairs at Toranmal Forest Range. No birds were found in a brief survey of its former eastern range in Orissa. More recently, survey effort in the Satpura Range (Maharashtra) has located another five sites, indicating that the species may prove to be widespread but previously overlooked in the western Satpuda Mountains. By 2005 over 100 individuals had been recorded in Melghat Tiger Reserve, Maharashtra, now recognised as the species' stronghold. Although there is some confusion over its former abundance, evidence strongly suggests it has always been rare.

It appears to be a sedentary resident with recent sightings from fairly open deciduous forest dominated by teak. It was rediscovered at an altitude of 460 m. Most historical records came from moist deciduous forest or dense jungle, the altitudinal range of which is unclear, although most specimens were collected in plains forest. This suggests that the recent observations from hill slopes may represent birds in suboptimal habitat. It appears to be quite strongly diurnal and fairly easy to detect, frequently perching on prominent bare branches. When calling it often perches near the top in larger trees. Lizards, small rodents, grasshoppers and nestlings of other birds are all prey items. It appears to partition resources with the similar and widespread Spotted Owlet *Athene brama*. It breeds between October and May laying a brood of two eggs, and can relay if its first nesting attempt fails.

Threats

Given its rarity, identification of threats is difficult, but habitat degradation seems to be a major threat. Deciduous forest has been severely depleted at the site of its rediscovery,

Melghat Sanctuary, Maharashtra, 2006

Photo: © Claudia Banwell

including total clearance of plains-level forest, and there is intense pressure from local people on the remaining forest resources in the area. It is likely that other forest areas where it occurs are under similarly intense pressure. The proposed Upper Tapi Irrigation Project threatens prime habitat used by Forest Owlet. The species suffers predation from a number of native raptors, limiting productivity and faces competition for a limited number of nesting cavities. It is hunted by local people and body parts are used in local customs. Overgrazing by cattle may also reduce habitat suitability. Pesticides and rodenticides are used to an unknown degree within its range and may pose additional threats.

Conservation actions to date

Since its rediscovery in 1997, fieldwork has been conducted into its status, ecology and threats. Interventions have been made to seek the prevention of further forest losses at the site of rediscovery. It has also been recorded in Khaknar Reserve Forest and Yawal Wildlife Sanctuary.

Conservation actions required

- Prevent illicit wood-cutting and hunting of wildlife in forests within the species' range.
- Conduct surveys in remaining suitable habitat, particularly sites not surveyed in 2000, in the 800 km gap between the east/west limits of the historical records, to establish its total range, current distribution and population status, habitat use, and to assess its main threats.
- An education and awareness raising programme is needed amongst local communities to promote the value and importance of this species and convey its potential benefits.
- Control the use of pesticides and rodenticides.
- Use nest site protection to avoid destruction of nests.
- Initiate a number of forest management measures and establish protected areas within its range.

Photo: © Ashley Banwell

Melghat Sanctuary, Maharashtra, 2006

Envirosearch believes that wildlife conservation research should be based on genuine scientific data. The areas of interest are conservation of large mammals and birds, management of protected areas, biodiversity conservation, management of human pressures on wildlife and biodiversity, man-animal conflict and ecotourism development.

www.envirosearch.in

Pernambuco Pygmy-owl
Glaucidium mooreorum
Population: < 50 ↓

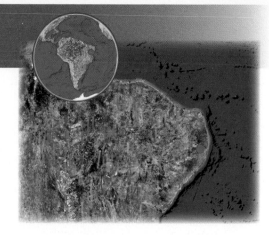

Painting: © Carl Christian Tofte
www.carlchristiantofte.dk/ctofte@hotmail.com

Range & population
This species was newly described from the Reserva Biológica de Saltinho (which covers just 4.8 km²) in Atlantic coastal forest in Pernambuco, Brazil and is the third new pygmy owl species to be discovered in South America since 1995. The species was also found in a 100 ha forest patch at Usina Trapiche in November 2001. It occupies a tiny and severely fragmented range. Playback surveys in lowland forests elsewhere in Pernambuco and Alagoas states since 2001 have failed to locate this species, and there are no records from other well-surveyed forest sites in the region. Its population has not been estimated accurately but is assumed to be tiny based on the lack of records outside its tiny range and continuing deforestation within the area.

It has been once, in 2001, recorded in the canopy of old secondary forest where it was observed eating a cicada. An unconfirmed report suggests the species is vocal during the rainy months of April and May. It has been recorded in forest up to 150 m but has not been found in other well surveyed forest in the region at elevations between 400 and 600 m.

Threats
The Pernambuco Center where this species was described is by far the most modified region of Atlantic Forest having declined in extent from c. 39,500 km² to c. 1,900 km² by 2002. The remainder is severely fragmented and legal restrictions have proven inadequate in halting deforestation from fire and illegal logging.

The Pernambuco Centre is biologically diverse even by Atlantic Forest standards, with 39 endemic bird species and subspecies and the largest number of threatened bird species in Brazil; 18 including Pernambuco Pygmy-owl, and Alagoas Curussow *Mitu mitu*, a species which is now Extinct in the Wild. Hunting is also reported to pose a threat to this species.

Conservation actions to date
The species occurs in the 4.8 km² Reserva Biológica de Saltinho. Approximately 240 km² of the remaining 1,900 km² of Pernambuco Atlantic Forest are protected within 52 reserves but these almost exclusively support small fragments. Legal restrictions exist to attempt to curb the rate of forest loss.

Conservation actions required
* Protection of remaining lowland forest fragments in the area.
* More effective law enforcement to prevent illegal deforestation.
* Further surveys are required to locate other populations outside the known range.

History
1980 – a small owl is collected by professor Galileu Coelho on 6 November at Reserva Biológica de Saltinho.

1990 – an owl is tape-recorded in October in the small Reserva Biológica de Saltinho.

2000 – José Maria Cardoso da Silva, of Conservation International Brazil, comes across the collected bird and realises it is an undescribed species.

2001 – a team consisting of Adrian Long, Luiz Gonzaga, Luis Silveira and nature photographer Luiz Claudio Marigo manages to film the owl when they followed up on alarm calls of other birds mobbing it.

2002 – the species is described by by Luis Pedreira Gonzaga, José Maria Cardoso da Silva and Galileu Coelho in December.

Jamaican Pauraque
Siphonorhis americana
Population: < 50 ↓

Painting: © David Nurney/HBWS (Lynx Edicions)

Range & population
This species is endemic to Jamaica, but has not been positively recorded since 1860. Three of the localities where it was collected are in the lowlands on the southern side of the island, and there is anecdotal evidence that the species could often be found in (what is now assumed to be) the Hellshire Hills. However, the specimen information is confused by the practice of labelling skins with the residence of the collector as the location of collection. There have been some recent, unconfirmed reports of *caprimulgids* from Milk River and Hellshire Hills, which apparently do not refer to other known species on the island.
The south side of the island is drier, suggesting that the species is (or was) found in either dry limestone forest, semi-arid woodland or open country at low elevations. It presumably nests (or nested) on the ground.

Threats
Introduced mammalian predators are considered primarily responsible for the possible extirpation of this species. The mongoose was introduced in 1872 (after the last confirmed record), but it can be assumed that rats were the cause of any decline prior to this date. As its ecological requirements are not known, the impact of habitat destruction is difficult to assess.

Conservation actions to date
None is known.

Conservation actions required
* Survey, especially Milk River and the Hellshire Hills, to locate any remaining populations.

New Caledonian Owlet-nightjar
Aegotheles savesi
Population: < 50 ↓

Painting: © Tim Worfolk/HBWS (Lynx Edicions)

Range & population
This species is endemic to New Caledonia. It is only known from specimens collected in 1880, 1915 and 1960 and a sighting in 1998 in the Rivière Ni valley. Given that local people do not know this distinctive species and that there have been no other records from recent surveys, it must occur in very low numbers and/or be restricted to the most remote forest massifs such as Kouakoue. The records are from Melaleuca savanna and humid forest. The 1998 sighting was of a single bird foraging for insects briefly at dusk, in evergreen riverine forest. New Caledonian Owlet-nightjar is larger and has much longer legs than congeners, which may indicate more terrestrial habits.

Threats
There is no direct information on threats. However, the ecologically similar Australian Owlet-nightjar is believed to suffer high predation rates of both adults and nests. It seems likely that New Caledonian Owlet-nightjar has declined through predation by introduced rats and possibly cats.

Conservation actions to date
The 1998 sighting was in the Reserve Speciale de Faune et de Flore de la Ni-Kouakoue, which has no formal protection although upgrading its protected status has been advocated.

Conservation actions required
* Conduct further field surveys close to the 1998 sighting.
* Publicise the search for this species amongst forest workers and villagers.
* Investigate feasibility and costs of rat control in the Ni-Kouakoue forest.
* Ensure stricter protected status for Ni-Kouakoue.

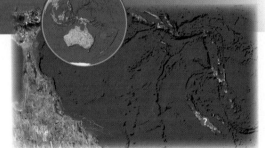

Puerto Rican Nightjar

Caprimulgus noctitherus

Maricao, Puerto Rico, 2004

Photo: © Rafael Rodríguez Mójica

Population: 1,400-2,000 ◄►

History

1877 – mongooses are introduced to Puerto Rico.

1888 – the species is discovered on 29th October near Bayamon, but thought to be a migrant Whip-poor-will *Caprimulgus vociferous*.

1919 – American biologist Alexander Wetmore (1886-1978) describes the species.

1961 – the second specimen is collected by Ricardo Cotte and William Blasini at Guanica Forest.

1984 – a population estimate gives 670 – 800 pairs. A Puerto Rican Whip-poor-will (nightjar) Recovery Plan is approved by the US Fish and Wildlife Service

2004 – 1,400 to 2,000 pairs are estimated to occur.

Range & population

This nightjar probably occupied large areas of Puerto Rico, but is now restricted to the south-west, notably Susúa-Maricao, Guayanilla-Peñuelas and Guánica-Bermeja. There are further recent records from the Parguera Hills and Sierra Bermeja (c. 10 km west of Parguera). Studies in 1985-1987, 1989-1990 and 1992 found 712 singing males in 98 km² of fragmented habitat, with 347 in the Guánica area, 177 in the Susúa-Maricao area and 188 in the Guayanilla area. The historical range probably comprised moist limestone and coastal forest, dry limestone forest, drier sections of the lower cordillera forest and perhaps dry coastal forest. It now occurs at higher densities in closed-canopy dry forest on limestone soils, composed mainly of semi-deciduous hardwood trees,

and an open understorey (little or no ground vegetation), at elevations up to 230 m, but more commonly above 75 m. It occurs at lower densities in dry, open, scrubby secondary growth, xeric or dry scrubland, open scrub-forest, thorny forest undergrowth, with a few birds in *Eucalyptus robusta* plantations. It feeds on night-flying insects by making forays from a perch. The male is territorial throughout the year but calling is at its peak during breeding which occurs from late February to early July, but mainly in April-June. One or two eggs are laid on the ground on leaf litter as it does not construct a nest. Birds are perhaps permanently territorial, exhibiting strong site fidelity. In Guánica forest, c. 87% of nests in one year produced at least one fledgling. It feeds on beetles, moths and other insects.

Threats

The introduction of mongooses is considered responsible for

172

the initial drastic population decline, but the differing habitat preferences of the two species suggests very little overlap in their current ranges. Habitat loss and degradation now have a more significant impact, especially from residential, industrial and recreational expansion, with associated increases in disturbance and fire risk. A proposed wind farm development in Karso del Sur IBA has the potential to wipe out 5% of the total breeding population. Young birds are predated by Short-eared Owls *Asio flammeus*, and young and eggs may be predated by Pearly-eyed Thrashers *Margarops fuscatus*, fire-ants and feral cats.

Conservation actions to date

It is legally protected. Guánica, Susúa and Maricao are public lands designated as state forests, and Guánica is a biosphere reserve. The Puerto Rico Conservation Trust has acquired lands in the Guayanilla Hills harbouring nightjars. Research is ongoing to generate current population estimates and develop landscape-level habitat models.

Conservation actions required

- Perform surveys to better quantify abundance throughout known range, identify additional areas for protection, and ascertain the species' status outside its current known range.
- Monitor to assess population trends and the effects of management.
- Effectively conserve existing reserves, including peripheral private lands.
- Reforest disturbed areas with native and selected plantation species.
- Acquire privately owned tracts of mature dry limestone forest.
- Lobby for priority site conservation through existing initiatives and Site Support Groups.

BirdLife Species Guardian **Sociedad Ornitológica Puertorriqueña, Inc (SOPI)**

Guanica State Forest, June 2007

Photo: © Jonathan Morel

Guanica State Forest, May 2007

Photo: © Michael J Morel

Short-crested Coquette
Lophornis brachylophus

Population: 250-999 ⬇

Painting: © Carl Christian Tofte
www.carlchristiantofte.dk/ctofte@hotmail.com

Range & population
This species is only known from a 25 km stretch of the Atoyac-Paraíso-Puerto el Gallo road in the Sierra de Atoyac (north-west of Acapulco), and is likely to be confined to the Sierra Madre del Sur in Guerrero, Mexico. All records have been near the villages of Arroyo Grande, Paraíso and Nueva Delhi in the months of January and March-May. At least seasonally, it can be locally fairly common to uncommon. It inhabits humid to semi-humid evergreen and semi-deciduous forest, forest edge and shade coffee plantations at elevations of 900-1,800 m, where it feeds on the flowers of Inga and Cecropia. There are local reports to 650 m suggesting that it may migrate altitudinally, breeding at higher elevations (possibly November-February), and spending March-August (possibly longer) at lower altitudes.

Threats
In the early 1990s, semi-deciduous forest between Paraíso and Nueva Delhi was being rapidly cleared for the cultivation of maize, fruit and coffee. Much of the remaining forest provides cover for illegal drug-growing making an evaluation of habitat quality difficult.

Conservation actions to date
No measures are known.

Conservation actions required
- Designate a protected area in the Sierra de Atoyac incorporating the range of this species.
- Survey to clarify the full extent of this species' distribution.
- Survey to assess the impact of shade coffee plantations on this species and understand its altitudinal movements.

Sapphire-bellied Hummingbird
Lepidopyga lilliae

Population: 50-249 ⬇

Painting: © Norman Arlott/HBW5 (Lynx Edicions)

This hummingbird is sometimes treated as a subspecies of Sapphire-throated hummingbird *Lepidopyga coeruleogularis*.

Range & population
This hummingbird is known locally on the Caribbean coast of Colombia. It appears to be either rare or sporadic at the few known localities. A male was captured in Vía-Parque Isla Salamanca in 2007 and the population size is presumably low. It is apparently restricted to coastal mangroves. A female has been observed nest-building and feeding in a mature mangrove tree.

Threats
Construction of a pipeline and road through the wetlands in the mid-1970s obstructed tidal flow and caused very extensive mangrove die-back although mangroves are now regenerating in some areas. Domestic and industrial pollution, sewage, urbanisation and mangrove cutting are further problems.

Conservation actions to date
Despite a number of searches, there have been very few records within the Isla de Salamanca National Park during the 1990s. However, a large-scale programme to allow water to flow between the sea and the Ciénaga Grange de Santa Marta is probably benefiting the species' habitat.

Conservation actions required
- Conduct field surveys to clarify its distribution and population.
- Research its taxonomic status and ecological requirements.

Honduran Emerald
Amazilia luciae
Population: 250-999 ↓

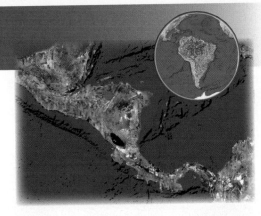

Aguan Valley, Honduras, 2005

Photo: ©Ronald Orenstein

History

1867 – American ornithologist and businessman Georg Newbold Lawrence (1806-1895) describes the species.

1988 – it is found to be common at two sites 16 km apart near Olanchito and Coyoles in the upper río Aguán valley, Yoro.

1991 – 22-28 birds are found in 2.5 ha of habitat near Olanchito.

2007 – an expedition using light aircraft to identify habitats in February find new populations in Olancho.

Range & population

This hummingbird occurs in the arid interior valleys of Honduras, where it is currently known from three sites and historically from 11 specimens at six additional sites. It was not recorded between 1950 and 1988. In 1996, it was found north-east of Gualaco in the Agalta valley, where there was less than 1 km² of suitable habitat. There is no suitable habitat at Santa Bárbara, Cofradía or in the Guayape valley, where the species was formerly recorded.

It inhabits arid thorn-forest and scrub apparently at elevations up to 1,220 m. The thorn-forest near Coyoles is c. 6-10 m high and dominated by *Mimosaceae*, *Cactaceae* and *Euphorbiaceae*, and the species is still found despite heavy grazing of the understorey and an apparent lack of flowers.

At Olanchito, birds occur in similar but more cut-over and heavily grazed thorn-forest and scrub. Feeding has been observed at several flowering plant species and a conspicuous orangepipe cactus. Insect-catching has also been noted.

Threats

At Santa Bárbara and Cofradía most of the thorn-forest has been cleared for grazing and what little remains is extremely dry with few birds of any species present. Most remaining habitat in the río Aguán and Agalta valleys is on large haciendas, managed (non-intensively) for cattle-grazing, but there is still clearance for plantation agriculture and cattle pastures. In the Agalta valley, bulldozers are removing thorn-forest for replacement with rice cultivation, and improved access to the río Aguán valley has facilitated the continuing conversion to pineapple plantations. Perhaps most concerning are plans to pave and extend a road through the range of this species, which would presumably lead to further habitat loss.

Conservation actions to date

The Honduran Air Force property known as Polígono in the río Aguán valley is now managed by the American Bird Conservancy and the Fundación Parque Nacional Pico Bonito as a core for a proposed 7,500 acre thorn forest reserve. An impact assessment of a proposed road is planned. The species is a conservation target of the The Hummingbird Society.

Conservation actions required

- Develop a system of core protected areas and work with neighbouring ranches to ensure that adjacent land is appropriately managed.
- Expand the Sierra de Agalta National Park to encompass suitable habitat within the valley.
- Survey to locate additional populations.
- Promote the species as a flagship for local and national conservation.
- Complete fencing thorn forest around Polígono to exclude cattle.

Aguan Valley, Honduras, 2005

Photo: ©Ronald Orenstein

Dusky Starfrontlet
Coeligena orina
Population: < 250 ↓

Reserva Natural Colibri del Sol, 2005

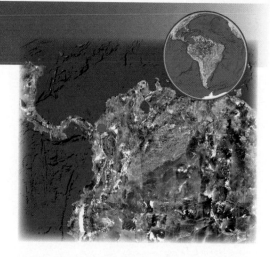

Photo: © Alosno Quevedo

History
1951 – Melbourne A. Carriker Jr collects an unknown hummingbird at 3,200 metres near the town of Urrao.

1953 – Alexander Wetmore (1886-1978) describes the species.

2004 – the species is rediscovered in August by an expedition organised by Fundación ProAves.

2005 – Dusky Starfrontlet Bird Reserve is established – first protected area for the species.

Range & population
This hummingbird has a very restricted range, being known from tiny forest fragments at Páramo Frontino and Farallones del Citará in north-west Colombia. There are only five other localities in the entire Western Andes that retain suitable habitat. The combined area of all potentially suitable sites is thought to be less than 25 km². It is apparently tied to elfin forest-timberline-páramo habitats and perhaps seasonally adjacent humid montane forest. At 3,500 m it was seen feeding on insects in the *Ericaceae*-clad canopy of elfin forest. Stomach content analysis has shown it feeds on parasitic wasps, spiders and dipterans; in addition to nectar. Very little is known about its habits and breeding ecology.

Threats
Páramo de Frontino contains rich deposits of gold, zinc and copper, which have attracted the attention of mining companies. However, political instability in the region has prevented exploitation of these resources to date. The future expansion of mining remains a serious potential threat. The area is currently wholly unprotected and is suffering from continuing deforestation. Future colonisation by human settlers is likely to lead to habitat loss and degradation; a process ongoing in the nearby Las Orquídeas National Park.

Conservation actions to date
In 2005, the Dusky Starfrontlet Bird Reserve was established by Fundacion ProAves. It protects over 5,000 acres of humid montane forest to páramo on Páramo de Frontino. A research and visitor station was established in 2007 with research on the Dusky Starfrontlet´s population and ecological requirements. There are proposals by National Parks Administration (UAESPNN) and Municipality of Urrao to extend Las Orquídeas National Park to encompass adjacent Páramo de Frontino. However, the benefit such a designation would have is questionable as the park is currently poorly protected and under great pressure from illegal colonists.

Conservation actions required
- Continue surveys to research the species' range, population size and trends.
- Support the expansion of the Dusky Starfrontlet Reserve in Páramo de Frontino.
- Establish a management plan for Páramo de Frontino and Dusky Starfrontlet Reserve.

Cerro Caramanta, 2007

Photo: © Luis Mazariegos

Chestnut-bellied Hummingbird
Amazilia castaneiventris
Population: 250-999 ↓

Soata, Boyaca, Colombia, 2007

Photo: © Luis Mazariegos

Range & population
This hummingbird is found only on the slopes of the Serranía de San Lucas and the East Andes, Colombia. Historically, it was locally common, but trends are difficult to assess because of the lack of observer coverage resulting (in part) from guerilla activity in its range. It mainly inhabits humid forest at 850-2,200 m. Many records come from forest borders or bushy canyons, with the most recent sighting in a semi-arid ravine vegetated with shrubs and low trees. The species benefits from bee-keeping which promotes the planting of melliferous vegetation used by hummingbirds.

Threats
The sites support large human populations and have long been areas of high agricultural production. Semi-arid habitats are affected by livestock-grazing and seasonal burning for farming. A gold rush began in the Serranía de San Lucas in 1996, and most of the eastern slopes have since been settled, logged and converted for agricultural and coca production. Immigration is continuing as road and oil pipelines extend into formerly inaccessible areas. It apparently suffers from subsistence hunting for food.

Conservation actions to date
Apart from one successful search in 2000, and its subsequent rediscovery in Soatá, Boyacá, none is known.

Conservation actions required
- Determine its status in the Serranía de San Lucas.
- Research its natural history and habitat preferences.
- Prepare action plans for conservation of habitat within its range.
- Protect areas of suitable habitat found to hold the species.
- Raise awareness of conservation issues through educational campaigns.

Purple-backed Sunbeam
Aglaeactis aliciae
Population: 250-999 ↓

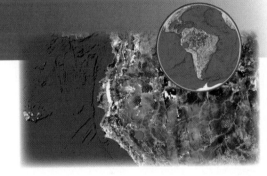

Peru, 2005

Photo: © Roger Ahlman

Range & population
This hummingbird is restricted to a tiny area of c.1 km² in the upper Marañón drainage of La Libertad and Ancash, west Peru. There is a recent unconfirmed sighting from the Llanganuco area in Ancash, c. 140 km south of the La Libertad sites. It is known from the temperate zone (c. 3,000 m) with vegetation comprising montane shrubs and Alnus and Eucalyptus trees, where it is found in the understorey of alder woodland. It feeds on mistletoe parasitizing alders and other trees. It has also recently been reported to feed and roost in introduced Eucalyptus trees. Juveniles and immatures have been recorded in February, March and June.

Threats
In 2005 less than 1 ha of alder woodland remained in the Molino area, the remainder having been replaced with Eucalyptus plantations providing timber for the mining industry. Alder woodland and montane shrubland is also impacted by cutting firewood and grazing livestock.

Conservation actions to date
No measures are known.

Conservation actions required
- Survey to investigate the reported occurrence in the Llanganuco area.
- Determine the distribution of Shining Sunbeam A. cupripennis to judge whether there are distributional gaps between the two hummingbirds.
- Research the species' ecological requirements.
- Investigate the species' taxonomic relationship with Shining Sunbeam.
- Safeguard the remaining habitat at the only known site.

Black-breasted Puffleg
Eriocnemis nigrivestis

Yanacocha, Ecuador, 2005

Population: 50-249 ↓

History
1852 – French naturalists Jules Bourcier (1797-1873) and Étienne Mulsant (1797-1880) describe the species.

1898 – three specimen are taken at Volcán Atacazo.

1983 – a possible sighting is made at Volcán Atacazo.

2005 – the species is adopted as the official emblem of Quito.

2006 – a second population, numbering 108 individuals, is discovered.

Range & population
This hummingbird is found seasonally on the northern ridge-crests of Volcán Pichincha, Pichincha province, north-west Ecuador. Seasonal distribution also seems to change from year to year. The large number of museum specimens (over 100) suggests it was formerly more common, but the only confirmed record between 1950 and 1993, was of three individuals in 1980. It has clearly declined and is now rare within a very limited range. The area of suitable habitat where the species is known to occur at this site has been dramatically reduced to c. 34 km², and supports an estimated 160 individuals. However, it may also occur on the unstudied western slope of the volcano where additional habitat remains. In 2006 another population was discovered in two remnant patches of forest of 24 km² and 30 km² respectively. It may also still occur on Volcán Atacazo.

Available records suggest that it is an altitudinal migrant, but its movements remain poorly understood and appear to have changed since it was first collected. It undertakes seasonal movements, occurring in dwarf, humid elfin forest and páramo, at 3,100-4,500 m, in November-February, and humid temperate forest at c. 2,400 m during other months. It has recently been recorded in bushy forest edges along road sides, steep slopes with stunted vegetation and from taller montane forest interiors and clearings. Although it is more of a generalist than previously reported, altitudinal migrations are thought to be determined by the seasonal flowering of specific vines and species such as fuchsias and ericaceous trees. It has been recorded using 27 different species of food-plants, thus it is not believed to be restricted in range owing to dietary constraints.

Threats

The main threat is the felling of forest for charcoal requirements. This leads to a subsequent increase in access to forest allowing the introduction of cattle and the eventual spread of the agricultural frontier for ranching and to a lesser extent production of crops. Until recently, suitable habitat on ridge-crests was disappearing more rapidly than surrounding vegetation, because the crests provide flat ground for cultivating potatoes and livestock-grazing within otherwise steep terrain. Some ridges where it formerly occurred are now almost completely devoid of natural vegetation and, even if it still occurs in these areas, it is unlikely to be numerous. Around 93% of the suitable habitat within its probable historic range has been degraded or destroyed, with 97% lost in Pinchincha Province. Human induced fires threaten large tracts of forest during the dry season. The construction of a pipeline at Cerro Chiquilipe led to habitat destruction to give way to the pipeline itself, an access road and a depressurization station despite the known presence of the hummingbird.

Volcán Pichincha has sporadically erupted since 1999, and ash-fall has been considerable in the area. The impacts of this on the species and its habitat are unknown. Future climate may push the climate zone for this species above the current treeline, and could lead to increased competition with Gorgeted Sunangel *Heliangelus strophianus* as that species expands its altitudinal range. However, the current treeline is thought to be lower than it was historically owing to centuries of anthropogenic stresses (particularly fire) causing the gradual loss and fragmentation of high altitude forest.

Conservation actions to date

Media coverage of recent research on the species and threats to its habitat has encouraged the authorities to control access and forbid charcoal production. Yanacocha Reserve was recently established by the Jocotoco Foundation and protects c. 1,000 ha of key habitat for the species. The reserve is situated only 45 minutes from downtown Quito. An additional 26 ha has recently been purchased adjacent to the reserve for reforestation (of native cloudforest) for a carbon offsetting scheme by Bird Holidays - a birdwatching tour company. A large part of the unexplored primary forest of Volcán Pichincha's western slopes are protected by Bosque Protector Mindo-Nambillo reserve. Western slopes of the Cordillera de Toisán are protected within the Cotacachi-Cayapas Ecological Reserve but forest cover outside the reserve is much reduced and local people plan to extend cattle pasture within the borders of the reserve.

Conservation actions required

- Assess current status and distribution on Volcán Pichincha.
- Survey Volcán Atacazo and neighbouring peaks for the species.
- Purchase critical primary and secondary habitats for the species.
- Initiate outreach amongst local communities to raise awareness of the species and integrate local people in the species' conservation strategy.
- Provide local people with alternative incomes that do not damage the species' habitat.
- Engage the government in the creation of protected areas on state-owned lands.
- Reforest corridors to link suitable habitat fragments.
- Pre-emptively restore native woody vegetation in at least 30% of grass páramo within the Cotacachi-Cayapas Ecological Reserve over the next 25 years in anticipation of future climate change.

The Hummingbird Society is dedicated to teaching about hummingbirds and working to protect them from extinction.

www.hummingbirdsociety.org

Photo: © Francisco Enriquez

Yanacocha, Eqaudor, 2001

Photo: © Nancy C Bell

Yanacocha, Eqaudor, 2004

Juan Fernández Firecrown
Sephanoides fernandensis
Population: 2,500-3,000 ↓

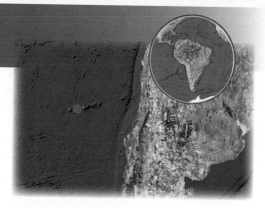

Juan Fernandez Island, 2006

Photo: © Fabrice Schmitt

History

1831 – the species is described by Captain Phillip Parker King (1791-1856).

1908 - the race *leyboldi* is believed to be last recorded on Isla Alejandro Selkirk.

1935 – the Juan Fernández Islands are designated a Chilean national park.

1977 – the Juan Fernández Islands are designated a UNESCO Biosphere Reserve.

2002 – a direct count census reveals 200 birds, of which only 60 are females.

2005 – first population estimate based on density measures indicates a population possibly over 2,500 individuals.

2007 – a citizen science project involving island residents in counts of firecrowns in town is performed.

Range & population

This species is endemic to the Juan Fernández Islands, Chile, where the nominate race is confined to c.11 km² on Isla Robinson Crusoe. Historical records indicate that densities on Robinson Crusoe were formerly much greater than the 684 individuals (varying between 804 birds in the austral summer and 445 in autumn) estimated in 1988-1989. Direct count surveys in 1995-1997 showed that the population is in the low hundreds. However, more thorough surveys conducted in 2005 and repeated in 2006, coupled with quantitative modelling, estimated population densities in different habitats and concluded that the global population may be considerably larger.

It inhabits remnant native forests, on which it appears to be completely dependent for breeding, but also utilizes non-native plant communities during the non-breeding season, feeding on introduced plants, such as *Eucalyptus globulus* and garden flowers. This usage of non-native plants is especially common in the austral autumn and winter when only one native species (*Rhaphithamnus venustus*) flowers. It is mostly nectarivorous, but small insects are taken from leaves or in flight. The proportion of insects in the diet increases during the chick-rearing period. The sex ratio is heavily skewed, with three males to every female. It may experience competition with Green-backed Firecrown *S. sephanoides*, especially over access to *Dendroseris litoralis* flowers post-breeding.

Threats

The clearance and degradation of vegetation by humans since the late 16th century, coupled with impacts of non-native herbivorous mammals (especially European rabbits), has limited the availability, quantity and quality of food resources. Habitat quality is also being degraded by the spread and dominance of invasive plants, most prominently by elm-leaf blackberry *Rubus ulmifolius*, maqui *Aristotelia chilensis* and murtilla *Ugni molinae*. Introduced predators, such as rats, cats and coatis, have been implicated in the mortality of some birds and may be responsible in part for its decline. Cats have been documented killing firecrowns in town during the non-breeding season. As is true with many island species, firecrowns are easily approached, thus rendering them highly susceptible to predation. Additionally, during its nocturnal torpor, this species is presumed to be vulnerable to predation. Males are able to defend territories with highly productive resources, but the smaller females are possibly being indirectly out competed by Green-backed Firecrown. Preliminary analyses of the population have revealed some genetic variation, but significantly less than in Green-backed Firecrown.

Conservation actions to date

The Juan Fernández Islands were designated as a national park in 1935 (protected from 1967) and a UNESCO Biosphere Reserve in 1977. The Chilean government began restoring habitat in 1997, and the islands have been nominated for World Heritage listing. Conservation is being led by the Juan Fernández Islands Conservancy, with support from the American Bird Conservancy, the Hummingbird Society, Conservation International, the Jeniam Foundation, and the Royal Society for the Protection of Birds. Key activities which have shown promising early results are control of invasive plants and herbivores (appears to increase nesting success of the firecrown), invasive predator control and a community outreach programme aimed at engaging local people.

Conservation actions required

- Continue to monitor the population using a quantitative census methodology that allows for statistical comparisons between surveys.
- Remove all introduced mammals, initially within an intensively managed, fenced, feasibility study area, with a long-term goal of acheiving complete eradications from the island.
- Replant native flora (including a 10 ha plot with shrubs that flower throughout the year) in areas free of introduced rabbits and cattle, initially within the feasibility study area but also at forest edges.
- Enforce grazing restrictions on national park land.
- Evaluate feasibility of establishing feeding stations in native forest.
- Replant fast-growing, soil-binding trees along highly eroded slopes for short-term relief.
- Implement systematic introduced plant control zonally.
- Continue to support ongoing efforts to remove alien invasive plants and mammalian predators, and increase awareness.

Chatham Islands Shag. Photo: © Brent Stephenson

Turquoise-throated Puffleg
Eriocnemis godini
Population: < 50, possibly extinct

Painting: © Carl Christian Tofte
www.carlchristiantofte.dk/ctofte@hotmail.com

Range & population
This hummingbird is known from only six 19th century specimens, and may be extinct. Only the type-specimen which was collected in 1850 has any locality information, having been taken at Guaillabamba, in ravines of the río Guaillabamba south of Perucho, Pichincha, in north Ecuador. Two 'Bogotá' trade-skins are the only evidence of its occurrence in Colombia, but it has been suggested that these originated from Pasto in south Nariño. The only subsequent record is an unconfirmed sighting near Quito, in the Chillo valley, in 1976. It was recorded at the type-locality between 2,100 and 2,300 m in a (presumably) arid ravine within a valley. It has been speculated that the 'Bogotá' trade-skins may have come from temperate zones. Altitude is 2,100-2,300 metres.

Threats
What is surmised to be suitable habitat at the type-locality has been almost completely destroyed, although remnants can be found in steep-sided stream-cuts in the arid upper Guaillabamba drainage.

Conservation actions to date
Searches specifically for this species at a large number of potential sites in the vicinity of the type-locality have been unsuccessful.

Conservation actions required
- Survey any remnant patches of habitat near the type-locality.
- Clarify its taxonomic status.

Colourful Puffleg
Eriocnemis mirabilis
Population: 50-249 ↓

Cauca, Colombia

Photo: © David Caro Sabogal

Range & population
This species remains known only from the vicinity of the type-locality, Cerro Charguayaco, in Cauca, south-west Colombia. It was known from four specimens and two observations before being rediscovered at the type-locality in 1997. It appears to be uncommon and incredibly localised. Preliminary studies suggest that it favours the understorey to mid-levels of lower montane, wet forest, feeding in the forest interior and edges within an extremely limited altitudinal range of 2,220-2,240 m.

Threats
In the 1960s and 1970s, the local economy was based on the fruit crop 'lulo', which was grown under the forest canopy, and hence deterred logging. However, a fungal disease and lepidopteran pest destroyed the crop in the 1980s, and logging recommenced.

Conservation actions to date
The type-locality is in Munchique National Park, but logging occurs within the park boundaries. The replanting of lulo fruits is being encouraged, with workshops targeting local communities located in impact zones. Funding from Swarovski Optik allowed the purchase of 5,000 acres of key forest habitat to safeguard the species. There are plans to extend the reserve by planting key tree species.

Conservation actions required
- Survey other areas of suitable habitat in Cauca.
- Research its status and annual ecological requirements.
- Continue to support the newly formed reserve.

Tuamotu Kingfisher
Todiramphus gambieri
Population: 200-250 ⟷ or ↓

Photo: © Pete Morris / Birdquest

French Polynesia, 2006

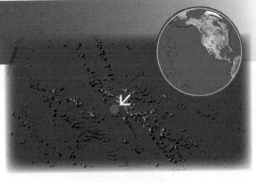

Range & population
This kingfisher is confined to the island of Niau in the Tuamotu Archipelago, French Polynesia. The race *gertrudae* was represented by 400-600 birds in 1974 the nominate *gambieri* having become extinct probably prior to 1922. Surveys in 2003 and 2004 estimated the total population as 39-51 individuals, but surveys involving radio tracking in 2006-2007 found more birds. It is found at the border of marshy areas, semi open bushes, coconut plantations and cultivated areas around villages. It feeds on insects (e.g. small *coleoptera*) and small lizards, and excavates nest-cavities in dead coconut trees (thus its choice of nest-site is limited).

Threats
Competition for food resources with the black rat *Rattus rattus* may pose a threat to the breeding success. Furthermore, rats may directly predate eggs and chicks and introduced cats are also predators of inexperienced, young birds calling for parents at ground level. The removal of suitable nesting trees in 1984, following a hurricane in 1983, has reduced the availability of nesting sites.

Conservation actions to date
The Fakarava Man and Biosphere Protected Area will include Niau.

Conservation actions required
- Conduct further fieldwork to validate the new population estimates.
- Research the impact of rats on the species.
- Provide nest boxes to increase the availability of nest-sites.
- Consider the possible translocation of birds to establish it on other islands.

Sulu Hornbill
Anthracoceros montani
Population: 40 ↓

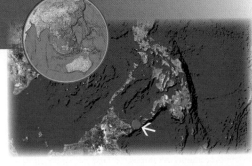

Photo: © Tim Worfolk/HBW6 (Lynx Edicions)

Range & population
This hornbill is endemic to islands in the Sulu archipelago in the Philippines; it persists with certainty only on Tawitawi and is thought to be extinct on Jolo (= Sulu) and on Sanga-sanga. It may survive on the small islands of Tandubatu, Dundangan and Baliungan. It inhabits primary dipterocarp forest, typically on mountain slopes (although this may simply reflect a constraint enforced by forest loss). It requires large trees for nesting.

Threats
Mainly deforestation. By the mid-1990s, rapid clearance of primary forest on Tawitawi had rendered remaining lowland patches highly degraded, with plans to replace even these with oil-palm plantations. Logging of remaining tracts, confined to rugged mountainous areas, is predicted to be followed by uncontrolled settlement and conversion to agriculture. High gun ownership in the recent past has resulted in it being shot for food and target practice. Young continue to be harvested for food, and there is evidence that it is collected for trade.

Conservation actions to date
Military activity and insurgency continue to present a serious obstacle to conservation work in the Sulus. There are no formal protected areas in the archipelago.

Conservation actions required
- Conduct surveys in all remaining forest patches in the Sulus.
- Urgently establish formal protected areas in the south-west of Tawitawi.
- Clarify the proposal for conservation funding for the Tawitawi/Sulu Coastal Area.
- Continue environmental awareness programmes.

Rufous-headed Hornbill
Aceros waldeni
Population: 120-160 ↓

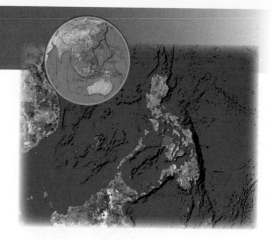

Northwest Panay Peninsula, Panay Island, The Philippines, 2001

Photo: © Callan Bentley

History
1874 – the first specimen is collected on Panay.

1877 – British ornithologist Richard Bowdler Sharpe (1847-1909) describes the species.

This species is also known as Visayan Wrinkled Hornbill.

Range & population
This species is endemic to the Western Visayas in the Philippines, where it is presumed to have occurred on three islands. It is presumed extinct on Guimaras and now survives only on Negros and Panay. In 1998, the total population was estimated at 60-80 pairs, based on extrapolation from fieldwork to all remaining forest areas on the islands. Of these, most are on Panay, with 30-40 pairs estimated to be present in the central mountains and a further 10-20 pairs on the Pandan peninsula. However, it has since almost certainly been extirpated in the latter area, despite pro-active anti-poaching and other forest wardening activities orchestrated by local support groups.

It inhabits closed-canopy forests, also frequenting logged areas and occasionally isolated trees in clearings. It is probably adapted to lower or mid-elevation forest, with records from 400-1,200 m on Panay and 300-950 m on Negros. It feeds in the canopy on figs and other fruits and may make local nomadic movements in response to food availability. It nests in large trees and seems to start breeding in March with eggs and chicks found in May-July.

Threats
Chronic deforestation has led to its extinction on Guimaras and its extreme scarcity elsewhere. An estimated 3% of Negros and 6% of Panay remains forested. Only 10% (c.144 km²) of this is thought to be below 1,000 m. The effects of deforestation have been exacerbated by its dependency on fruit, the availability of which is spatially and temporally variable. Hunting is an equally serious threat, given that up to a quarter of the population of north-west Panay was shot on one day in 1997. Collection for trade and local zoos is an additional threat, as well as the poaching of nest sites.

Conservation actions to date
The proposed Central Panay Mountains National Park and Mt Talinis/The Twin Lakes Balinsasayo Natural Park benefit from conservation funding. Other sites with recent records include Mt Kanla-on Natural Park (Negros) and Northern Negros

Natural Park, which receives nominal protection. Public awareness campaigns target the species.

Conservation actions required
- Publish results from surveys, particularly on Panay, to identify important sites.
- Gazette Central Panay Mountains National Park and propose further key sites on Negros and Panay for urgent establishment as strict protected areas.
- Conduct community awareness programmes to reduce hunting and promote local economic support for key sites.

Northwest Panay Peninsula, Panay Island, The Philippines, 2001

Photo: © Callan Bentley

Photo: © Callan Bentley

Okinawa Woodpecker
Dendrocopus noguchii
Population: 146-584 ↓

Oku, Yambaru, Okinawa, Japan, 2002

Photo: © Atle Ivar Olsen

Although both forage on dead and live trunks, males have also adapted to feed on the ground on soil-dwelling arthropods, as well as berries, seeds, acorns and other nuts.

Threats
Its decline is primarily attributable to deforestation, which continues at a significant rate as a result of logging, dam construction and associated road-building, agricultural development and golf course construction. Its limited range and tiny population make it vulnerable to extinction from disease and natural disasters such as typhoons.

Conservation actions to date
It is legally protected in Japan and has been declared a 'National Monument' and a 'Special bird for protection' by the japanese government. It occurs in Yonaha-dake Prefecture Protection Area and small protected areas on Mt Ibu and Mt Nishime and conservation organisations have purchased sites where it occurs.

Conservation actions required
* Continue to monitor its population.
* Designate a special protected area to cover all the mature forest (40 years old or more) on the central ridge of northern Okinawa.
* Connect fragmented forests in the north with planted forest corridors and ensure all forests of more than 25 years old are protected and logging is prohibited.
* Provide nest-boxes in young secondary forest.
* Institute a conservation education programme using Okinawa Rail *Gallirallus okinawae* and Okinawa Woodpecker as flagship species.

History
1877 – British ornithologist Henry Seebohm (1832-1895) describes the species.

1928 – an expedition to Okinawa finds that the species should be considered as in danger of extinction.

1955 – the Ryuku Islands government declares the species a 'National Monument'.

1972 – Lester L. Short estimates the population to 20-60 pairs.

1996 – Yambaru is designated as a national park.

2003 – a lawsuit is filed by the Centre for Biological Diversity to protect the areas belonging to the US Marine Corps where the species occurs.

This species is sometimes placed in the genus *Sapheopipo*.

Range & population
This woodpecker is endemic to Okinawa Island, Japan, where it is confined to Kunigami-gun (locally known as Yambaru) with the main breeding areas along the mountain ridges between Mt Nishime-take and Mt Iyu-take. It also occurs in coastal areas. It was considered close to extinction in the 1930s and, in the early 1990s, the breeding population was estimated to be c. 75 birds and the total population between 146-584 birds. A density of 12.1 birds per km² has been estimated at the US Forces Northern Training Area in north-eastern Okinawa.

It occurs in subtropical, evergreen broadleaved forest at least 30 years old, with tall trees of more than 20 cm in diameter, much of which is now confined to hill-tops. Foraging takes place in old-growth forest. Nesting is between late February-May, often in hollow *Castanopsis cuspidata* trees which it excavates by itself. The nest is only used for one breeding and may be used for roosting in winter. Nestlings have been recorded in May and June. There is an extraordinary difference in the foraging niches of males and females.

Oku, Yambaru, Okinawa, Japan, 2002

Photo: © Atle Ivar Olsen

Kaempfer´s Woodpecker
Celeus obrieni
Population: < 50 ↓

Photo: © Advaldo Dias do Prado/Museum de Zoologia, Universidade de Tocantins

Tocantins state, Brazil, October 2006

History

1926 – a female is collected by Emil Kaempfer in Uruçuí, north-east Brazil on 16ᵗʰ August.

1973 – Lester S. Short describes it as a new subspecies of Rufous-headed Woodpecker *Celeus spectabilis*.

1980 – a search is made for the taxon but it is not found.

2006 – Advaldo Dias do Prado and his team net and photograph an individual on 21ˢᵗ October.

2007 – a total of 23 different individuals are known. The species is changed from Not Evaluated to Critically Endangered.

This species has previously been called Caatinga Woodpecker

Range & population
This woodpecker was rediscovered in October 2006 after a gap of 80 years. It was refound during surveys near Goatins in Tocantins state, central Brazil, c. 350 km from the type locality at Uruçuí in the state of Piauí. Recent surveys have located more individuals in an area spanning 750 x 620 km. A number of searches have failed to locate the species in the area where the type specimen was collected. However, suitable habitat can also be found in the states of Tocantins, Piauí, Maranhão and Bahía, all in the eastern part of central Brazil. Given that it went unrecorded for many years and is only currently known from one locality the species is assumed to have a tiny population in an extremely small range.
The type specimen and a recently mist-netted bird were from cerrado woodland with open gallery forest and babaçu palm forest. It seems to have a large home range and low density. Within this habitat it shows strong association with the bamboo *Gadua paniculata*. The species' habits are unknown and it seems to occupy markedly different habitat to its sister species, Rufous-headed Woodpecker *Celeus spectabilis*.

Threats
The main threats are probably from habitat loss and conversion through fires, infrastructure development and conversion to soya crop. The species was recently rediscovered during surveys prior to the building of a new section of the Belém-Brasília highway. If built this may impact on habitat, resulting in cerrado being burnt to give way for cattle and soya agriculture. Fires may destroy the species habitat, or may play an integral role in maintaining it.

Conservation actions to date
There are currently no known conservation actions underway for this species. However, it remains a focus of ongoing research. The company responsible for the construction of the new road is supporting a monitoring study of the species. Through the GTB Programme, BirdLife and SAVE Brasil will start a project to elucidate some aspects of the species biology. The research will measure the home range and try to estimate the total population considering the range and suitable habitats. There is no formal protection of habitat within the current known range.

Conservation actions required
- Conduct further surveys to ascertain the species' range, numbers, population trends and the threats it faces.
- Survey the existing Protect Areas along the species range (Jalapão National Park, Jalapãp State Park, Lageado State Park and Indigenous Reserve Craos) to confirm the presence of the species.

Tocantins state, Brazil, October 2006

Photo: © Advaldo Dias do Prado / Museum de Zoologia, Universidade de Tocantins, www.untins.br

Imperial Woodpecker
Campephilus imperialis
Population: < 50, trend unknown

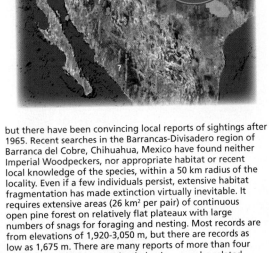

Painting: © Mark Hulme/HBW6 (Lynx Edicions)

but there have been convincing local reports of sightings after 1965. Recent searches in the Barrancas-Divisadero region of Barranca del Cobre, Chihuahua, Mexico have found neither Imperial Woodpeckers, nor appropriate habitat or recent local knowledge of the species, within a 50 km radius of the locality. Even if a few individuals persist, extensive habitat fragmentation has made extinction virtually inevitable. It requires extensive areas (26 km² per pair) of continuous open pine forest on relatively flat plateaux with large numbers of snags for foraging and nesting. Most records are from elevations of 1,920-3,050 m, but there are records as low as 1,675 m. There are many reports of more than four individuals, and this grouping behaviour may be related to its foraging specialisation. The main food source, beetle larvae in snags, is probably patchily distributed and peaks within a short period of time. Consequently, feeding-sites are probably best exploited by "nomadic" groups. If it operated in groups of seven or eight individuals, the minimum area of old-growth forest for a group would be 98 km². Breeding has been recorded between February and June, and probably 1-4 eggs are laid.

Threats
The chief threats are the combined and interconnected impacts of hunting and habitat loss. It has been hunted for pleasure, food and supposed medicinal purposes over a long period of time. Locals' uses of it have included eating young as delicacies, carrying its feathers as earmuffs to prevent headache, letting women in labour inhale fumes from singed feathers as a stimulant and to use the bill to draw disease out from the body. The expansion of lumber operations into remote parts of the sierra opened up areas for settlement (and hunters) in the early 1950s. Although over-hunting probably precipitated the initial decline, this was compounded by the widespread removal of dead pines for pulp and mature pines for timber. By 1996, only 22 km² of suitable breeding habitat remained and even the area from where a pair was reported in 1993 had been logged. The species' social nature made it particularly susceptible to both types of threat; it frequently occurred in groups of four to eight (sometimes up to 20) individuals and therefore required large tracts of forest and was easily exploited by hunters.

Conservation actions to date
A number of specific searches have been undertaken since the 1960s, including an extensive 11 month search in 1994-1995. There are no confirmed records from protected areas. Searches are ongoing and anecdotal reports are regularly pursued. The species' range and potential habitat fragments have been comprehensively mapped, and identified areas thoroughly explored.

Conservation actions required
- Prepare to follow-up any further local reports.
- Continue searching areas of old-growth forest in the former range.

History
1832 – the first specimens are exhibited at the Zoological Society of London on August 14th when the ornithologist John Gould (1804-1881) describes the species.

1887 – a note in The Auk by R. Ridgway describing a record only 50 miles from Arizona speculates in that the species will "doubtless soon be added to the American fauna". The record was made by Lieutenant H. C. Benson who was there scouting for Apache Indians.

1898 – W. E. Nelson estimates the density as 6 birds per 80 km². He also finds the first nest, containing 2 eggs, in February.

1956 – the last confirmed observation is made from Durango.

1993 – a pair are claimed in Durango and a single female in Sonora.

1995 – a single male is claimed from a site 20 km away from the 1993 site.

2005 – a bird is reported in November in the Barrancas-Divisadero region of Barranca del Cobre, Chihuahua, Mexico.

Range & population
This woodpecker was formerly distributed throughout the Sierra Madre Occidental of Mexico in Sonora, Chihuahua, Durango, Nayarit, Zacatecas (possibly) and north Jalisco with more isolated populations in west Jalisco and Michoacán. It was not historically a rare species within suitable habitat, but the total population probably never numbered more than 8,000 individuals. The last confirmed record was from 1956

188

Indian Vulture. Photo: © Ganesh H Shankar

Ivory-billed Woodpecker
Campephilus principalis
Population: < 50, trend unknown

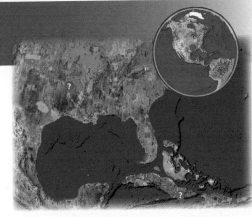

Painting from "The 50 Rarest Birds of the World" by Blake Twigden

History
1758 – Carolus Linneaus (1707-1778) describes the species.

1938 – an estimated 20 individuals are in the wild.

1987 – the last sighting of the Cuban subspecies is made.

1999 – an unconfirmed sighting is made by forestry student David Kulivan in the Pearl River region of southeast Lousiana.

2006 – a $10,000 reward is promised for information leading to nest, roost or feeding sites feeding. Several unconfirmed sightings are reported from Pearl River.

Range & population
Two subspecies of this large woodpecker occurred at low densities throughout the south-east USA (nominate *principalis*) and on Cuba (race *bairdii*). Sixty years after the last confirmed North American record in north-eastern Louisiana in 1944, the species was reported to have been rediscovered in 2004 in the Big Woods region of eastern Arkansas. Evidence for the rediscovery comes in the form of seven sightings, a short poor-quality video, over 100 sound recordings indicative of this species from automatic recording stations, and a number of additional possible encounters. The sound and video recordings have been analysed in detail. However, some consider that this evidence is not yet conclusive, and intensive searches are currently underway that hope to provide unequivocal documentation of the species' continued existence. There were also unconfirmed reports by researchers working in forests along the Choctawhatchee river in Florida reporting 14 sightings and 41 acoustic encounters heard during 2005-2006 and further sightings and calls in the 2006-2007 field season, but again incontrovertible evidence is still required. Between the last confirmed sightings in 1944 and the 2004 records discussed above there were a further 20 credible unconfirmed reports from within its historic range. The species is considered likely to be extinct in Cuba, as intensive searches have not found any new records subsequent to those of the late 1980s. Calls heard in 1998 suggested that it might survive in the highest reaches of the Sierra Maestra in south-east Cuba, an area from which there

had been no historical records and at an elevation higher than the known altitudinal range of the species. Follow-up searches in the area found poor habitat and no indications of presence of the species. Any remnant population in either the USA or Cuba is likely to be tiny.

It was originally found in both bottomland hardwood and montane (pine, mixed and broadleaf) forests in the USA and Cuba. Historic accounts indicate that it has a very large home range and occurs naturally at low densities, suggesting that large contiguous tracts of mature woodland would be required to support a viable population. The Big Woods area comprises several distinct types of swamp and bottomland hardwood forests, covering a total area of c. 220,000 ha. In Cuba, extensive habitat loss and degradation in the lowlands mean that any remaining population may be restricted to intact montane pine forests. The primary requirement is for dead trees, which harbour wood-boring beetle larvae, its preferred food source. It forages by stripping bark from dead trees, using its bill like a carpenter's chisel, and also takes fruit, nuts and seeds. The breeding season is March-June in Cuba and February-May in the USA.

Threats
Logging and clearance for agriculture are responsible for the dramatic decline in numbers and range. These factors are likely to threaten any remaining population.

Conservation actions to date
After rediscovery in February 2004, intensive surveys involving dozens of observers, automatic cameras and recording equipment have been carried out in the Big Woods area. Searches have also continued in other parts of the south-east USA that have historic records of the species, with specific searches planned for 21 locations across that area in 2006-2007. An endangered species recovery team of c. 50 members has been appointed, and a recovery plan is being drawn up. Funds totalling $10.2 million have been allocated by the federal government to the recovery effort. Part of the Big Woods area falls within the Cache River and White River National Wildlife Refuges. In Cuba there have been a number of searches for the species.

Conservation actions required
- Carry out further surveys in the south-east USA (particularly near recent reported sightings) to try to locate further individuals, document their continued existence and determine the population size and distribution.
- Ensure strict protection of any nests and nesting trees, if found.
- Continue to carry out searches for the species in Cuba.
- Ensure the implementation of appropriate protective measures if a population is found in Cuba.
- Engage birdwatchers in the search for the woodpecker and raise awareness about the importance of reporting any sightings.

Gurney's Pitta
Pitta gurneyi

Krabi province, Thailand, 2007

Population: 10,000-17,000, trend unknown

History

1875 – Allan Octavian Hume (1829-1912) describes the species.

1914 – what is considered the last record is made in Myanmar.

1986 – the species is rediscovered in the wild in Thailand, after a specimen is found at a Bangkok bird dealer. 44-45 pairs are estimated to exist.

1987 – Khao Nor Chuchi, an important site in Thailand is declared a non-hunting area.

1993 – Khao Nor Chuchi is upgraded to Wildlife Sanctuary.

2003 – a new population is discovered at four sites in Myanmar.

2006 – an expedition is mounted to the Lenya area, Myanmar with the purpose of refining census methods for future surveys.

Range & population

This colourful pitta occurs in peninsular Thailand and adjacent southern Tenasserim, Myanmar. Formerly common across much of its range, there were no field observations in Thailand between 1952 and 1986. Since 1986, intensive surveys have found it in at least five localities, although it has disappeared from all but one of these, Khao Nor Chuchi. This population has declined from 44–45 pairs in 1986 to just nine pairs in 1997, most of which are outside protected-area boundaries. A search for it in Myanmar in 2003 was successful and the species was discovered at four sites with a maximum of 10-12 pairs at one location. Further surveys have revealed that this population numbers over 10,000.

It occurs in secondary, regenerating, lowland semi-evergreen forest, usually below 160 m, with understoreys containing Salacca palms, in which it nests. A central element of its territories is gully systems where moist conditions exist year-round and there is usually access to water in small streamlets. Moisture and shade appear to be crucial. It breeds during the wet season in April–October, with peak activity in June. The domed nest is made of leaves and placed low in a tree or rattan. 3-4 eggs, sometimes 5, are laid and both sexes incubate them. It feeds on insects, spider, slugs, frogs and other small animals

Threats
The key reason for its decline has been the almost total clearance of lowland forest in southern Myanmar and peninsular Thailand through clear-felling for timber, unofficial logging and conversion to croplands, fruit orchards, coffee, rubber and oil-palm plantations. By 1987, only 20–50 km² of forest below 100 m remained in peninsular Thailand and this area continues to decline. Snare-line trapping for the cage-bird trade is also a serious threat, and birds were traded in Bangkok during the 1950s to 1970s when it was not known in the wild among ornithologists. In 1986 sources in Bangkok claimed that 5-6 birds, perhaps as many as 50, were supplied annually to the bird trade.

Conservation actions to date
Following its rediscovery in Thailand, a series of breeding season censuses were conducted, from 1987–1989, to locate and quantify populations in peninsular Thailand. The Khao Nor Chuchi Lowland Forest Project was established in 1990 and engaged the local community in participatory management, education programmes and ecotourism, to help reduce pressure on remaining forest. However, this has met with limited success as economic incentives continue to govern land-use decisions. A project in Myanmar aimed at conserving remaining lowland forest in southern Tenasserim commenced in 2004. There are currently no protected areas in this region.

Conservation actions required
- Conduct comprehensive surveys of remaining populations in southern Myanmar.
- Extend strict protected area status to all remaining suitable habitat currently outside Khao Nor Chuchi Wildlife Sanctuary boundaries.
- Establish an *in situ* protection unit with direct responsibility for safeguarding all remaining habitat, to facilitate cooperation with sanctuary officials and strengthen management and community participation.

Krabi province, Thailand, 2007

Photo: © Kanit Khanikul

Krabi province, Thailand, 2007

Photo: © Kanit Khanikul

Araripe Manakin
Antilophia bokermanni

Chapada do Araripe, state of Ceará, Brazil, 2005

Population: 800 ↓

History

1998 – the species is described by Galileu Coelho and Weber Girão Silva.

2002 – first population assessments and genetic studies conducted, with a grant from the Brazilian 'Fundação O Boticário de Proteção à Natureza'.

2004 – the BP Conservation Leadership Programme and the Brazilian Ministry of Environment co-sponsor an extensive field effort to determine the population size, present range, reproductive biology, and major threats to the Araripe Manakin, conducted by the Brazilian NGO Aquasis.

2005 – team members of the conservation project become fire fighters in order to protect nests from a blazing forest fire.

2006 – a conservation plan is published by Aquasis.

2007 – a new award is granted by the BP Conservation Leadership Programme to establish a Wildlife Refuge for the Araripe Manakin.

Range & population

This manakin was described in 1998 and, until recently, was only known from the type-locality in the foothills of the Chapada do Araripe, south Ceará, Brazil. An extensive search conducted in 2004-2006 increased the known localities for the species to 42, estimated the overall population size at 800 individuals, and determined its present range as a 28km² patch of moist forests along the north-eastern slope of the Chapada do Araripe. It inhabits the lower and middle storey of tall, second growth forest (where there is an abundance of vines), edge and adjacent clearings, preferring more humid areas of moist forest near springs and streams. It reportedly feeds on small fruits of *Cordia sp.* and *Cecropia sp.*, however, an ongoing study has already identified 15 species of plants - from 12 families - that form part of the Araripe Manakin's diet. It occurs in pairs, and immature males have been found in March and January. Vocal activity among males peaks between 10.00 and 14.00 hours, and is highest during September-October when rainfall is at its lowest. The breeding follows during the wet season when around three quarters of tree species bordering gallery forests occupied by

Araripe Manakin are fruiting. Nests are built on the marginal vegetation of narrow streams, always above running water.

Threats
Lowlands adjacent to the Chapada have mostly been cleared for agriculture (e.g., bananas, maize, beans, passion fruit and tomatoes), cattle raising and urban expansion. There are several recreational facilities along the slopes of the Chapada do Araripe. These include large open parks and swimming pools, which have affected deforestation and water diversion in their development, particularly in areas where there is spring water. A new, large facility involving road-building and land clearance is under construction very close to the type-locality. Fires in 2004/5 largely destroyed an area of forest known to contain 7 active nests of the species. The species is not known to be trapped either by wildlife traders or by the local population as pets. However, the springs that supply the numerous streams along the slopes, which in turn support the unique moist forest habitat of the Araripe Manakin, have suffered an average reduction of ¾ in their outflow in the past hundred years. Thus, the deforestation on the slopes and the plateau of the Chapada do Araripe seem to be affecting the rainwater collection that supplies the aquifer that forms the springs, posing a threat to the manakin's remaining habitat. Diversion, channeling and piping of the springs and streams are also greatly reducing the viable gallery forest nesting areas of the species.

Conservation actions to date
The type-locality is within the large Chapada do Araripe Environmental Protection Area, and adjacent to the Araripe National Forest, but both Protected Areas are of 'sustainable use' designation, and neither is preventing loss of moist forest habitat, and future exploitation or disturbance. However, the owner of the land adjacent to the type-locality has decided to protect the forest following the discovery of this species. The British Petroleum (BP) Conservation Leadership Programme has been supporting a Conservation of the Araripe Manakin Project, in the Chapada do Araripe region of Brazil since 2004, conducted by the local NGO Aquasis. The project was granted a new award in 2007 to undertake intensive research to better understand the species conservation status to create a Conservation Plan for the Araripe Manakin. The project team is now focusing on the creation of a fully protected area in the Araripe, encompassing the remaining moist forest habitat and potential areas for recovery.

Conservation actions required
- Formally protect the remaining habitat as a Wildlife Refuge.
- Provide incentives for landowners to establish a network of private reserves as a buffer zone.
- Work with environmental and water management authorities to protect springs and streams and their associated gallery forests along the slopes of the Chapada.
- Increase awareness campaigns in the Araripe region to value the biodiversity and water resources in this unique moist forest habitat in the middle of the semi-arid caatinga biome, using the Araripe Manakin as symbol for the conservation of the Chapada.
- Promote research on moist forest species composition and ecology, in order to support future conservation actions related to habitat recovery.

Arajara Park, Ceará, Brazil, 2006

Photo: © Alberto Campos (Aquasis)

Arajara Park, Near Crato, Ceará, Brazil, 2006

Photo: © Charles Hesse

Chapada do Araripe, state of Ceará, Brazil, 2005

Photo: © Ciro Albano

Kinglet Calyptura
Calyptura cristata
Population: < 50 ↓

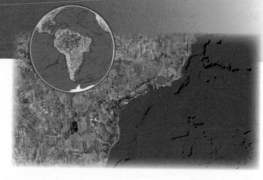

© Blake Twigden, www.inventas.co.nz/50rarestbirds/

Range & population
The Kinglet Calyptura has a very restricted range to the north of Rio de Janeiro city, Brazil. The only 20th century record was of two birds observed in the Serra dos Órgãos on several days in October 1996. It is apparently restricted to foothill forest, but tolerates secondary habitats. It has been recorded eating fruit, seeds and insects.

Threats
Deforestation, historically driven by gold and diamond mining and the creation of coffee plantations, appears to have brought this species to the brink of extinction. The harvesting of bromeliads, mistletoes and orchids from the forest of the region may further threaten the species by reducing food supply, but also by altering habitat structure and microclimate.

Conservation actions to date
It is protected by Brazilian law. Some areas of apparently suitable habitat are protected within the park of the 1996 sighting, and there are adjacent tracts of forest to elevations of c.50 m. Suitable habitat also occurs within the Reserva Ecologica Guapiaçu.

Conservation actions required
- Develop and follow a standardised survey protocol involving focal watches at suitable fruiting trees, focusing particularly in suitable habitat in the Serra dos Órgãos including the Reserva Ecologica Guapiaçu, and in the Serra do Mar near Ubatuba.
- Protect all remaining low-altitude forest in the vicinity of the rediscovery site.

Minas Gerais Tyrannulet
Phylloscartes roquettei
Population: 50-249 ↓

Parque Nacional Cavernas do Peruaçu, Brazil, 2003

Photo: © Dante Buzzetti

Range & population
This tyrannulet is only known from three areas in the São Francisco valley, in north and central Minas Gerais, east-central Brazil. It was recorded at the Projeto Jaíba, Mocambinho in September 1996 and the species may occur in contiguous habitat in south-west Bahia. Three were observed in dry forest at Sítio Duboca in 2000 and 2005. It occurs in mesophytic, semi-deciduous woodland and gallery forests. Birds occasionally also descended to the green cotton *Gossypium* bushes of a plantation. In both dry and gallery forests, it appears to prefer the upper branches of taller, emergent trees, where it sallies for insect prey. Nest building has been observed in October.

Threats
Its habitat is probably the most threatened in central Brazil owing to its valuable Aroeira *Astronium urundeuva* wood and relatively fertile soils. Charcoal-burners were fully active at the type-locality in 1986, where there was also extensive forest cutting for pasture and agricultural development. The São Francisco basin is also threatened by limestone quarrying and a large-scale irrigation project that has already resulted in the loss of large areas of forest.

Conservation actions to date
It is protected under Brazilian law but no other measures have been taken.

Conservation actions required
- Survey to locate additional populations.
- Urgently protect the known area near Pirapora.
- Conduct an environmental awareness campaign directed at landowners, local communities and schools.
- Reinforce the protection of the region's gallery forests.

Kaempfer´s Tody-tyrant
Hemitriccus kaempferi
Population: 1,000-2,499 ⬇

Salto do Piraí, Joinville, Santa Catarina, Brazil, 2006

Photo: © Vítor de Q. Piacentini

Range & population
This tody-tyrant is known only from three localities, namely Salto do Piraí near Vila Nova, Brusque and Reserva Particular do Patrimônio Natural de Volta Velha, near Itapoá, in Santa Catarina, Brazil. The species is apparently very rare, with a very small and extremely fragmented range. It inhabits humid, lowland Atlantic forest. It feeds predominantly in the midstorey of medium-sized trees, usually at a height of 1.5-2 m, hover-gleaning and flycatching during short sallies. It has not been observed to join mixed-species flocks: instead, pairs appear to remain within small, well-defined territories.

Threats
Deforestation has been extensive in the Atlantic forest, and lowland forest remaining in the vicinity of both sites continues to be cleared.

Conservation actions to date
It is protected by Brazilian law, and occurs in one protected area, and in forest adjacent to another.

Conservation actions required
- Survey remaining patches of lowland forest in Santa Catarina and adjacent areas of Paraná to clarify distribution and status.
- Survey forest within the vicinity of the second historical locality, Brusque, which has not been visited subsequently.
- Investigate ecological requirements of the species at both current localities.
- Expand the Reserva Particular do Patrimônio Natural de Volta Velha to incorporate adjacent patches of lowland forest.
- Include the Salto do Piraí locality within an enlarged Bracinho State Ecological Station.

Rondonia Bushbird
Clytoctantes atrogularis
Population: < 50 ⬇

Painting: © Carl Christian Tofte
www.carlchristiantofte.dk/ctofte@hotmail.com

Range & population
This species' centre of distribution is probably the upper rio Madeira/Tapajós interfluvium, Brazil. It may be naturally rare. It is very poorly known. Its habitat is mature terra firme forest dominated by dense vine-tangles, where it appears to feed 0.2-5 m above ground. The species appears to be resistant to some degree of forest degradation and occurs in man-made secondary growth.

Threats
The principal threats are the expansion of the agricultural frontier as a direct result of highway construction (which has declined in the 1990s) and commercial logging (which is increasing significantly). Although its range almost certainly includes adjacent parts of Amazonas and Mato Grosso, deforestation in Rondônia proceeds at a high rate. Hydroelectric schemes in Rondônia are apparently moving ahead and can pose a threat.

Conservation actions to date
The vicinity of type-locality has been extensively surveyed but the incredible paucity of information makes effective conservation action difficult. The state government of Amazonas, Brazil, as part of its Programa Zona Franca Verde, has created a mosaic of nine protected conservation areas, including the important Madeira/Tapajós interfluvium.

Conservation actions required
- Reassess forest state and species's status at the type-locality.
- Survey for the species elsewhere in Rondônia and adjacent areas of Mato Grosso and Amazonas.
- Perform future surveys using playback.
- Establish reserves in this area of the Brazilian Shield to protect this and other threatened species.
- Eliminate incentives for cattle-ranching and other inappropriate forms of agriculture within the region.

Rio de Janeiro Antwren
Myrmotherula fluminensis
Population: 50-249 ↓

Painting: © Carl Christian Tofte
www.carlchristiantofte.dk/ctofte@hotmail.com

Range & population
This species was discovered as recently as in 1982, when a single individual was mist-netted, in central Rio de Janeiro state, Brazil. The only subsequent reports come from the Serra do Mar Ecological Reserve (now called the Guapi Açu Ecological Reserve, or REGUA). The type-specimen was collected in a partially isolated and highly disturbed woodlot. Birds have most frequently been observed in mixed-species flocks with other insectivorous species, including Unicoloured Antwren *Myrmotherula unicolor*, but typically forage lower than the latter species, mainly within 2 m of the ground, among dense vine-tangles.

Threats
The virtually complete loss of all lowland forest on the coastal plain south of the Serra dos Órgãos has likely deprived this species of almost all habitats within its probable range.

Conservation actions to date
Guapi Açu Ecological Reserve encompasses privately-owned land at an altitudinal range of 35–2,000 m. The Fazenda Serra do Mar forms the core of this reserve, and the adjacent seven landowners are expected to sign buffer-zone management agreements.

Conservation actions required
* Determine whether the type-specimen and birds at Guapi Açu represent the same taxon and determine the taxonomic validity.
* If it is a valid species, assess its status at Guapi Açu.
* Survey suitable habitat in the surrounding areas to clarify distribution and status.
* Conduct ecological studies to determine habitat requirements.

Alagoas Antwren
Myrmotherula snowi
Population: 50-249 ↓

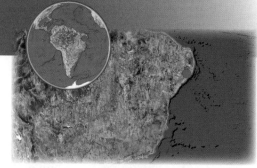

Murici Ecological Station, State of Alagoas, Brazil, 2007

Photo: © Ciro Albano

Range & population
This species has only ever been recorded in Alagoas and Pernambuco states, north-east Brazil. It was first discovered at Murici (Alagoas) in 1979. Recently, it has also been discovered at two sites in Pernambuco.
It forages in pairs and small mixed-species flocks in the middle strata of upland semi-humid forest at 400-550 m.The diet consists of arthropods, including spiders, beetles, ants and cockroaches. Breeding probably occurs in February, and juveniles have been recorded in May.

Threats
Forest at Murici has been reduced from 70 km² in the 1970s to 30 km² of highly disturbed and fragmented habitat in 1999, largely as a result of logging and conversion to sugarcane plantations and pastureland. In January 1999, new logging roads were evident and such forest fragments are severely threatened by fires spreading from adjacent plantations. The massive clearance of Atlantic forest in Alagoas and Pernambuco has left few other sites likely to support populations of this species.

Conservation actions to date
Although land at Murici remains privately-owned and vulnerable to clearance, international efforts to effect its conservation are ongoing. Frei Caneca is a private reserve protecting c.6 km² of forest.

Conservation actions required
* Survey other remnant patches of upland Atlantic forest in Alagoas and Pernambuco for this species.
* Ensure the de facto protection of Murici Ecological Station.
* Secure the long-term conservation of Mata do Estado.
* Investigate the expansion of Frei Caneca Private Reserve to include adjacent forest.

Restinga Antwren
Formicivora littoralis
Population: 250-999 ↓

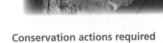

Cabo Frio, Brazil, 2007

Photo: ©Luiz Freire

Conservation actions required
- Survey to ascertain and monitor its status, especially in the Maçambaba area.
- Conduct research into the species' ecology.
- Ensure continued support for the protected areas where it occurs.
- Conduct impact assessments prior to real-estate projects.
- Implement an environmental awareness campaign in the area.

BirdLife Species Guardian ✓ **Pingo D'água**

History
1990 – Luis A. Pedreira Gonzaga and José Fernando Pacheco describe the form.
1992 – it is split as a species.

This species was previously treated as a subspecies of Serra Antwren *Formicivora serrana*.

SAVE Brasil strives to conserve birds, their habitats and global biodiversity, working with people towards sustainability in the use of natural resources.

www.savebrasil.org.br

Range & population
This antwren occupies a highly restricted range around Cabo Frio in Rio de Janeiro state, Brazil. The type-locality, near Arraial do Cabo, is a strip of dunes some 30 km long and up to 400 m wide. The species is found at high densities within suitable habitat and has been considered abundant on Ilha do Cabo Frio. Although no population estimates are available, it is likely to have declined rapidly owing to habitat loss, and recent assessments have indicated that its occupied range is extremely small.

It occupies restinga (beach-scrub habitat, rich in *cactii* and *bromeliads*, growing on sand-dunes) and other scrub vegetation on coastal hillsides, and can persist in tiny areas of habitat around holiday homes. Birds usually forage in pairs, remaining close to the ground in dense thickets. Nests have been found in June, October and November on Ilha do Cabo Frio, and breeding would appear to be almost year-round, as judged from the state of the gonads of collected specimens. The nest is constructed from fibres attached to horizontal branch forks. The clutch-size is two with both sexes sharing parental duties.

Threats
The species' range is within a major holiday development area, where suitable habitat is under pressure from clearance for real-estate projects and the increasing presence of squatters. The type-locality is severely threatened by the salt industry and the development of beachfront housing.

Conservation actions to date
Small amounts of restinga habitat are protected by three designated areas: the Jacarepiá and Maçambaba State Reserves, and the Maçambaba Environmental Protection Area. Access to Ilha do Cabo Frio is restricted by the Brazilian navy, thereby providing some protection.

Praia Seca, Brazil, 2006

Photo: ©Nancy C Bell

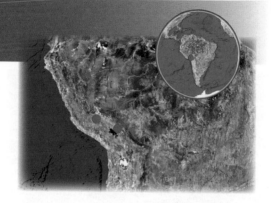

Royal Cinclodes
Cinclodes aricomae
Population: 50-249 ↓

Abra Malaga, Cusco area, Peru, 2000

Photo: © Tuomas Seimola

History
1876 – the first and, for some time, last record in Bolivia when Samuel Botsford Buckely collects an individual north of the Rio Unduavi valley.

1932 – Melbourne A. Carriker describes the species.

1997 – a record in the Cordillera Apolobamba, La Paz, Bolivia is the first in Bolivia for over 120 years.

2000 – a record is made in the Ilampu valley, Bolivia.

2003 – another record is made near Sanja Pampa, La Paz, Bolivia.

This species has sometimes been treated as a subspecies of Stout-billed Cinclodes *Cinclodes excelsior.*

Range & population
Royal Cinclodes occurs in the Andes of south-east Peru (Cuzco, Apurímac and Puno) and adjacent Bolivia (La Paz). Historically, it was probably common, at least locally, and distributed along the entire Cordillera Real range of mountains. Its scarce and patchy habitat now occupies c. 10% of the estimated potential cover in Bolivia, and possibly less than 3% in large parts of Cuzco, where natural habitat halved in extent during the 1980s. All Peruvian records are from near Cuzco city, Cuzco/Apurímac, Peru, including the Cordillera Vilcanota, with numbers estimated at 100-150 individuals in 1990. Surveys in three river valleys of the Cordillera Vilcanota in 2003-2005 confirmed the species' presence at only one of ten sites visited and estimated just two birds in 1.71 km² of *Polylepis* forest. It is confined to tiny, humid patches of Polylepis woodland and montane scrub, mainly at 3,500-4,800 m. It forages, presumably for invertebrates, in moss, leaf-litter and decaying wood, descending temporarily to lower elevations during periods of snow. The breeding season probably begins in December but, in the Cordillera Vilcanota, pairs are territorial during the austral winter, and have been seen carrying nesting material into a hole in a cliff face in September.

Threats
The main threats are the uncontrolled use of fire and heavy grazing, which combine to prevent *Polylepis* regeneration. Cutting for timber, firewood and charcoal is locally destructive, but could be sustained if regeneration were not prevented. Less significant threats to *Polylepis* are the change from camelid to sheep and cattle-farming, afforestation, especially where exotic tree species (e.g. *Eucalyptus*) are planted, and erosion and soil degradation caused by agricultural intensification.

Conservation actions to date
Local successes include the Runtacocha highland near Cuzco, where local people are reacting positively towards better environmental control. High-altitude habitats have been surveyed and conservation measures proposed. The 1997 Bolivian record was within Madidi National Park, but *Polylepis* is threatened at the site. The Ilampu valley is in the south-west corner of Cotapata National Park. For the last three years there has been a *Polylepis* conservation program working with local communities on the known sites for the Royal Cinclodes.

Conservation actions required
- Survey remaining habitat in the relatively inaccessible Cordillera Vilcanota, to determine the species´ distribution and investigate its ecology.
- Protect Yanacocha forest and other *Polylepis* habitat in the Cordillera Vilcanota.
- Improve land-use management by segregating agricultural, grazing and forest areas.
- Expand *Polylepis* planting programmes and plant buffer zones below *Polylepis* woodland to provide an alternative firewood source.
- Evaluate conservation problems and socio-economic issues.
- Encourage local people to develop land-use management and restoration schemes.
- Establish private nature reserves in key sites.

Abra Malaga, Peru, 2006

Photo: © Ian Merrill

Stresemann´s Bristlefront
Merulaxis stresemanni
Population: 50-249 ↓

Painting: © Carl Christian Tofte
www.carlchristiantofte.dk/ctofte@hotmail.com

Range & population
This species was known until recently from just two Brazilian specimens taken near Salvador in the 1830s, and near Ilhéus in 1945, in coastal Bahia. In 1995, it was rediscovered in the wild when a male was observed and tape-recorded at Fazenda Jueirana, near Una Biological Reserve, Bahia. The species has also been found in the Jequitinhonha valley, Minas Gerais, near the border with Bahia. The male in 1995 was observed foraging on the ground and on fallen tree trunks in an area of drier forest between two humid valleys. It was found in humid forest at 700-800 metres around the Jequitinonha and Murcuri River valleys.

Threats
Most humid forest in Bahia has been cleared or converted to cacao plantations, and remaining patches are disappearing very rapidly.

Conservation actions to date
It is protected by Brazilian law. The sighting in 1995 was in a privately-owned fazenda adjacent to the Una Biological Reserve. The best preserved forest tract where the species was discovered in Macarani County in 2005 is owned by individuals reportedly interested in declaring the area a Private Natural Heritage Reserve.

Conservation actions required
- Carry out surveys in the Jequitinhonha valley to determine the size and status of this population.
- Search for additional populations in lowland forests in and around Bahia, using the voice cut now available.
- Safeguard the forest in the Jequitinhonha valley, and remaining tracts of humid forest in Bahia.

Bahia Tapaculo
Scytalopus psychopompus
Population: 50-249 ↓

Painting: © Carl Christian Tofte
www.carlchristiantofte.dk/ctofte@hotmail.com

Range & population
This secretive species was until recently known only from three specimens taken at two localities in coastal Bahia, Brazil: a male collected in July 1944 at Ilhéus and a pair obtained in October 1983 at Valença. The species is no longer present close to these towns, but it has been found at two other sites, where small populations survive. It seems that the mature wet lowland forests are an obligatory condition for its presence, in Una and Igrapiúna areas. It is restricted to patches in river and stream valleys with small swamps around the main river course or swampy parts of the river. Its preferred micro-habitat appears to be areas with dense agglomerates of vines and, shrubs, covered by trunks and branches of fallen trees.

Threats
Destruction of coastal Atlantic forest has been extensive in Bahia, south of Salvador, and only small fragments remain totalling perhaps 10% of its original extent in the area. The species is presumed to be at great risk from the continuing loss of suitable habitat.

Conservation actions to date
Una Biological Reserve is a small protected area.

Conservation actions required
- Continue studying the known population at Ituberá.
- Search for the species in other fragments of remaining habitat in the area.
- Determine its population size, habitat requirements and status at the known localities.
- Effectively safeguard Una Biological Reserve and the habitat at Ituberá.

Masafuera Rayadito
Aphrastura masafuerae
Population: 140 ↓

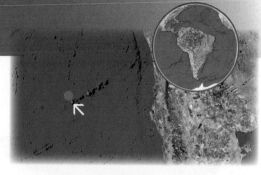

Masafuera Island, 2006

Photo: © Andrea K Suardo

Range & population
This species is endemic to Alejandro Selkirk (Más Afuera) in the Juan Fernández Islands, Chile. The population was estimated at c.140 individuals in 2001-2002, representing a decline of 30% in just under a decade. It is found primarily in *Dicksonia externa* fern forest. Records are from 600 m - 1,300 m. It nests during December to January in small natural holes in steep rock walls, usually at least 5 m above the ground.

Threats
A large proportion of natural vegetation on the island has been degraded and fragmented by goat-trampling, fire and timber cutting. Mammalian predators, such as rats and possibly mice impact on brood survival, and feral cats impact on adult survival. Recent declines may be related to an increase of Red-backed Hawks *Buteo polyosoma exsul*.

Conservation actions to date
The Juan Fernández Islands were designated a biosphere reserve in 1977 and sheep were removed from the island in 1983. A habitat restoration programme in 1997 and nest boxes were installed in 2006. Other monitoring work is ongoing and efforts continue to improve current population estimates and knowledge of the species' ecology and habitat preference.

Conservation actions required
- Eradicate goats from Alejandro Selkirk.
- Establish a continuous monitoring scheme of the species.
- Compare with the ecological requirements of other species to develop management strategies.

Alagoas Foliage-gleaner
Philydor novaesi
Population: 50-249 ↓

Reserva Particular Frei Caneca, Jaqueira, Pernambuco, Brazil, 2003

Photo: © Dante Buzzetti

Range & population
This species has only ever been recorded at two sites in Alagoas and Pernambuco, north-east Brazil. It was first discovered at Murici (Alagoas) in 1979. Indications are that the species is (barely) extant. It was discovered at Frei Caneca Private Reserve (Pernambuco) in April 2003.
It inhabits interior upland forest at 400–550 m, from the understorey to the subcanopy, and has been observed in selectively logged and old secondary forests. Food consists of insects, including larvae taken from dead wood, beetles, grasshoppers and ants. There is little breeding information, but an immature was collected in January.

Threats
Forest at Murici has been more than halved from the 1970s, to 1999, largely as a result of logging and conversion to sugarcane plantations and pastureland. The massive clearance of Atlantic forest in Alagoas and Pernambuco has left few other sites likely to support populations of this species.

Conservation actions to date
It is protected under Brazilian law. Although land at Murici remains privately-owned and vulnerable to clearance, international efforts to effect its conservation are ongoing. Frei Caneca is a private reserve protecting 630 ha of forest. BirdLife purchased a property adjacent to the Frei Caneca Private Nature Reserve, increasing the protected area size to 1,000 hectares along the Serra do Urubu.

Conservation actions required
- Survey any remnant patches of upland Atlantic forest in Alagoas for this species.
- Ensure the *de facto* protection of Murici Ecological Station.

Uluguru Bush-shrike
Malaconotus alius
Population: 2,400 ↓

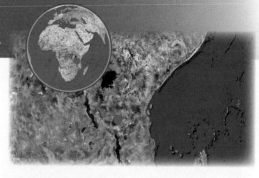

Painting: © Kim Franklin

Range & population
This species occurs only in the Uluguru Mountains, Tanzania. It seems to prefer areas where precipitation is highest and the forest least disturbed, but has also been found in degraded forest at the edge of forest reserves or where mature and tall trees still remain. It probably forages alone and in pairs, feeding on large arthropod.

Threats
Forest area declined from 300 km² in 1955 to 230 km² in 2001, caused by clearance for farms by an expanding human population on the lower slopes. Most of this clearance occurred between 600 and 1,600 m which constitute the preferred habitat. Slow but continuous loss and degradation of habitat remains a threat. This consists mainly of cutting for firewood and some timber.

Conservation actions to date
Uluguru North is a Forest Reserve and some areas outside the reserve have been protected. Conservation action in the Ulugurus focuses on assisting local initiatives and increasing the involvement of local communities in forest management. The area is proposed as a Nature Reserve that would include Uluguru North and South Forest Reserves and connect these across the Bunduki Gap

Conservation actions required
- Monitor population status.
- Clarify its preferred habitat-types.
- Increase efforts to reduce firewood collection and timber harvesting within the reserve.
- Plant new forest below 1,500 m
- Take greater care of riverine forest corridors.

Bulo Burti Boubou
Laniarius liberatus
Population: < 50, unknown trend

Bulo Burti, Somalia, 1989

Photo: © E F G Smith

Range & population
This boubou was described on the basis of blood and feather samples from a single live individual first observed in August 1988 in the grounds of a hospital at Bulo Burti (Buulobarde), 140 km inland on the Shabeelle river in central Somalia. It was netted in January 1989 and, after 14 months in captivity and because believed to be a highly threatened species, was released as near as possible to its site of capture, in March 1990. Searches in the Bulo Burti area in July 1989 and April 1990 failed to produce any more records. The individual was netted in Acacia scrub.

Threats
The area of Acacia scrub in the region is rapidly diminishing due to excessive tree-cutting, logging and clearance.

Conservation actions to date
Searches in the area of Bulo Burti in 1989 and 1990 were unsuccessful.

Conservation actions required
- Continue searching for the species at its known location and in nearby areas of similar Acacia habitat.
- Gather DNA samples from the black morph of Tropical Boubou *L. aethiopicus* to resolve ongoing taxonomic uncertainty regarding this species.

São Tomé Fiscal
Lanius newtoni
Population: < 50, trend unknown

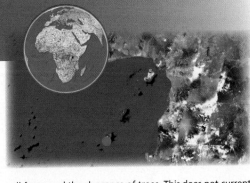

São Tome, 2006

Photo: © Jonathan Rossouw

Range & population
This fiscal is endemic to the island of São Tomé, São Tomé e Príncipe. Previously known only from records in 1888 and 1928, it was rediscovered in 1990, with the observation of a single bird in the south-west of the island. Since 1994, there have been regular records in the centre of the island, in the south-east and in the Bombaím area. All records are from primary lowland and mid-altitude forest, predominantly under closed canopy, in sites with little or no under-growth, but with bare ground and rocks. Many records are from ridgetops.

Threats
Land privatisation is leading to an increase in the number of small farms and the clearance of trees. This does not currently affect primary forest but may be a threat in the future. Road developments along the east and west coasts are increasing access to previously remote areas. Introduced black rat and mona monkey *Cercopithecus mona* are potential predators.

Conservation actions to date
Protection of primary forest as a 'zona ecologica' and a national park has been proposed. A new law providing for the gazetting of protected areas and the protection of threatened species awaits final ratification.

Conservation actions required
- Research its population, distribution, requirements and key threats in order to produce conservation recommendations.
- Ensure protection of remaining lowland primary forest.
- List it as a protected species under national law.

BirdLife Species Guardian **Virgínia Carvalho d'Almeida Godinho (Associação dos Biólogos Santomenses)**

Isabela Oriole
Oriolus isabellae
Population: 50-249 ↓

Ambabok, San Mariano, 2004

Photo: © Merlijn van Weerd

Range & population
This oriole is endemic to Luzon in the Philippines. It has been recorded recently at just three localities in the north-east despite an increasing number of fieldworkers attempting to locate it. This indicates considerable rarity and that its distribution is probably patchy. It frequents the canopy and middle storeys of forests, especially thick bamboo, but also forest edge, from 50-440 m. It appears to tolerate secondary growth.

Threats
It may be a lowland specialist and lowland forest destruction is assumed to be its primary threat. By the late 1980s, only 24% of Luzon was estimated to remain forested, with most remaining areas under logging concession. There is virtually no forest left near San Mariano, a key historical site, and one recent record was from a small, degraded forest tract isolated from the Sierra Madre forests. Competition with the closely related White-lored Oriole *O. albiloris* may impact this species.

Conservation actions to date
Mansarong, where the species was recorded in 1994, and Ambabok, where the species was recorded in 2003 and 2004, are located within the Northern Sierra Madre Mountains Natural Park. The Bataan Natural Park/Subic Bay protected area probably encompasses one of the historical localities.

Conservation actions required
- Conduct extensive surveys, particularly in bamboo forests, around historical sites in Bataan, the Mariveles Mountains and Mt Cetaceo, around Mansarong, and also Diffun (Quirino Province) where it has recently been reported.
- Propose key sites found for formal protection.

Sangihe Shrike-thrush
Colluricincla sanghirensis
Population: 50-249 ↓

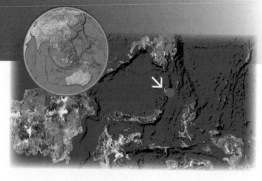

Mount Sahengbalira, Sangihe, Indonesia, 1999

Photo: © Jon Riley

This species has been split from Little Shrike-thrush *Colluricincla megarhyncha*.

Range & population
This shrike-thrush was rediscovered on the island of Sangihe, north of Sulawesi, Indonesia, in 1995. It is resident in lower montane forest between 600 m and 750 m, occurring singly and, perhaps more frequently, in small groups.

Threats
Original forest on Sangihe has been almost completely converted to agriculture. The largest habitat tract in which the species has been found is undergoing clearance in its lower reaches by shifting cultivators.

Conservation actions to date
The Gunung Sahendaruman 'protection forest' nominally conserves some remaining habitat, although few measures have been taken to ensure its efficacy. Further forest is protected as watershed for a hydroelectric scheme in the Kentuhang valley. Since 1995, the 'Action Sampiri' project has been working for biodiversity conservation in Sangihe and Talaud, conducting fieldwork and developing ideas for future land-use through agreements.

Conservation actions required
- Conduct further surveys for the species.
- Ensure effective protection of habitat on Gunung Sahendaruman.
- Continue education programmes.
- Encourage forestry staff to establish a permanent presence on the island.

Caerulean Paradise-flycatcher
Eutrichomyias rowleyi
Population: 19-135 ↓

Mount Sahengbalira, Sangihe, Indonesia, 1998

Photo: © Jon Riley

Range & population
This flycatcher is endemic to the island of Sangihe, Indonesia. The survival of the species was confirmed in October 1998 around the base of Gunung Sahendaruman. It is a sedentary insectivore, resident in primary forest on steep-sided valley slopes and valley bottoms with streams. It generally feeds in the canopy and sub-canopy of c. 15 m tall trees but will also descend to feed in the low understorey. Prey is taken in active flight, perch-gleaning, by undertaking looping sallies and by descending to the ground.

Threats
Virtually the entire island of Sangihe has been deforested and converted to agriculture, leaving very little habitat for the species. Forest continues to be cleared at its fringes by shifting cultivators. Harvesting of forest products and hunting may constitute minor threats.

Conservation actions to date
See also Sangihe Shrike-thrush whose conservation actions also benefit Caerulean Paradise Flycatcher. There is now a small bird tourism industry on the island which, it is hoped will provide an economic incentive to island residents to conserve remaining forest.

Conservation actions required
- Conduct further surveys to quantify the population and monitor trends.
- Support proposals for the rapid establishment of remaining forest on Gunung Sahengbalira as a strict nature reserve.
- Continue education programmes.
- Encourage forestry staff to establish a permanent presence on the island.

Seychelles Paradise-flycatcher
Terpsiphone corvina
Population: 208-278 ◀▶

La Digue, Seychelles, 2002

Photo: © Håkan Carlestam

History

1867 – British zoologist Alfred Newton (1829-1907) describes the species.

1995/1996 – surveys find 69-83 pairs (c.150-200 birds).

2000 – surveys find 104-139 pairs in 2000.

2006 – A project 'Investing in island biodiversity; restoring the Seychelles Paradise Flycatcher' funded by Darwin Initiative starts in September.

Range & population

This flycatcher was thought to remain only on western La Digue, Seychelles. Recently a few birds have been found sporadically on neighbouring Marianne, though this may represent a non-viable overspill. Sightings on Félicité have also been reported. Comprehensive surveys on La Digue show that the population is increasing.

It requires mature stands of indigenous Badamier *Calophyllum innophylum* and Takamaka *Terminalia catappa* trees. It appears strictly insectivorous and birds breed at one year of age. Nesting in this species was generally believed to be dependent on a proximity to wetland areas but this relationship appears to be an artefact of its dependence on native woodland which is important for both nesting and foraging: territories are smaller where native tree density is high. The species occurs densely (60% of all territories) on the forested plateau areas of La Digue. The reasons for the population increase are not clear but probably involve the species utilisation of forest fragments and forest-edge habitat.

Threats

Alarming rates of habitat loss and fragmentation, due to tourism and private housing developments, may be the greatest threats on La Digue. A wilt disease affecting *C. innophylum* has lead to increased woodland loss on the La Digue plateau. Plants, such as water lettuce *Pirtia stratiotes*, introduced to La Digue's marshes, may possibly have reduced favoured invertebrate prey, though this is unproven. Alien mammals and also some endemic bird species have recently been shown to be nest predators, though Seychelles Paradise Flycatcher can resist their impacts more effectively than other endemic birds in the Seychelles. The level of nest predation is highest at the forest edge, compounding the already negative impact of habitat fragmentation. Adult birds appear to have lower survival rates in areas with more alien species.

Conservation actions to date

A 0.1 km² area of mature woodland was established as a nature reserve on La Digue in 1991. Wardening staff have been recruited, a few wells and pools established to increase standing water, an education centre constructed, and public awareness programmes initiated. In 2002 a further 13 ha of land was purchased increasing the reserve size to 21 hectares. Pollution monitoring has been ongoing for some time - a sluice gate was built to protect water quality in the wetland and the groundwater supply was protected when a new land-fill site was established. The introduced water lettuce is routinely removed from marshland. A programme to assess the best islands to which future translocations could be considered has been completed. Cat and rat eradication programmes were conducted on Curieuse (28 ha), Denis (140 ha) and Frégate (210 ha) in 1999 in preparation for translocation, but in 2001, Curieuse and Denis still harboured rats and the habitat of Frégate is less favourable for new populations to establish. In 2002, a second rat eradication programme on Denis (which holds the best quality habitat) was successful. In addition, rat and cat eradications programmes on North (201 ha) in 2005 were also successful. Currently preparations to translocate flycatchers to Denis Island in late 2007 are underway.

Conservation actions required

- Through translocation programmes, increase the number of populations to at least three.
- Conserve woodland habitat on La Digue, and consider replanting native forest. Reforestation should focus on large patches to minimise the level of predation.
- Continue population and nest monitoring and research into territory quality and food requirements.
- Assess the impact of habitat loss, predation and historical changes in land-use.
- Encourage placement of new development away from the western plateau or in areas with no existing woodland.
- Continue removal of invasive water plants on La Digue.
- Conduct field surveys to clarify the status of this species.

La Digue, Seychelles, 2007

Photo: © Christer Sundström

Tahiti Monarch
Pomarea nigra
Population: 40-45 ↑

Tahiti, French Polynesia, 2007

Photo: © Tun Pin Ong

Range & population
This species is endemic to Tahiti in the Society Islands, French Polynesia. It has apparently been rare throughout the 20th century. By the end of 2004, it was starting to recover with new pairs even becoming established in abandoned territories. It is highly territorial, foraging both in the canopy and the undergrowth for insects.

Threats
Its decline might be related to the replacement of the high, dense forest by introduced shrubs. A decline in habitat quality is a likely threat elsewhere, as forest is largely composed of introduced invasive species and usually confined to a narrow strip along the floor of steep basalt canyons. Predation by rats is an important factor. Introduced birds such as Red-vented Bulbul *Pycnonotus cafer* and Common Myna *Acridotheres tristis* may also be an important threat.

Conservation actions to date
In 1998, rat control around known nests (using poisoning and tree-banding) was started, and continued during several breeding seasons.

Conservation actions required
- Regularly monitor known territories.
- Search for birds in previously known and possible new areas.
- Continue rat control.
- Conduct experiments to improve the quality of the habitat.
- Confirm the impact of introduced birds and investigate their control.

Fatuhiva Monarch
Pomarea whitneyi
Population: 274 ↓

Painting: © Douglas H. Pratt / Oxford University Press

Range & population
This monarch is endemic to Fatu Hiva in the Marquesas Islands, French Polynesia. In 1975, the population was estimated at several hundred pairs and, in 1990, it was still common. A 2006 survey indicated a decline of over 30%. It occurs in dense, native forest from 50 m to 700 m, with some non-breeding birds found up to 775 m on a crest below the highest summit on Mt Touaouoho in native wet forest. It feeds on insects (e.g. *Coleoptera*), spiders and seeds.

Threats
Fatu Hiva is a relatively well preserved, well forested island (with no overgrazing or destruction of vegetation by fire). Black rat *Rattus rattus* was observed for the first time on the island in February 2000. Identified as serious threat as its presence is strongly correlated with the decline and extinction of monarch populations, rats already appear to have caused a rapid population decline and represent the principal threat.

Conservation actions to date
The population has been regularly checked since the 1970s. Conservation efforts have been increased owing to the recent rapid decline in the population.

Conservation actions required
- Permanently control rats and investigate total eradication.
- Conduct surveys elsewhere on the island using the same methodologies and continue to monitor the population in the Omoa Valley.
- Conduct a more thorough study over several months into the species' ecology and the threat that rats pose.
- Consider translocation.
- Continue a public awareness programme.

Black-chinned Monarch
Monarcha boanensis
Population: 100-200 ↓

Photo: © C W Moeliker /Natural History Museum Rotterdam

Boano Island, Moluccas, Indonesia, 1994

Range & population
This monarch is confined to the island of Boano off north-west Seram, South Maluku, Indonesia. Known from just one specimen collected at an unspecified locality in 1918, it was rediscovered in 1991, in a foothill gorge of Gunung Tahun. It is presumably a sedentary resident, and is believed to be restricted to the higher parts of the island (c.150–700 m), although recent observations come from dense secondary semi-evergreen forest, comprising trees up to 20 m high, in a gorge between 150 m and 200 m.

Threats
Forests on the island of Boano have long been exploited for human needs. However, although recent cutting is deemed to have irreversibly affected the island's ecosystem, patches of valley-bottom forest remain wherein the monarch persists. Its extremely low estimated population size and the apparent ease with which forest at the single known site could be cleared or burnt renders it highly vulnerable.

Conservation actions to date
No measures have been taken, other than the survey to relocate the species in the early 1990s.

Conservation actions rqeuired
- Conduct extensive surveys on Boano (and the neighbouring islands of Kelang and Manipa which may prove to support the species) to establish its range, distribution and status, and assess its habitat requirements and threats.
- Assess the suitability of Gunung Tahan (the site of rediscovery) as a protected area.
- Devise and implement a conservation strategy for the species involving the establishment of an appropriate protected area if necessary.

Banggai Crow
Corvus unicolor
Population: < 50, trend unknown

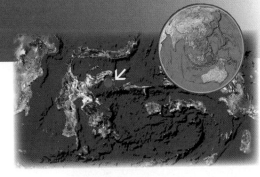

Painting: © Hilary Burn

Range & population
This crow is only known from two specimens taken on an unspecified island in the Banggai archipelago, immediately east of Sulawesi, Indonesia in the 1880s. In 1991 and 1996, visits to the island group yielded no unequivocal records of this species. Crows the size of Slender-billed Crow *C. enca* (which occurs on neighbouring Sulawesi and the Sula Islands) were seen at six localities during these visits, with only one sighting of a smaller crow, perhaps this species. Nothing is known about its habits. The small crow seen on a recent visit to the islands was in mossy forest at 660 m.

Threats
Given that it is so poorly known, it is impossible to identify any specific threats. However, it may have been severely impacted by extensive deforestation, as by 1991 logging had begun in the last remaining areas of primary habitat, which will probably lead to further encroachment by shifting cultivators as a result of improved access.

Conservation actions to date
No action has been taken.

Conservation actions required
- Conduct a comprehensive search for the species throughout the archipelago (paying close attention to the use of vocalisations to aid detection) to establish its range, distribution, population status, and assess its habitat requirements and potential threats.
- Identify its conservation needs based on results of this survey, and thereby work towards the establishment of an appropriately sized and situated protected area supporting viable populations of this and other threatened species known to occur on the islands.

White-eyed River-martin
Eurochelidon sirintarae
Population: < 50 ↓

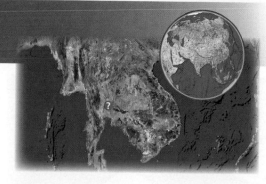

Photo: © H. E. McClure

Range & population
This species is only known as a probable non-breeding visitor to one area of central Thailand where it was discovered in 1968 amongst roosts of wintering swallows. The most recent unconfirmed report from Thailand was in 1986 and potentially suitable habitat remains in Cambodia but Myanmar may be a more likely refuge of any remaining population. Its ecology is almost totally unknown. It has only been recorded between December and February roosting in reedbeds.

Threats
There has been a massive decline in the number of swallows roosting at Beung Boraphet as a result of intensive trapping for food and roost habitat destruction. A number of threats could have contributed to its overall decline, including disturbance of riverine sand-bars, flooding upstream and the alteration of downstream hydrology caused by dams, extensive deforestation, and agricultural intensification.

Conservation actions to date
Beung Boraphet has been declared as a Non-Hunting Area. Several unsuccessful searches have been made for it at this site since its discovery. In 1969, a survey, based on village interviews, of the Nan Yom and Wang rivers in northern Thailand did not reveal any further information. Similarly, a brief survey in 1996 of rivers in northern Laos was unsuccessful.

Conservation actions required
- Conduct surveys for the species along all major rivers within its putative breeding range.
- If a population is rediscovered, immediately implement appropriate conservation measures.

Archer's Lark
Heteromirafra archeri
Population: 50-249 ↓

Painting: © Martin Woodcock

Range & population
This lark is known from a very restricted area from Jifa Medir to Ban Wujaleh, west of Hargeisa in north-west Somalia, along the Ethiopian frontier. It was not seen at its original site, or in the area of Ethiopia adjacent to its range in Somalia, during five visits to the region between the 1970s and 1990s, nor on ten occasions during 1996-2006, although a possible sighting was reported from there in 2003, and another was claimed in Jijiga, extreme eastern Ethiopia in 2004. However, its secretive habits make it very difficult to observe. This species is found in an area with 300-400 mm rainfall per year. Habitat at its two known sites varies: one is open grassland and the other fairly open, rocky country with scattered and sparse bush and limited grass cover. It avoids open spaces, creeping through grass cover, and flies reluctantly. Its diet is unknown. Nests have been observed in June, and clutch-size is three.

Threats
The original grassland site in Somalia has been settled and cultivated by refugees, resulting in the disappearance of the tussocky perennial grasses described as the species' habitat in 1922.

Conservation actions to date
No conservation action or fieldwork relating to this species is currently being undertaken.

Conservation actions required
- Conduct surveys to establish its range, distribution and population status. Intensive searches are needed along the Ethiopian-Somali border, perhaps in April-May when it may be singing and more conspicuous.

Raso Lark
Alauda razae
Population: 130 ⬍

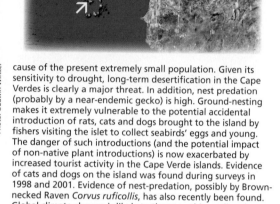

Raso Island, Cape Verde, 2006

Photo: ©Edwin Winkel

History

1898 – English Ornithologist Boyd Alexander (1873-1910) describes the species.

1985 – a survey shows at least 150 birds to be present.

1986 – number is 75-100 pairs.

1989 – 200 birds are counted.

1990 & 1992 – surveys based on day visits produce 250 birds.

2003 – a complete survey produces 98 birds.

2004 – following rains, the population is up to 130 individuals.

Range & population

This lark is restricted to the very small (7 km²), arid, un-inhabited island of Raso in the Cape Verde Islands, although ancestrally it may have occurred on Branco, Santa Luzia and Sao Vicente which were a single island during the last glacial low. Suitable breeding habitat represents less than half the area of Raso. Its population is believed to fluctuate in response to climate. From the mid 1960s to the early 1980s, the population was estimated at only 20-50 pair but after rains in the early 21st century it was up to 130 individuals. Only a third of these are female. Whether this is a real decline or a pattern in the naturally fluctuating population is unclear. The present population size is approximately the same as that believed to exist in the 1960s.

It is found on level plains with volcanic soil and is associated with small vegetated patches in which it feeds and breeds. It has probably adapted to exploit the plant and insect life resulting from nutriment provided by seabird colonies. There is significant difference in bill size between males and females enabling the species to exploit limited food resources, with both sexes having larger bills than congeners. Flocks have also been observed feeding among rocks close to the sea, and it (particularly males) excavates holes in sandy soil to extract the small bulbs of nutsedges *Cyperus bulbosus* and *C. cadamosti*. Breeding is erratic and governed by the slight and irregular rains. The population fluxes rapidly and significantly in response to rain; a prerequisite for breeding, and has fallen to extremely low levels during droughts. During the non-breeding season birds aggregate into tight flocks. Adult survival appears to be high and the species is thought to be relatively long-lived.

Threats

Drought over successive breeding seasons is undoubtedly the cause of the present extremely small population. Given its sensitivity to drought, long-term desertification in the Cape Verdes is clearly a major threat. In addition, nest predation (probably by a near-endemic gecko) is high. Ground-nesting makes it extremely vulnerable to the potential accidental introduction of rats, cats and dogs brought to the island by fishers visiting the islet to collect seabirds' eggs and young. The danger of such introductions (and the potential impact of non-native plant introductions) is now exacerbated by increased tourist activity in the Cape Verde islands. Evidence of cats and dogs on the island was found during surveys in 1998 and 2001. Evidence of nest-predation, possibly by Brown-necked Raven *Corvus ruficollis*, has also recently been found. Global climate change is likely to threaten this small and precipitation-dependent species.

Conservation actions to date

Raso Lark has been officially protected under Cape Verde law since 1955 and in 1990, Raso was declared a National Park. To date there has been no enforcement of these laws on the ground. Surveys have revealed the absence of cats on the island and annual population monitoring and a research project are underway.

Conservation actions required

- Conduct research into other potential nest predators.
- Investigate the suitability of Santa Luzia to establish a second population by conducting appropriate ecological research.
- Investigate reasons for the male biased sex ratio.
- Raise awareness amongst tourists and tour operators visiting Raso to ensure precautions are taken to avoid the accidental introduction of alien species and safeguard the fragile island ecology.
- Maintain good relations with fishers using the island and engage them in conservation activities.
- Continue regular monitoring of the population and the status of introduced predators.

BirdLife Species Guardian **Paul Donald (RSPB) & Michael Brooke (University of Cambridge)**

Raso Island, Cape Verde, 2003

Photo: © Adam Riley

Liberian Greenbul
Phyllastrephus leucolepis
Population: 250-999 ↓

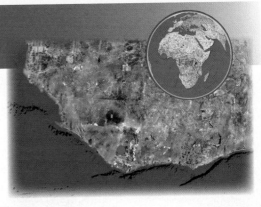

Painting: © Martin Woodcock

Range & population
This species was described in 1985 and is obviously very rare. It is known only from two forest patches 20 km north-west of Zwedru, near Cavalla river, Grand Gedeh County, south-east Liberia, in the Upper Guinea rainforest. Despite much fieldwork in Liberia before the civil war started and in adjacent countries, there have been no further records. This is a rainforest species found in the transition zone between evergreen and semi-deciduous forest, where it follows mixed-species flocks and forages on branches near trunks 4–8 m above ground.

Threats
Forest in the region of the type-locality is being logged and cleared for smallholder agriculture and is already highly fragmented. The civil unrest undoubtedly adds to short term exploitation of these resources.

Conservation actions to date
The civil war, which has recently flared up again, has prevented research or conservation efforts for a number of years.

Conservation actions required
- Establish the extent of remaining habitat and estimate the population and distribution, once the security situation permits.
- Determine its taxonomic status and whether it merely represents an aberrant form of Icterine Greenbul *Pyllastrephus icterinus*.

Taita Apalis
Apalis fuscigularis
Population: 600-930 ↓

Ngangao Forest Reserve, Kenya, April 2001

Photo: © Ken Norris

This species has been split from Bar-throated Apalis *A. thoracica*

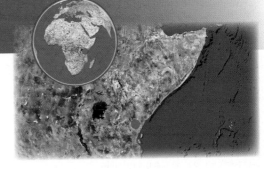

Range & population
It is now restricted to just three tiny fragments of forest in the main Dabida massif of the Taita Hills, Kenya. The species inhabits the understorey of montane forest. It is highly sociable feeding on small invertebrates and occasionally berries and seeds, and has a clutch-size of 2-4.

Threats
Most of the original forest in the Taita Hills has been cleared for cultivation or reforested with non-native, timber-tree species, and the remaining tiny area is under serious threat.

Conservation actions to date
The Forest Department is safeguarding the remaining forest fragments of the Taita Hills. The Taita Hills have been designated as an IBA. Recent conservation work in the Taita Hills has resulted in the reduced attrition of indigenous forests.

Conservation actions required
- Study its ecology and assess its population size.
- Evaluate the possibility of (re)introduction to Mbololo.
- Initiate an outreach programme to local communities.
- Draw up management plans based on the results of the ongoing ecological surveys, in close conjunction with the Forest Department and local communities.
- Remove non-native trees from within indigenous forest and reforest cleared areas with native trees.
- Initiate sustainable forest-use schemes based on ecotourism and the harvest of forest products.

Long-billed Apalis
Apalis moreaui
Population: 50-249 ↓

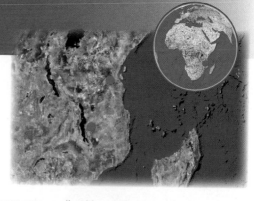

Amani, East Usambara, Tanzania, 2000

Photo: © Norbert J Cordeiro

History

1931 – William Lutley Sclater (1863-1944) describes the species.

1945 – the species is collected in Mozambique.

2001 – a visit to the Serra Jeci massif in Mozambique reveals that it is still present there.

This species is also known as Long-billed tailorbird *Orthotomus moreaui*

Range & population

This apalis occurs at low density in two widely separated forests, the East Usambaras in Tanzania (nominate subspecies) and the Njesi Plateau in northern Mozambique (subspecies *sousae*), where it was recently rediscovered, the area not having been visited since 1945. These two subpopulations are 1,000 km apart, and despite much recent fieldwork, there are still no records from any of the intervening forests. In the East Usambaras it is more common than previously suggested, but still somewhat local and infrequent. There are recent records from Mt Nilo and five sites near Amani; Amani Nature Reserve is conservatively estimated to hold 15-200 individuals. Only c. 110 km² of suitable habitat remain in the East Usambaras. Given that it is uncommon, elusive and exists at low densities, it may yet be found in other forests of the Eastern Arc now that the microhabitats and vocalisations are known.

In the East Usambaras, its primary habitat is now believed to be wetland forest edge. It has been found in submontane and montane forest, chiefly in open forest edge-type habitat with a high density of vines and climbers such as clearings and drainage lines, in addition to wetland glades on the edge of, or inside forest. Occasionally it can be found in degraded forest, in tea plantations, or even at a considerable distance from the forest edge in suitably thick clumps of vegetation. However, forest areas disturbed by humans are clearly not favoured. It is often absent from large areas of apparently suitable habitat. It forages alone or in mixed-species parties in the lower and middle storeys (up to 18 m), preferring the tangled vegetation in the lower storeys where it searches foliage for invertebrates avoiding sunlit places. It is apparently territorial, but its breeding ecology remains unknown. In one study, 26% of records were of pairs. *O. m. sousae* has recently been confirmed to inhabit the forest canopy.

Threats

Despite favouring some open forest-edge habitats, it remains vulnerable to forest destruction, especially as it may not cross open spaces easily. Although the extent of protected forest in the East Usambaras has recently been increased, there is heavy pressure on most unprotected forest, especially for pole-cutting, cultivation and firewood-collection. As this forest becomes depleted, pressure on reserves is likely to increase. The activities of an adventure-tourism company, with research programmes using a large number of volunteers on closely-spaced transects, may also have contributed to forest disturbance affecting this species. Nothing is known of the recent status in the forests in northern Mozambique.

Conservation actions to date

Two current projects in the East Usambaras are working to increase the amount of forest, including all lowland remnants, in protected areas. In particular the Amani Nature Reserve has an active conservation programme which engages with local stakeholders such as plantation owners.

Conservation actions required

- Revisit the Njesi Plateau and nearby areas to assess its status and population size.
- Search for the species at Monte Sanga, the areas between Monte Gatala and Chiconono, the Lupilichi Highlands and the Serra Juzagombe.
- Evaluate the effectiveness of selected forest-management techniques that could benefit this species.
- Engage stakeholders on the Amani Plateau in forest management and raise awareness of this species' status.
- Protect forest edge wetland habitats from uncontrolled opportunistic agriculture.
- Consider methods to reduce disturbance in and around tea plantations.
- Conduct ecological surveys to understand why it is apparently so rare and thinly distributed.
- Concentrate searches in new areas using the newly understood habitat requirements, particularly its preference for wet glades or a proximity to water.

BirdLife Species Guardian   **Norbert Cordeiro**

Amani, East Usambara, Tanzania, 2000

Photo: © Norbert J Cordeiro

Blue-crowned Laughingthrush
Garrulax courtoisi

Population: 50-249 ⬇

Photo: © Zhao Dongjiang

Wuyuan, China, June 2007

History

1919 – French missionary Père A. Riviere collects two specimen, probably in Wuyuan County, Jiangxi Province.

1923 – French biologist Henri Auguste Ménégaux (1857-1937) describes the species and names it after Père F. Courtois.

1956 – specimen collected near Simao, Yunnan Province.

1982 – Chinese ornithologists, Professors Cheng Tso-hsin and Tang Rui-chang collect a new subspecies *simaoensis*, considered by them to belong to Yellow-throated Laughingthrush.

1988 – birds of Chinese origin arrive in Europe.

2000 – the species is rediscovered in Wuyuan county, 80-90 birds are found in two breeding flocks 40 km apart.

2001 – a census finds 150-160 individuals in four flocks. Over 20 nests are found.

2006 – Chester Zoo organizes searches for the species in in Jiangxi, Yunnan and Guangxi provinces.

This species has previously been considered a subspecies of Yellow-throated Laughingthrush, *Garrulax galbani* which has its nearest occurrence 2,000 km from Wuyuan

Range & population

This laughingthrush is endemic to China and had been unrecorded in the wild for nearly 50 years. The entire known wild population is restricted to 5 or 6 fragmented sites during the breeding season with a population thought to number fewer than 200 individuals. In addition, there are 51 individuals known in captivity. It occupies an extremely small known breeding range in Jiangxi Province below 100 metres. The wintering grounds are not known but are thought to be near to the breeding sites. Three birds collected near Simao belong to a separate subspecies *simaoensis* which has not been seen in the wild since.

It breeds in loose colonies in tall, old trees adjacent to villages and human habitation, also near rivers. This habitat has been termed fung shui wood and includes camphor and maple trees and may be dependent on a regional tradition of protecting centuries-old village trees. It forages both on the ground and in trees in vocal groups.

Threats

Relatively unknown; however, road building developments have destroyed nesting and roosting habitat at more than one breeding site. The birds receive no legal protection against building developments such as holiday resorts, which are being promoted in Wuyuan County. The species was recorded in captivity in 1988 in Europe, suggesting that trade may represent an additional threat, although wild-caught birds are legally banned from Europe.

Conservation actions to date

Over 180 small, Special Protected Areas were established by Wuyuan County local government following the signing of several Memoranda of Understanding with local villages. A studbook is maintained by a partnership of captive breeders to support *ex situ* conservation efforts.

Conservation actions required

- Conduct further surveys in an attempt to identify the wintering range and any additional breeding sub-populations.
- Survey Wuyuan of NE Jiangxi and Simao of Yunnan to try to find the occurrence of the subspecies *simaoensis*.
- Establish formal protection for the species against infrastructure development.

Photo: © Zhang Bin

Wuyuan, China, June 2006

Millerbird
Acrocephalus familiaris
Population: 31-731 ↓

Photo: © Mark Alexander MacDonald

Nihoa, Hawaiian Islands, 2006

Range & population
This warbler is endemic to the steep, rocky island of Nihoa in the Northwestern Hawaiian Islands. It became extinct between 1916 and 1923 on Laysan. No long-term trend is evident, but fluctuations between successive surveys appear to be real. Pairs show year-to-year territory fidelity, with nesting occurring from at least January to September, but possibly throughout the year. Nests are located in dense shrubs (mainly *Sida fallax*) and two eggs are generally laid.

Threats
Its extinction on Laysan was ultimately caused by the intro-duction of rabbits, which denuded the island of vegetation (causing severe insect food shortage). On Nihoa, the population size is probably regulated primarily by the weather, apparently being linked to precipitation levels, with droughts, storms and hurricanes inevitably having a negative impact. Fire is a past and potential threat and introduction of detrimental non-native species is a permanent possibility.

Conservation actions to date
Strict protocols are followed to ensure that legal permittees do not accidentally introduce new species via seeds, eggs or insects travelling on clothes and equipment. Visiting scientists make efforts to control alien plants by hand weeding.

Conservation actions required
- Continue monitoring.
- Ensure strict protocols to prevent further accidental introductions of alien species.
- Translocate birds to Laysan, Kaho`olawe or Midway.

Mauritius Olive White-eye
Zosterops chloronothus
Population: 186-296 ↓

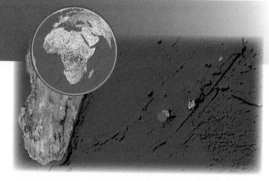

Photo: © Vikash Tatayah

Black River, Mauritius, 2006

Range & population
This white-eye is endemic to Mauritius. The species' core distribution has contracted since 1975, it has disappeared from three outlying sites and the core area has halved. It is restricted to the wettest native upland forests. It feeds on both nectar and insects, and travels considerable distances to productive flowers. Some introduced plant species have become important nectar sources. In recent decades pairs have not fledged more than one offspring per nesting attempt.

Threats
It has suffered chronically from continuing habitat destruction and degradation as a result of invasion by exotic plants. Nest predation by introduced mammals is also a major threat.

Conservation actions to date
The species has long been protected by law. The Black River National Park partly covers its distribution. Rehabilitation of native vegetation in small plots has been initiated through exclusion of exotic plants and animals, and there is ongoing research to assess benefits to native birds. In 2005-6 a captive breeding programme was initiated, allowing the release of four individuals on Ile aux Aigrettes in 2006.

Conservation actions required
- Compulsory purchase of habitat around Bassin Blanc.
- Continue population monitoring.
- Continue rehabilitation of native forest in appropriate areas.
- Develop Conservation Management Areas (CMAs) which have high densities of important nectar-producing plants and where predators are strictly controlled.

Rota Bridled White-eye
Zosterops rotensis
Population: 1,100 ↓

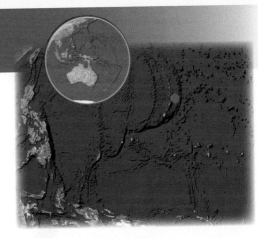

Rota, Mariana Islands, 1997

Photo: © Jack Jeffrey

History
1931 – S. Takatsukasa and Dr. Y. Yamashina (1900-1989) describes the species.

1935 – Black Drongos are introduced to Rota from Taiwan to control insects.

1982 – the population estimate is 10,763 individuals.

1990 – surveys estimate 300-1,500 birds.

1996 – surveys estimate 1,165 birds with 94% of the population restricted to four patches of forest covering only 259 ha.

1999 – surveys estimate 1,092 birds.

2006 – a final rule designating critical habitat for Rota bridled white-eye is released by the U.S. Fish and Wildlife Service. The final designation consists of 3,700 acres of government land and 258 acres of private land.

Bridled White-eye *Zosterops conspicillatus* has been split into *Z. conspicillatus* and *Z. rotensis*.

Range & population
This white-eye is endemic to Rota in the Northern Mariana Islands (to USA), where it was once thought to be common and widespread, but is now largely restricted to the upper escarpments of the Sabana plateau, where it is found in mature wet forest above 200 m. The population has declined by a rate equivalent to 74% over 10 years. The outline recovery plan presents a long-term goal of restoring the population to a stable 10,000 individuals.
Its ecological requirements are poorly known. It may favour native, mature, wet limestone forest appearing to prefer *Hernandia labyrinthica* mixed forest and *Merrilliodendron megacarpum* forest, though this apparent relationship could simply be a factor of its decline in recent decades. It feeds on insects, seeds, and fruit, and perhaps nectar. Its absence from some areas of apparently suitable native forest is unclear, but may relate to prey availability. Nesting has been recorded from December to August and clutch size is one to two eggs.

Threats
The recent rapid declines and the current localised distribution are most likely to be primarily a result of habitat loss and degradation owing to agricultural activities, development, typhoons and use of pesticides. The recent introduction of the Brown Tree Snake *Boiga irregularis* is a serious concern. If the snake becomes established serious future declines are likely. Predation by introduced rats and Black Drongo *Dicrurus macrocercus* has been implicated in its decline.

Conservation actions to date
The species was listed as endangered under the US Endangered Species Act in 2004 and following lengthy and committed court action against the Bush Administration in October 2006, c.1,600 ha of Critical Habitat was designated for the species. The US Fish and Wildlife Service published a draft recovery plan. Funding was acquired in 2003 to start a nest predation study and experimental trapping of predators observed raiding nests.

Conservation actions required
- Monitor population trends through detailed censuses.
- Control and monitor population of Brown Tree Snake *Boiga irregularis*.
- Control rats and Black Drongos in case they pose a threat.
- Enact the proposed Habitat Conservation Plan, including the protection and replanting of native forest in the Sabana region.
- Research its breeding ecology and life history in order to determine its habitat preferences and reasons for decline.
- Establish additional wild populations in predator-free sites.
- If Brown Tree Snake becomes established, the establishment of a captive population will become a priority as an insurance measure against the likely rapid declines that could occur in the wild population.

Rota, Mariana Islands, 1997

Photo: © Jack Jeffrey

Sangihe White-eye
Zosterops nehrkorni
Population: < 50 ↓

Painting: © John Anderton / OBC

This species has recently been split from Black-crowned White-eye *Zosterops atrifrons*.

Range & population
This species is restricted to Sangihe, Indonesia, where it has not been seen since 1999. It frequents the mid-storey to upper canopy of primary broad leaved ridgetop forest, often with a high density of *Pandanus* sp., where it gleans insects from leaves and presumably also forages on fruit. It appears to be strictly confined to altitudes between 750 m and 1,000 m.

Threats
Virtually the entire island of Sangihe has been deforested and converted to agriculture. Potential threats can be the requirement for large ranges in which to search for fruit, or perhaps the depredations of introduced rats.

Conservation actions to date
Since 1995, the 'Action Sampiri' project has been working for biodiversity conservation in Sangihe. As a result, plans are in progress to reclassify the existing of "protection forest" on Gunung Sahengbalira as a wildlife reserve (with core areas as a strict nature reserve), although this process is likely to take 2-3 years.

Conservation actions required
- Conduct further surveys for the species.
- Ensure effective protection of habitat on Gunung Sahendaruman.
- Continue conservation education programmes.
- Encourage forestry staff to establish a permanent presence on the island.

White-chested White-eye
Zosterops albogularis
Population: < 50 ↓

Painting: © Lyn Wells / BirdLife International

Range & population
This white-eye is endemic to Norfolk Island (to Australia). There have only been scattered sightings since the 1970s, most recently unconfirmed from the Norfolk Island National Park in 2005. It feeds high in shrubs and trees.

Threats
The principal threat is probably predation by introduced Black Rat *Rattus rattus*. The clearance of much native forest and invasion of the remainder by exotic weeds has also contributed. Competition from the self-introduced Silvereye *Z. lateralis* may also have contributed to the decline.

Conservation actions to date
Rat baiting, cat trapping and control of other invasive plants and animals occurs in Norfolk Island National Park. The species is being considered in a multi-species management plan for Norfolk Island National Park. Possibilities of captive breeding and securing additional funding to finance recovery efforts are being pursued. A predator exclusion fence has been proposed for Norfolk Island National Park to create a predator free 'island' within the park.

Conservation actions required
- Determine a method for finding the birds reliably and conduct thorough surveys.
- Establish cooperative rodent control programmes throughout Norfolk Island.
- Enhance rat baiting and cat trapping on Norfolk Island and monitor their efficacy.
- Establish a captive-breeding population.
- Introduce it to Phillip Island.

Philippine Eagle. Photo: © Rich Lindie

Faichuk White-eye
Rukia ruki

Population: 526 ↓

Tol Island, Chuuk, Federated States of Micronesia, 2005

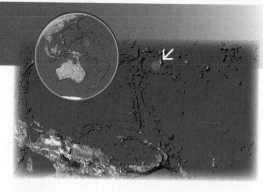

Range & population
This white-eye occurs on the four tiny islands Tol South, Wonei, Pata and Polle in the Faichuk Group of the Chuuk (= Truk) lagoon, Federated States of Micronesia. The species is confined mostly to old-growth stands of native forest, particularly the rich and well-developed forest above 400 m on Mt Winipot (Tol South), where fig trees *Ficus spp.*, native palms *Clinostigma spp.*, *Parinarium*, *Randia* and the endemic poison tree *Semecarpus kraemeri* predominate. The latter possibly plays an important ecological role in the species' survival. It is also found in lower densities in areas of native trees mixed with plantations. It feeds by foraging for insects in the foliage. It is territorial, breeding has been observed in April.

Threats
Mature stands of native forest have virtually disappeared from most of Chuuk and *S. kraemeri* is purposefully cut by local people who consider it a nuisance. The potential introduction of alien species to the islands is a concern, particularly Brown Tree Snake *Boiga irregularis*, although the lack of an airport and major port facilities reduces this possibility.

Conservation actions to date
None is known.

Conservation actions required
- Conserve native forest above 250 m on Mt Winipot.
- Identify and protect native forest on Polle.
- Promote local awareness through an education programme.
- Re-visit the islands to establish the current population size and trends.

Golden White-eye
Cleptornis marchei

Population: 57,522 ↓

Saipan, Mariana Islands, 1997

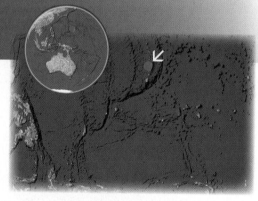

Range & population
This white-eye is endemic to the Northern Mariana Islands (to USA), occurring on Saipan and on the uninhabited Aguijan. On Saipan, estimated densities from surveys in 1991-1992 are among the highest ever reported for birds, suggesting that numbers are likely to be at carrying capacity for the island. On Saipan, it occurs in all wooded habitats and in urban areas. However, it is decidedly more common in limestone forest than in disturbed areas. It forages predominantly in the foliage of trees, particularly *Cynometra ramifolia*, feeding on invertebrates, flying insects, nectar, fruit and flowers and also taking insects from tree bark.

Threats
The species' ability to utilise different habitats may help to explain its persistence despite periodic typhoon damage and extensive, human-caused habitat change The establishment of Brown Tree Snake *Boiga irregularis* on Saipan poses a major threat to the population and is very likely to lead to extremely rapid declines. Aguijan is difficult to get to and it is unlikely that snakes will be accidentally introduced there.

Conservation actions to date
Although not directed solely at the conservation of this species, extensive efforts are underway to determine the status of Brown Tree Snake on Saipan and should an established population be identified, to control it immediately.

Conservation actions required
- Monitor population trends through detailed censuses.

Munchique Wood-wren
Henicorhina negreti
Population: 376-560 ↓

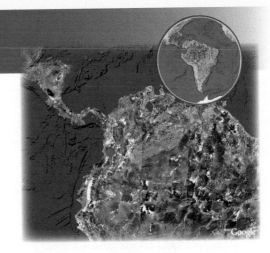

Photo: © Iain Campbell

RNA Mirabilis-Swarovski, Cauca department, Colombia

History
1984 – Steven Hilty records a song which probably belongs to this species.

1996 – Paul Coopmans also notes the different song and gathers more evidence the following years.

2000 – Paul Salaman collects the holotype in July.

2003 – the species is formally described by Paul Salaman and others and honours Colombian conservationist Alvaro José Negret (1949-1998).

Range & population
This species is restricted to a tiny range in the western Andes of Colombia where the departments of Chocó, Antioquia and Risaralda meet; and in Munchique massif (Valle de Cauca). A Fundación ProAves monitoring team discovered a tiny population in extreme eastern Chocó and SW Antioquia department. It appears to have very specific habitat requirements, being restricted to the Pacific slope of the very peaks of the highest mountains/ridges on the Western Cordillera, the lowest and narrowest of Colombia's three Andean ranges. As a result this species' global area of occupancy is tiny. 5-8 territorial pairs or males were registered along a 2 km transect. This represents a much lower density than parapatric populations of Grey-breasted Wood-wren *H. leucophrys*. The population density of 1 km² may be as few as 10 pairs or as high as 16 pairs. Further declines in the future may be unavoidable if climatic conditions change. There have been many surveys of the high peaks along the Western Cordillera (both historically and in the past decade) that have failed to record this species, suggesting there are unlikely to be many undiscovered populations remaining.
It is very specific in its habitat requirements, occurring in extremely wet, stunted cloud forest where it is common in naturally disturbed forest with patchy successional habitat, typically preferring an extremely dense understorey smothered in epiphytes at forest borders, landslides and along stream gullies. This forest is characterized by almost continuous cloud or fog cover. It has been recorded between 2,250 m and 2,640 m. It feeds on arthropods gleaned from near to the forest floor, typically below two metres. It will associate briefly with multi-species flocks as they pass through its territory.

Threats
Forest clearance affects this species directly, but it also leads to reduced cloud and fog cover and a general drying of the habitat. This allows congeners to colonise the areas where Munchique Wood-wrens currently occur in isolation. Global warming has the potential to shift the elevation at which Munchique and Grey-breasted Wood-wrens replace one another (presumably upwards with increasing temperature), potentially reducing the possible range of the species. More immediately, global warming has contributed to increasing severity of dry seasons in the region, that has resulted in many man-induced fires in otherwise extremely wet forests. Human pressure in Munchique is escalating. Consequently deforestation within Munchique national park, until recently essentially pristine, is now a serious issue and continues within the two protected areas which support this species.

Conservation actions to date
It is known from two protected areas: Munchique National Natural Park and Tambito Nature Reserve. However, forest clearance continues within their boundaries. In 2004 it was found that the core population on Cerro Munchique was unprotected (Tambito reserve was much smaller than projected) and threatened by forest clearance for farming. Fundación ProAves, with the support of the American Bird Conservancy and Swarovski Optik were able to purchase five key properties that encompassed the majority of the species' range, and are now protecting the site as 'Mirabilis-Swarovski Bird Reserve'.

Conservation actions required
- Continue monitoring existing populations and survey new areas for additional subpopulations.
- Lobby the government to adequately protect known sites, which support this and other Globally Threatened species, by directing resources more effectively.
- Support local organisations seeking to protect key sites.

ProAves Colombia's mission is to protect birds and their habitats in Colombia, through research, conservation actions and community outreach.

PROAVES
C·O·L·O·M·B·I·A

www.proaves.org

Iquitos Gnatcatcher
Polioptila clementsi

Population: 50-249 ↓

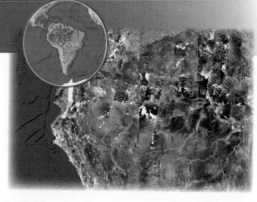

Photo: © José Alvarez-Alonso

Allpahuayo-Mishana National Reerve, Peru

Range & population
This recently described species occurs in Reserva Nacional Allpahuayo-Mishana just west of Iquitos, Department of Loreto, Peru. Extensive surveys of available habitat within the reserve have only located 15 pairs. Since its discovery, the species has apparently become more difficult to locate year on year.

It appears to be rare or uncommon within white-sand forest with a variable canopy height between 15 and 30 m. Consistently found in tall, humid varillal forest.

Threats
Available habitat continues to be threatened by clearance for agriculture facilitated by government incentives to encourage colonization of land surrounding Iquitos; and illegal logging of forest within a national reserve, for construction, fuel wood and charcoal.

Conservation actions to date
The entire known population occurs within the boundaries of the recently established Reserva Nacional Allpahuayo-Mishana.

Conservation actions required
- Conduct further surveys for the species in suitable habitat outside the known range.
- Enforce protection of remaining habitat within the Reserva Nacional Allpahuayo-Mishana.

Niceforo´s Wren
Thryothorus nicefori

Population: < 50 ↓

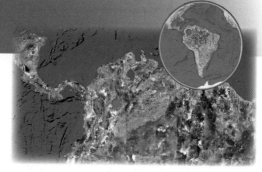

Photo: © David Caro Sabogal

Santander, Colombia, 2005

Range & population
This wren occurs on the west slope of the East Andes in Santander, Colombia. The only known site is the type-locality at San Gil on the río Fonce south of Bucaramanga, where ten specimens were collected between 1944-1948. There were no further records until two birds were observed and recorded in 1989, and then again in 2000. In 1989, birds were found in dense Acacia scrub in a semi-arid valley of the large, intermontane río Sagamosa drainage basin, at 1,095 m, in the upper tropical zone. None was found in the coffee plantations that dominate the hills north of San Gil.

Threats
Threats are unclear. The region generally comprises coffee plantations, light woodland and, to a lesser extent, pastures and plantain and sugarcane plantations. Suitable habitat may have been lost during this agricultural conversion. Acacia scrub is threatened by goat- and cattle-grazing, and seasonal burning for farming.

Conservation actions to date
None is known.

Conservation actions required
- Determine its taxonomic status.
- Conduct field surveys to determine its population size and distribution.
- Study its ecological requirements and natural history.
- Assess threats to the species.
- Use any new data collected to draft and execute a conservation strategy for the species.

Socorro Mockingbird
Mimus graysoni
Population: 285-420 ↓

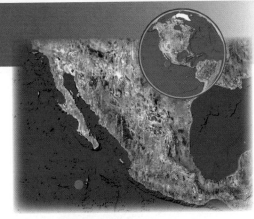

Isla Socorro, Mexico, 1993

Photo: © Robert L. Curry

History

1871 – American businessman and amateur ornithologist George Newbold Lawrence (1806-1895) describes the species.

1925 – it is considered the most abundant and widespread landbird on Socorro.

1958 – the species is considered common.

1978 – only 2-9 mockingbirds are found on the island.

1988-1990 – 50-200 pairs are estimated.

1993-1994 – c. 350 individuals are estimated with the highest densities around Cerro Evermann.

Formerly treated in the monotypic genus *Mimodes*; but now transferred to the genus *Mimus* based on molecular data by Brian Barber et al.

Range & population
This mockingbird is endemic to Socorro island in the Revillagigedo Islands, Mexico. It was considered widespread on the island in 1925, and was still abundant in 1958. By 1978, it had declined dramatically and was feared on the verge of extinction. Of 170 birds ringed in 1994, 56% were subadults, suggesting that productivity is high and the population would be capable of increasing if habitat quality improves across the island.
It occurs principally in moist dwarf forest and ravines with a mixture of shrubs and trees at elevations above 600 m. Vegetation in these areas is dominated by the trees *Ilex socorrensis*, *Guettarda insularis* and *Oreopanax xalapensis* and the understorey species *Triumfetta socorrensis* and *Eupatorium pacificum*. It is less common at low and mid elevations (0-500m), and absent from areas of *Croton masonii* scrub near sea-level and sheep-damaged habitat in the south. However, at lower elevations across the island fig groves, *Ficus cotinifolia* acts as regeneration nuclei for the species, supporting birds when a suitable understorey is present. Nesting may occur from November-July with a peak in March-April. Three eggs are laid and the incubation period is no more than 15 days. Food includes crab remains, small invertebrates and fruit, particularly those of *Ilex socorrensis* and *Bumelia socorrensis*.

Threats
Sheep had intensively grazed almost one third of the island by 1990, leaving no suitable nesting or foraging habitat in the south of the island. Predation by feral cats was initially thought responsible for the species' decline, but cats were introduced sometime after 1972, and examinations of cat stomach contents and scats have not provided any substantial evidence. Competition with the immigrant Northern Mockingbird *Mimus polyglottos* is probably not a factor because Socorro Mockingbird is much larger, has different habitat preferences and is not outcompeted in undisturbed habitats. Since 1994 c. 30 ha of forest has been lost owing to a now permanent locust swarm on the island which erupts twice yearly. Its effects are thought to be more severe owing to the degradation of native vegetation by introduced grazing mammals, and the suppression of native bird populations (which typically exert top-down control of insect populations on the island) by introduced cats. Locusts cut leaves, flowers and fruit from trees and thus represent a serious threat to fruit eaters such as Socorro Mockingbird. War games by the US and Mexican Navies also represent a threat.

Conservation actions to date
The Revillagigedo Islands were declared a biosphere reserve in 1994. There is an ongoing eradication programme of cats and sheep in the region, and there are plans to eradicate cats and sheep from Socorro.

Conservation actions required
● Eradicate cats and sheep from Socorro.
● Implement a vegetation and soil restoration plan after sheep have been removed.
● Establish a research monitoring station on Socorro.
● Monitor the population, especially before and after the proposed eradications.

Isla Socorro, Mexico, 1993

Photo: © Robert L. Curry

Cozumel Thrasher
Toxostoma guttatum
Population: < 50 ↓

Painting: © Sophie Webb / Oxford University Press

Threats
Hurricane Gilbert appears to have had a severe effect on the species, whose status may have deteriorated further following hurricanes Roxanne, Emily and Wilma between 1995 and 2006. Further hurricanes are likely because Cozumel lies within the area of Mexico most frequently hit by hurricanes, and these may extirpate any surviving, small populations. However, this seems an unsatisfactory explanation of its current rarity because it must have evolved with a relatively high hurricane frequency. The reasons behind its decline are poorly understood, but introduced Boa snakes and cats are the leading hypothesised threat.

Conservation actions to date
There have been several recent searches for the species and efforts are ongoing to determine the remnant population size and distribution, and to evaluate the threats and reasons behind its decline. These are led by Villanova University and the American Bird Conservancy and involve Island Endemics, Conservation International and Philadelfia Zoo.

Conservation actions required
- Urgently survey in the breeding season (when it is most conspicuous) to determine whether the species is still extant and identify appropriate conservation measures.
- Investigate its former status and ecology through interviews with local people to ascertain the reasons for its decline.
- Conduct an awareness raising campaign to raise the profile of this species and educate visitors about the potential to damage the island's ecosystem.
- Establish formal protection for interior lands on Cozumel.

History
1885 – American ornithologist Robert Ridgway (1850-1929) describes the species.

1971 – Boa snakes *Boa constrictor* are introduced to the island.

1988 – hurricane Gilbert hits the island on September 14 and contributes to the species' decline.

1995 – a bird captured in a mist net is the last definitive record. Hurricane Roxanne hits the island on October 11.

1998 – the form is recognised as a species by the American Ornithologist's Union. The last confirmed sighting is made.

2004 – several observations are made.

2006 – a field sighting at the Cozumel Golf Club is reported in April.

The Cozumel Thrasher has in the past been considered a subspecies of the Long-billed Thrasher *Toxostoma longirostre*.

Range & population
This thrasher is endemic to Cozumel Island, Mexico, where it was formerly fairly common, and at times was considered the most common bird on the island. It became rare immediately after Hurricane Gilbert in September 1988, with only four records obtained during monthly visits to the island during August 1994-August 1995. Only a few sightings have been recorded subsequently, the most recent being five observations in 2004, possibly involving fewer birds and one from 2006.

Recent records originate from semi-deciduous forest and deciduous forest away from scrubby areas. However, it was formerly reported to inhabit scrubby woodland and thick undergrowth bordering fields, and the edges of tropical deciduous and semi-deciduous forest. The closely related Long-billed Thrasher prefers drier habitat. It is typically known to skulk on or near the ground, but often sings from conspicuous perches. The breeding season is May-July.

Photo: © Jon Hornbuckle

Bali Starling
Leucopsar rothschildi
Population: 24 ↓

Miami Metrozoo, 2005

History

1911 – German ornithologist Erwin Stresemann (1889-1972) collects the holoytpe and describes it the year after.

1970 – the species becomes protected under Indonesian law.

1975 – 200 birds are estimated in September.

1983 – the Bali Starling project is established.

1990 – wild population estimated at c. 15 birds.

1999 – an estimated 3,000 birds are in captivity, of which a third are registered in a studbook.

2001 – 6 birds are found.

2005 – 24 individuals are recorded, following releases.

2006 – 37 birds are released in Nusa Penida.

2007 – 12 birds released in Nusa Penida and offered to the gods in religious ceremonies performed by Hindu priests. 10 birds bred in Japan are prepared for release in the West Bali National Park in May.

Range & population

This starling is endemic to the island of Bali, Indonesia, where it formerly ranged across the north-west third of the island. It has perhaps long been uncommon, but the population has declined drastically and contracted its range. In the early 1900s, when it was discovered, the numbers have retrospectively been guessed at 300-900, although this is thought to be a gross underestimate. Illegal poaching reduced numbers to a critically low level in 1990. Conservation intervention coupled with the release of a few captive-bred birds raised this to between 35 and 55. However, despite excellent breeding success and continuing conservation efforts, including releases, the population continues to fluctuate. A second population on Nusa Penida island derived from 49 released individuals appears to have adapted to the island and is breeding. The total number to date of birds born in the wild on Nusa Penida is 16. A further 1,000 Bali Starlings are believed to survive in captivity.

In the breeding season, which usually takes place in October and November, it inhabits fire-induced open shrub, tree and palm-savanna and adjacent closed-canopy monsoon-forest (tropical moist deciduous) below 175 m. In the non-breeding season, birds disperse into open forest edge and flooded savanna woodland. In the past they also occurred, and even nested, in coconut groves near villages. Previously thought to rely on cavities excavated and vacated by other birds, released individuals on Nusa Penida have nested in sugar palm, coconut, mangrove and fig trees.

Threats

Its decline to virtual extinction in the wild is primarily attributable to unsustainable, illegal trapping in response to worldwide demand for the cage-bird trade. This threat continues despite the fact that the whole population is now confined within a national park and has been the subject of a specific conservation programme. The park and programme have, however, suffered from repeated mismanagement and corruption. In 1999, while black-market prices soared (US $2,000 in mid-1990s), an armed gang stole almost all the 39 captive individuals in the park awaiting release into the wild. These serious problems are compounded by habitat loss. With the population now at such a critically low level, other threats may include genetic erosion, inter-specific competition, natural predation and disease.

Conservation actions to date

The species has been protected under Indonesian law since 1970, while the remaining world population occurs entirely within Bali Barat National Park. Since 1983, the Bali Starling Project has helped to improve the guarding of the park, bolstered the wild population through release of captive-bred birds, and provided the foundation for the development of the Bali Starling Recovery Plan. It also appears to be benefiting from efforts within the Nusa Penida Bird Sanctuary. Plans are being developed to legalise breeding and trading of Bali Starling to open up the market and undermine illegal trade.

Conservation actions required

- Commence strict implementation of the Bali Starling Recovery Plan.
- Continue to monitor the success of the release and subsequent breeding of released birds in the wild on Nusa Penida, in particular investigating interactions with Black-winged Starling *Sturnus melanopterus*.

Pohnpei Starling
Aplonis pelzelni
Population: < 50, trend unknown

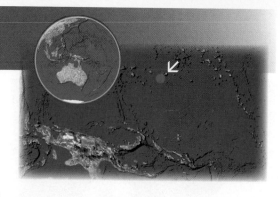

Range & population
This starling is endemic to the island of Pohnpei, Federated States of Micronesia, where it declined drastically sometime after 1930. It has not been seen since 1995. This is reputedly a species of dark, damp montane forest above 425 m, although it has also been observed in plantations. It usually occurs in pairs, feeding on insects and fruit. Small berries from shrubs form a large part of the diet, although seeds and grubs are also taken from the ground. The nest is reportedly placed in the hollows of trees, but this has not been confirmed.

Threats
The reason for the decline of this species is unknown, although habitat loss, bird hunting (a common practice among Pohnpeians), and predation by introduced rats are all possible contributory factors. The cultivation of sakau (= kava) *Piper methysticum* as a major cash-crop has reduced undisturbed upland forest. Long-standing tradition and custom surround its use, but this has given way to more widespread recreational use with the result that clear-cutting 1-2 ha plots for sakau has increased in recent years, reaching to the edge of cloud-forest at c. 600 m in some areas.

Conservation actions to date
None is known.

Conservation actions required
- Continue to search exhaustively for this species and investigate any records of its presence.
- Protect upland forests.

Olomao
Myadestes lanaiensis
Population: < 50, trend unknown

Range & population
This bird is endemic to the central Hawaiian Islands (USA), where it is (or was) known from Maui, Lana`i and Moloka`i. It was last seen on Lana`i in 1933. Most of the historical range on Moloka`i in Kamakou-Pelekunu has been resurveyed and the species probably has been extirpated from that area. Any remaining population in non-surveyed areas is likely to be tiny. It is a shy and retiring bird of the montane forest canopy. Like its congeners, it is primarily frugivorous.

Threats
This species' drastic decline is probably attributable to the introduction of disease-carrying mosquitoes and habitat destruction. Mosquitoes were, until recently, restricted to the lowlands, but have followed the penetration of feral pigs into remote native rainforests over the last 25 years, and Moloka`i's uplands are probably too small to provide disease-free refugia. Pigs also modify native forests as they carry alien weeds to new areas and their rooting destroys the shrub layer, and introduced Axis Deer *Axis axis* are an additional problem.

Conservation actions to date
The Kamakou Preserve and neighbouring land have been partially fenced and control programmes exist for feral ungulates. The Oloku`i Natural Area, established in 1986, protects pristine native forest where Olomao may persist.

Conservation actions required
- Conduct surveys to locate any remaining populations and, if found, urgently assess action required for its recovery such as establishing captive breeding.

Puaiohi
Myadestes palmeri
Population: 300-350 ◄►

Kaua`i, Hawaii, 2006

Photo: © Janos Olah

History
1893 – Walter Rotschild describes the species.

1907 – the Forest Reserve Act protecting forests in Hawaii is introduced.

1967 – the species is listed as endangered in the US.

1995 – a recovery project involving US Fish & Wildlife Service, Biological Resources Division (USGS), Hawaii Division of Forestry and Wildlife and the Peregrine Fund commences.

1996 – a captive-breeding programme begins.

1999 – 8 males and 6 females from the captive population are released into the wild and raise four fledglings.

2007 – 9 birds released into the wild bringing the total number of releases to 132.

Range & population
This species is endemic to Kaua`i in the Hawaiian Islands (USA), where recent records are all from the Alaka`i Wilderness Preserve above 3,500 feet. It has recently been lost from the Waiau and possibly the Halekua drainages. It formerly occurred in lowland habitats, but probably only locally, and was extirpated from these areas by the end of the 19th century. During 1998-2000, the population was estimated at c. 200, possibly up to 300, wild individuals.
A captive-breeding programme has facilitated the successful reintroduction of individuals, resulting in successful breeding in the wild by captive-bred birds.
It is now restricted to high-elevation `ohi`a forests. It is a ravine specialist, favouring stream banks with a rich under-storey and many nests are placed on cliffs above streams. It is primarily frugivorous, with arthropods (particularly insects) forming an important dietary component. Some birds may be disease resistant, but it is not known what proportion exhibit this characteristic. It has high, but variable, productivity and many pairs rear multiple broods during the season.

Threats
The destruction of the understory by feral pigs has been implicated in this species' rarity. Avian pox-like lesions have been observed on a mist-netted bird, and avian malaria is suspected to cause some mortality. Although hurricanes have caused serious damage to its habitat, the species appears to recover relatively well, probably because ravines are better sheltered. Predation by native Short-eared Owls *Asio flammeus* and alien mammals (e.g. rats) suppresses productivity and competition for food with introduced insects, birds and mammals may also have negative impacts. Several plants, including blackberry *Rubus argutus*, Australian tree fern *Cyathea cooperi*, Kahili ginger *Hedychium gardnerianum*, daisy fleabane *Erigeron annuus* and strawberry guava *Psidium cattleianum* have significantly altered area currently and recently occupied by Puaiohi, and have the potential to convert the forest canopy, understorey and cliffs used for nesting substrate to unsuitable habitat.

Conservation actions to date
It is protected in the Alaka`i Wilderness Preserve. Rat poison bait stations have placed near a few nests with moderate success. Bait stations are also placed around the release sites for captive-bred individuals at the time of release. Several types of rodent-resistant nest boxes have been installed in nesting habitat, and one pair was documented to nest successfully in one box. Control of feral ungulates has proved difficult in less accessible areas of the Alaka`i Wilderness Preserve which is rarely visited by hunters and alternatives are expensive and of limited effectiveness. 132 birds have been released and confirmed breeding has occurred in the wild. Releases include lowering the birds with helicopters to release sites in remote locations.

Conservation actions required
- Protect the Alaka`i Wilderness Preserve from the invasion of introduced plants.
- An ungulate exclusion fence is planned for a portion of the Alaka`i plateau, which will include 5-10% of the species' range.
- Remove rats and cats from the Alaka`i Wilderness Preserve.
- Continue captive breeding and release efforts.

Alakai Wilderness Preserve, Kaua`i, Hawaii, 2007

Photo: © Pauline Roberts

Taita Thrush
Turdus helleri
Population: 1,350 ↓

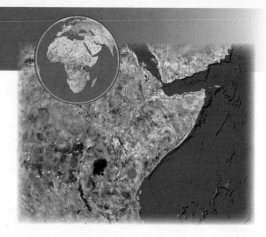

Taita Hills, Kenya, 2006

Photo: ©Tom Callens

History
1913 – Edgar Alexander Mearns (1856-1916) describes the form.

1985 – Taita Thrush is split from Olive Thrush *Turdus olivaceus* and is awarded specific status. It is named after American zoologist Edmund Heller (1875-1939).

This species has been split from Olive Thrush *Turdus olivaceus*.

Range & population
This thrush is confined to three or four tiny forest patches in the Taita Hills, southern Kenya: Mbololo (c.200 ha), Ngangao (c.92 ha), Chawia (c.50 ha) and Yale (2 ha) at an altitude of around 1,200 m. Although there have been reported sightings at Mt Kasigau, 50 km south-east of the Taita Hills, survey work in 1998 did not record the species there. Research in 1997 indicated a total population 1,060 birds in Mbololo, 250 in Ngangao and 38 in Chawia.
It is confined to montane cloud-forest, not venturing into secondary growth, scrub or cultivated areas, although the areas where it occurs have been heavily logged in the past. Despite much research, very few inter-fragment movements have been recorded. It prefers well-shaded areas with a dense understorey, high litter-cover and little or no herbaceous cover, and consequently is found at greater density in Mbolobo, the least disturbed forest area, and is rarest in Chawia, which has a more open canopy and a very shrubby understorey. Birds in poor body condition have been shown to have lower survival rates. Rarely ascends more than 2 m above ground. The diet is predominantly fruit. It is monogamous and terrestrial, with overlapping home ranges and breeding between January and July. The clutch-size is 1–3.

Threats
Most indigenous forest has been cleared in the Taita Hills for cultivation or reforestation with non-native timber, and the remaining tiny area is under serious threat from both clearance and degradation, although habitat quality in the largest two fragments remains good. A highly male-biased sex ratio in Chawia (only 10% of birds were female) might have significant negative consequences for the subpopulation's long-term survival. The species' reproductive rate may thus be lower than expected. Where habitat disturbance leads to deteriorations in body condition, the long-term survival of sub-populations may be put at risk.

Conservation actions to date
The Forest Department is now safeguarding the remaining forest fragments of the Taita Hills. An ongoing collaborative research project includes a large ornithological component, which aims to provide the necessary ecological data to plan conservation policies for this and other endemic species in the area.
The Taita Hills holds three endemic species, of which the Taita Thrush is one, and another 30 threatened species. The Kenya Forests Working Group with input from Nature Kenya and local community have produced a draft management plan for the Ngangao Forest. It aims at preventing further biodiversity and habitat loss at this critical site.

Conservation actions required
• Initiate an outreach programme to local communities, in particular to discuss the benefits of conserving the remaining forests.
• Draw up management plans, based on results of ongoing ecological surveys, in close conjunction with the Forest Department and local communities.
• Remove non-native trees from within indigenous forest.
• Reforest cleared areas with native trees.
• Initiate sustainable forest-use schemes, based on ecotourism and harvesting forest products.

BirdLife Species Guardian Mwangi Githiru

Taita Hills, Kenya, 2005

Photo: © Toon Spanhove

Somali Thrush
Turdus ludoviciae
Population: 10,000-19,999 ↓

Painting: © Martin Woodcock

Range & population
This thrush occurs on mountain-top woodlands in northern Somalia. It was considered to be locally common in 1979, most notably in Daloh Forest Reserve.

It is found in juniper woodlands and neighbouring open areas of mountain-tops at 1,300–2,000 m. It often feeds in small parties, sometimes in groups of up to 30 birds when feeding on fruiting juniper. Four nests have been found, all containing two eggs, and several pairs have been observed feeding young in the nest in May.

Threats
Even in 1979 the species' habitat was greatly threatened by forest destruction, including burning, felling and cattle-grazing, against which Forest Reserve status provides no protection in the current political situation. There were unconfirmed reports, in 1998, that the juniper woodlands in the species' range had been completely felled. Such reports are credible and, if true, imply a drastic decline.

Conservation actions to date
No conservation action or fieldwork has been carried out recently, due to the political instability in the area, nor is any likely to occur in the near future.

Required conservation actions
- Establish how much of its habitat remains.
- Assess the size and trend of its population.

Rueck's Blue-flycatcher
Cyornis ruckii
Population: < 50, trend unknown

Painting: © Karen Phillipps

Range & population
This blue-flycatcher is known from two specimens collected in 1917 and 1918, at Tuntungan and Delitua in the lowlands of northern Sumatra, Indonesia. Two further specimens are purportedly from Malaysia, but their provenance has been questioned. Its ecology is virtually unknown. Specimens were collected at 150 m and 200 m in 'exploited forest', suggesting it may tolerate some habitat degradation. The fact that they were taken in January and April raises the possibility that the species may be migratory.

Threats
There is apparently no remaining forest cover at the two known collecting localities (they are situated on the outskirts of a large city: Medan), and its range may therefore have shrunk considerably. However, the description of its habitat as 'exploited' forest raises the possibility that it may persist in adjacent disturbed wooded areas.

Conservation actions to date
This species has been protected under Indonesian law since 1972. No other measure is known.

Conservation actions required
- Examine the two skins in detail to improve understanding of its taxonomic status.
- Conduct surveys (including use of mist nets) for the species between January and April in remaining forest patches ranging out from the two historical locations.
- Develop a conservation plan for the species, pending results of these surveys, including the establishment of protected areas, where appropriate, at any sites supporting populations.

Cebu Flowerpecker
Dicaeum quadricolor
Population: c. 100 ↓

Painting: © Melinda Bitting

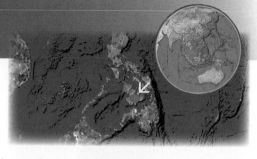

Range & population
This flowerpecker is endemic to the island of Cebu in the Philippines. Early in the 20th century, it was feared to have become extinct but in 1992 it was rediscovered at Tabunan and has since been found at three further sites. It evidently frequents secondary and selectively logged areas, but always next to a larger patch of native vegetation. It has been observed feeding on mistletoe-like plants (*Loranthus sp.*) and small, ripe *Ficus* fruits.

Threats
The few remaining tracts of forest are variously threatened by illegal settlement, road construction, shifting cultivation, illicit logging, charcoal making, firewood collection and habitat clearance for mining. Competition with Red-striped Flowerpecker *D. australe* may have accelerated the species' decline given the extreme shortage of available habitat.

Conservation actions to date
Tabunan is located within the Central Cebu National Park, which was declared a Strict Protection Zone in 1996. In 1997, a three-year management plan was drawn up to ensure long-term sustainability, and funding has been received for its implementation. Reforestation schemes have been implemented at Mt Lantoy, and the area has been proposed for designation as a national park.

Conservation actions required
- Identify all remnant forest tracts on Cebu and urgently survey them for remaining populations.
- Research the species' ecology, particularly interactions with *D. australe*.
- Continue to fund and implement management activities at Tabunan.
- Support the proposal to designate Mt Lantoy as a national park.
- Propose strict formal protection for remaining forest tracts.

Mauritius Fody
Foudia rubra
Population: 210-250 ↓

Mauritius, July 2006

Photo: © Natasha Lloyd

Range & population
This species, restricted to south-west Mauritius, has suffered a 55% decline from 1975 to 1993. Since 1993, the population decline rate has slowed. It holds territories in all types of native forest. In fact its use of exotic vegetation increased markedly during a recent increase in range between 1994 and 2003. Its diet is comprised primarily of insects, but also fruit and nectar.

Threats
Historically, clearance of upland forest affected this species. Introduced predators, notably Black Rat *Rattus rattus* and Crab-eating Macaque *Macaca fascicularis*, and their nest predation is regarded as the major cause of present-day decline. Introduced Madagascar Red Fody *F. madagascariensis* may compete and restrict its range.

Conservation actions to date
Rats and Macaques are controlled as part of a programme to rehabilitate plots of native vegetation. A captive-rearing programme implemented by the Mauritian Wildlife Foundation, the Gerald Durrell Endemic Wildlife Sanctuary and the National Parks and Conservation Service is proving highly effective. Research into the species' ecology is ongoing and prospective surveys to assess the suitability of Round Island for translocation have been conducted.

Conservation actions required
- Develop a Conservation Management Area at Combo.
- Increase breeding productivity by supplemental feeding, double clutching and captive-rearing of harvested wild clutches.
- Continue releases on offshore islands and monitor the population on Ille aux Aigrettes.
- Pursue the possibility of releasing birds onto Round Island.

São Tomé Grosbeak
Neospiza concolor
Population: < 50 ↕

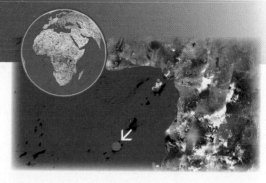

Photo: © Martim Melo

São Tomé Island, Southwestern forests, 2005

Range & population
This species was known from just one 19th century specimen from southern São Tomé. It was rediscovered in 1991. Since then, there have been a possible sighting in 1992, and of adults and a juvenile in 1997. Given the limited area of suitable habitat and the paucity of records it probably has a tiny population. It occurs in lowland, closed-canopy primary forest and is reportedly quite silent, which could partly explain why it has so rarely been seen.

Threats
Historically, large areas of lowland forest were cleared for cocoa plantations. Today, land privatisation is leading to an increase in the number of small farms and the clearance of trees which may be a threat in the future. Road developments along the east and west coasts are increasing access to previously remote areas. Introduced mammals are potential threats.

Conservation actions to date
Protection of primary forest as a 'zona ecologica' and a national park has been proposed. A new law providing for the gazetting of protected areas and the protection of threatened species awaits final ratification.

Conservation actions required
- Research its population, distribution and ecology.
- Ensure legal protection of all remaining lowland primary forest.
- List it as a protected species under national law.

BirdLife Species Guardian **Maria Manuela Bandeira (Associação dos Biólogos Santomenses)**

Azores Bullfinch
Pyrrhula murina
Population: 203-331 ↓

Photo: © Ruben Heleno

Sã Miguel, Azores, 2006

Range & population
This finch is endemic to the island of São Miguel, Azores, Portugal. It was locally abundant, but became rare after 1920 as a result of forest clearance and hunting. Today it is almost entirely confined to native forest on the slopes around Pico da Vara. The diet consists of plants and it appears entirely dependent on native trees for food during certain months of the year. Movements of up to 3 km from elevations of 700 m down to 300 m have been recorded as birds move to feed on ripening seeds. Birds breed from mid-June to late August.

Threats
The historical decline and its extremely small range are believed to be a consequence of the widespread clearance of native forest for forestry plantations and agriculture. The spread of alien invasive plant species suppresses the natural food supply of the species. Predation by introduced rats may also be affecting nesting success.

Conservation actions to date
The species is protected under Portuguese law. Pico da Vara/Ribeira do Guilherme has been designated as a Special Protected Area. A species action plan was published in 1996.

Conservation actions required
- Continue and expand the population monitoring scheme.
- Investigate the possibility of breeding at Salto do Cavalo.
- Continue the removal and exclusion of exotic flora.
- Continue the replanting of native vegetation.
- Monitor the species' response to ongoing habitat restoration.
- Promote land use changes in the buffer areas around the SPA.
- Investigate the impact of rat predation on nesting success.

Nihoa Finch
Telespiza ultima
Population: 3,177 ⬍

Photo: © Jack Jeffrey

Nihoa, Hawaiian Islands, 1996

Range & population
This finch is endemic to the steep, rocky island of Nihoa in the Northwestern Hawaiian Islands (USA). It once occurred at least on the island of Molokai in the Main Hawaiian Islands, but was extirpated in prehistory. The population ranged from 6,686 in 1968, to 946 in 1987. It occurs in low shrubs and grasses covering some two-thirds (0.43 km²) of the island. It feeds on eggs, seeds, invertebrates and flowers. It nests in cavities in cliffs, rock crevices or in piles of loose rock.

Threats
The main threats are the potential introduction of detrimental non-native species (especially irruptive grasshoppers) and diseases and stochastic events, such as droughts, storms and hurricanes.

Conservation actions to date
Nihoa is part of the Hawaiian Islands National Wildlife Refuge, and legal access is controlled by a permit system and strict protocols. Visiting scientists make regular efforts to control one of the three species of alien plant on Nihoa by hand weeding. A process to evaluate and prioritize potential translocation sites throughout the archipelago is underway. Disease susceptibility may preclude reintroduction of the Nihoa finch to the Main Hawaiian Islands, and translocation efforts may focus on the Northwestern Islands. An attempted introduction to French Frigate Shoals in 1967 failed.

Conservation actions required
- Continue monitoring.
- Ensure strict protocols prevent further accidental introductions of alien species.

Ou
Psittirostra psittacea
Population: < 50, trend unknown

Painting: © H. Douglas Pratt / Oxford University Press

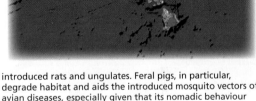

Range & population
This species was originally widespread but the last confirmed sighting was in 1987. However, since 1995 there have been unconfirmed reports from Kaua`i and Hawai`i. It is restricted to wet to mesic `ohi`a forest between 800 and 1,900 m, mainly 1,200–1,500 m. Its bill is adapted to feeding on `ie`ie, an understory vine, and outside the `ie`ie fruiting season, it is nomadic in response to seasonal fruit and invertebrate abundance.

Threats
Habitat has been lost and modified by logging and agriculture, and `ie`ie has declined because of pressure from introduced rats and ungulates. Feral pigs, in particular, degrade habitat and aids the introduced mosquito vectors of avian diseases, especially given that its nomadic behaviour may increase its exposure to disease. On Kaua`i, hurricanes and, on Hawai`i, lava-flows have decimated the population.

Conservation actions to date
Recent reports of this species come from three protected areas. A Rare Bird Search Project was implemented to find the species and make recommendations for its conservation, but none were located. Feral pig elimination is being carried out in a number of protected areas in Hawai`i which could hold remnant populations.

Conservation actions required
- Perform further surveys to locate any remaining populations.
- Manage ecosystems where the species could still occur.
- Plant and encourage food-plants.
- Remove feral ungulates.

Maui Parrotbill
Pseudonestor xanthophrys

Population: 500 ↓

Hanawi Natural Area Reserve, Maui, Hawaii, 2006

Photo: © Eric Vander Werf

Range & population
This species is endemic to Maui in the Hawaiian Islands and is restricted to montane mesic and wet forest at 1,200-2,150 m. It feeds mainly on the larvae and pupae of wood- and fruit-boring beetles, moths and other invertebrates. During the breeding season (November - June), one chick is usually raised per year and young are dependent on parents for 5-8 months.

Threats
From 1945 to 1995, the invasion of feral pigs on Haleakala caused chronic habitat degradation and facilitated the spread of disease-carrying mosquitoes into remote rainforests. Habitat is now being degraded by goats, and feral deer pose an imminent threat. Weather influences the survival of young and thus potential recruitment rates. Other limiting factors include predation and competition from exotic bird and insect species.

Conservation actions to date
The East Maui watershed is cooperatively managed with fencing and removal of feral ungulates. In the Waikamoi Preserve, Hanawi Natural Area Reserve and Haleakala National Park, conservation practices additionally combat the establishment of alien plants and feral pigs have been controlled. Progeny from a captive population will be used for a pilot release program in the forests of East Maui.

Conservation actions required
- Complete and routinely check ungulate exclusion fences.
- Complete ungulate eradication programme.
- Control alien plants and replant koa forest in areas adjacent to its current distribution.
- Improve techniques for captive breeding and release.

Nukupuu
Hemignathus lucidus

Population: < 50, trend unknown

Painting: © H. Douglas Pratt / Oxford University Press

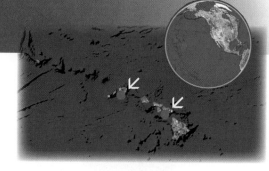

Range & population
This species is endemic to the Hawaiian Islands (USA). On Kaua`i, it is probably confined to the `Alaka`i Wilderness Preserve but recent surveys on Kauai have failed to find it. On Maui, it is found on the eastern and north-eastern slopes of Haleakala, where a single male seen in 1995 in the same place as a report from 1994 provided strong evidence of its persistence. If any population remains, it is likely to be tiny. It inhabits dense, wet `ohi`a forest and the higher parts of mesic koa-`ohi`a forest. On Maui, all recent sightings were between 1,450 and 2,000 m,. On Kaua`i, the Koai`e Valley (where it was seen in 1995) is at 1,000–1,300 m. It feeds on wood-borers, spiders and beetles.

Threats
The lower-elevation koa forests (possibly the species' key habitat) have been nearly eliminated by cattle-ranching. Remaining higher-altitude forests are degraded by introduced ungulates. Feral pigs facilitate the spread of alien plants and introduced disease-carrying mosquitoes.

Conservation actions to date
On Maui, fencing and feral pig eradication has been completed in a c. 650 ha area where the male was recorded in 1994. In Waikamoi Preserve, Hanawi Natural Area Reserve and Haleakala National Park, efforts have been made to combat the establishment of alien plants.

Conservation actions required
- Conduct surveys to locate any remaining populations.
- If any birds are found, attempt to increase the population by captive propagation.
- Research competition from exotic bird and insect species.

Akikiki
Oreomystis bairdi
Population: 1,472 ↓

Pihea Trail, Kauai, Hawaii, 2004

Photo: © Jack Jeffrey

History
1887 – Norwegian zoologist Leonhard Hess Stejneger (1851-1943) describes the species.

1890s-1900s – early naturalists consider the Akikiki common at elevations as low as 300 m.

1973-1981 – island wide population confined to Alaka'i swamp and estimated at about 6,800.

1983 and 1992 – hurricanes Iwa and Iniki, respectively, devastate forests throughout Kaua'i affecting all bird populations.

2000 – population estimated at 1,500 and confined to 36 km² area.

Range & population
Akikiki was common and widely distributed in the 1890s on Kaua'i in the Hawaiian Islands (USA). During 1968-1973, the total population was estimated at 6,832, when it was recorded on the Laau ridge and was fairly widespread in Koke'e. Since then, it has declined in and retreated from the Koke'e region and the fringes of the Alaka'i region and is now uncommon to rare in Alaka'i. Recent unpublished survey data indicate dramatic declines (85-89% since 1968-1973) and a decline of c. 64% in its core area in the Alaka'i Swamp from 1970 to 2000. It is found in high-elevation 'ohi'a and koa-'ohi'a forest, but the latter is mainly distributed in the Koke'e region, from where it is retreating. The Alaka'i stronghold is at 1,000–1,600 m. It feeds on invertebrates.

Threats
Lowland forests have been cleared for timber and agriculture, with feral livestock causing further degradation and destruction. Feral pigs continue to be particularly detrimental, additionally dispersing alien plants and facilitating the spread of introduced mosquitoes which transmit avian malaria and avian pox. Domestic and introduced birds provide reservoirs for these diseases, to which there is little resistance in Hawaiian honeycreeper populations. Predation by introduced animals and competition for arthropod resources by introduced taxa (especially Japanese White-eye *Zosterops japonicus*, wasps and ants) are additional threats. Introduced plants such as Kahili ginger (*Hedychium gardnerianum*), blackberry (*Rubus argutus*), strawberry guava (*Psidium cattleianum*), Australian tree fern (*Cyathea cooperi*) and firetree (*Myrica faya*) have degraded much native forest in Koke'e, and provide reservoirs for breeding mosquitos.

Hurricanes have had major impacts on population size in the past and can displace birds from the small area of suitable habitat at altitude and push them into the lowlands where avian malaria is more prevalent. A growing concern is that rising temperatures could allow mosquito abundance to increase at higher altitudes and further transmit avian malaria and avian pox.

Conservation actions to date
It is protected by the Alaka'i Wilderness Preserve. The Zoological Society of San Diego is developing techniques for rearing *Oreomystis* creepers from eggs and breeding them in captivity, using the related Hawai'i creeper, at the Keauhou Bird Conservation Center. The Hawai'i creeper has been successfully propagated in captivity, and release of the captive population is planned. Starting in April 2007 the Hawaii Department of Land and Natural Resources conducted population surveys of forest birds on Kauai to determine trends. The U.S. Fish and Wildlife Service announced in 2005 that the Akikiki should be officially designated an endangered species, but declined to move forward with the listing for budgetary reasons.

Conservation actions required
- Protect the Alaka'i Wilderness Preserve from the invasion of introduced plants and feral ungulates.
- Restore as much native vegetation to the Alaka'I region and remove as many introduced mammals (primarily pigs) as possible.
- Continue to monitor its population status and distribution.
- Develop a programme for captive rearing and release, before the population falls to a critical level.

Pihea Trail, Kauai, Hawaii, 2004

Poo-uli

Melamprosops phaeosoma

Population: < 50 ↓

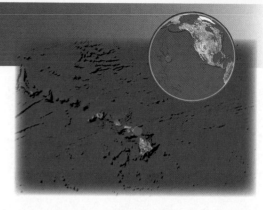

Hanawi, Maui, Hawaii, 2003

Photo: © Jack Jeffrey

History

1973 – Betsy Harrison Gagne, a college student from Hawaii University discovers the species.

1974 – the species is described by biologists Tonnie Casey and Jim Jacobi.

1980 – the Hawaii Forest Bird Survey takes place and is the first survey to target the Poo-uli. Three birds are recorded, too few to make any population assessments.

1981 – a population estimate gives 150 birds.

1986 – the first nest is found.

1992 – the Hawaii Forest Bird Survey is repeated, using the same transects, but no Poo-uli are detected.

1996 – only four individuals could be found. The last immature bird is seen.

1997 – only three individuals known.

2002 – on April 4th a female is captured. The idea was to also capture a male, but this had to be given up. The female fed in captivity, was fitted with a transmitter and released in a territory of a male. She stayed for half a day in that territory, without connecting with the male, and then headed to where she was caught where she could be followed for ten days.

2004 – one of three known individuals is captured in September but dies on 28 November.

Range & population

This species, whose Hawaiian name means 'black head', is endemic to Maui in the Hawaiian Islands (USA), where it was discovered in 1973, in the Ko`olau Forest Reserve on the north-eastern flanks of Haleakala, and estimated to number fewer than 200 birds. During 1975-1985, there was a 90% decline in density in the upper Hanawi watershed, the only area where it now persists. In 1995, only five to seven birds were known but two years later only three individuals could be found (two male, one possibly female), each with distinct home ranges in Hanawi Natural Area Reserve (NAR) and the immediately adjacent Haleakala National Park. The two other individuals known to be a male and a female have not

been seen since 2003 and 2004, and are likely to have now died (if alive, both birds would be a minimum of 10 years old in 2008). No other individuals have been located since 1998 despite almost constant presence of researchers in the field in recent years, but it is still possible, albeit unlikely, that a few unlocated individuals may exist in the wild.

It is found in remote `ohi`a forest at 1,400–2,100 m, but this may be suboptimal habitat as subfossil evidence indicates that it occurred in much drier habitat at 300–1,500 m. It feeds primarily on snails, insects, and spiders, and occasionally fruit. It is the only Hawaiian bird known to feed on snails. The two known nests were found in `ohi`a trees.

Threats

Habitat destruction and modification, and the rapid spread of disease-carrying mosquitoes in the lowlands are thought to be responsible for past declines, and the latter continues to be a threat. The precise causes of the recent population decline are unknown, although a correlation with a concurrent 473% increase in pig activity within the Hanawi NAR has been hypothesised, as indexed by ground-cover disturbance. Predation by introduced rats, cats and small Indian mongoose *Herpestes auropunctatus* is also possible. Rats and the introduced garlic snail *Oxychilus alliarius* have been blamed for the decline of native land snails, an important food source for the Po'o-uli. Helicopters may disturb birds, especially during the nesting season.

Conservation actions to date

In 1986, the 30 km² Hanawi NAR was created to protect this species and, during 1990-1997, all feral pigs were systematically eradicated from three fenced areas. However, there was evidence of pig activity within one of these areas in 1998. An environmental assessment has been produced and a management plan proposed. Two wild birds were briefly united when one was caught and moved into the home range of another. However, after just one day the translocated bird had returned to its own territory.

Conservation actions required

- Survey all remaining `ohi`a forest on East Maui.
- Create more pig-free areas below the existing fence-lines to help prevent the spread of mosquitoes into upper elevation forests and abet the restoration of more lower elevation habitat.
- Intensify habitat management in Hanawi NAR and adjacent areas.

The Hawaii Audobon Society's mission is to foster community values that result in the protection and restoration of native ecosystems and conservation of natural resources through education, science and advocacy in Hawaii and the Pacific.

www.hawaiiaudobon.com

Oahu Alauahio
Paroreomyza maculata
Population: < 10, trend unknown

Painting: © H. Douglas Pratt / Oxford University Press

Range & population
This species is endemic to O`ahu in the Hawaiian Islands (USA) where the last well-documented observation was in 1985. Sightings have been in remnant (extensively degraded) native, lowland mesic to wet forest containing many introduced plants. It was reported to eat quantities of carabid beetles as it was seen feeding on the dead branches of koa trees.

Threats
Some native forests remain on O`ahu, so habitat loss and alteration cannot fully explain the decline of this species. Disease spread by introduced mosquitoes is prevalent in the

lowlands and is a likely contributory factor. The construction of the H-3 freeway (for which the US Congress gave specific exemption from the Endangered Species Act) destroyed habitat around North Halawa Valley, from which most of the recent confirmed sightings have come.

Conservation actions to date
Surveys have been carried out during the 1990s to search for this species, but have failed to find any birds.

Conservation actions required
- Continue to conduct intensive and extensive surveys to locate any remaining populations.
- If any birds are found, start intensive monitoring, including the collection of data on vocalisations, foraging and breeding behaviour.
- If active nests are found, ensure localised predator control.
- Consider captive propagation, following development of specific techniques.

Akohekohe
Palmeria dolei
Population: 3,750 ↓

Waikamoi, Hawaii, 1991

Photo: © Jack Jeffrey

Range & population
This species occurs on Maui in the Hawaiian Islands (USA) but is extinct on Moloka`i. It occurs in mesic `ohi`a-koa and wet `ohi`a forest from 1,100-2,300 m. It primarily feeds on `ohi`a nectar, also taking invertebrates, especially caterpillars. It usually nests twice seasonally, in November to June. Birds, perhaps especially immatures, may disperse to lower elevations.

Threats
Habitat destruction and modification and the rapid spread of disease-carrying mosquitoes in the lowlands are thought to be responsible for past declines. Predation by introduced rats,

cats and Barn Owl *Tyto alba* and possibly small Indian mongoose *Herpestes auropunctatus* is a further limiting factor.

Conservation actions to date
Cooperative management of the East Maui watershed includes fencing at c.1,070 m and removal of feral ungulates. In the Waikamoi Preserve, Hanawi Natural Area Reserve and Haleakala National Park, conservation practices combat the establishment of alien plants and, from the late 1980s, feral pigs have been controlled. Research into captive breeding is underway, and six individuals have been hatched from late-stage wild eggs.

Conservation actions required
- Preserve remote and ecologically diverse areas, especially on the northern slopes of Haleakala.
- Extend plant control to areas outside reserves.
- Establish a population in historically occupied habitat.
- Continue population monitoring and captive-breeding efforts.

Bachman´s Warbler
Vermivora bachmanii
Population: < 50, trend unknown

© Jerry A. Payne, USDA Agricultural Research Service

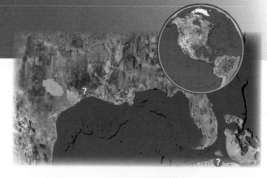

Range & population
This wood warbler is known to have bred in Missouri, Arkansas, Kentucky, Alabama and South Carolina, USA, and there are breeding-season records from various other south-east states. Birds wintered in Cuba and occasionally Florida, USA. The last nest was found in 1937, but there have been recent (unconfirmed) sightings. Small areas of suitable habitat remain, and the species may still survive. It bred in seasonally flooded swamp-forest, always near standing water, apparently showing a strong association with canebrakes of the bamboo *Arundinaria gigantea*. Winter habitat requirements are much less specific, with records from dry forest, wetlands and urban areas, but apparently favouring wooded areas with flowering *Hibiscus* trees. Breeding occurred from March–June, with the nest constructed in the shelter of a dense bush or tangle of vegetation.

Threats
The drainage of river-bottom swamplands, and the near-total clearance of canebrakes in the USA, combined with the conversion of much of Cuba to sugarcane plantation, offer the best explanation for the disappearance of this species.

Conservation actions to date
There is currently no action being taken for this species. Searches within the large expanses of suitable habitat that remain on the wintering grounds would be costly and most probably futile.

Conservation actions required
- Systematically search the small areas of remaining breeding habitat.

Semper´s Warbler
Leucopeza semperi
Population: < 50, trend unknown

Painting: © Don Radovich

Range & population
This species is endemic to St Lucia, where it is extremely rare and very possibly extinct. It eluded almost all 20th century efforts to find a population. There are a mere handful of reports since the 1920s and no certain records since 1961. Sightings in 1965, 1989, 1995 and 2003 have not been confirmed. It was apparently more abundant in the 19th century, and has clearly undergone a significant decline. It is known from the undergrowth of montane and elfin forest. The ecology is virtually unknown, but it is apparently largely terrestrial and possibly even nests on the ground.

Threats
The introduction of mongooses in 1884 portended the disappearance of this species, as they probably preyed on adults, nestlings and eggs. The decline may have been compounded by habitat loss, but suitable forest still remains on the island.

Conservation actions to date
There have been no adequate searches for the species in recent years.

Conservation actions required
- Survey to locate any remaining population.

Belding´s Yellowthroat
Geothlypis beldingi
Population: 1,000-2,499 ↓

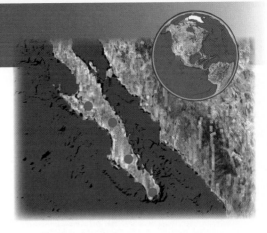

Baja California, 2006

Photo: © Steve Mlodinow

Range & population
This warbler has a fragmented distribution on the Baja California peninsula, Mexico. The nominate race occurs at Punta San Pedro (70 birds) and San José del Cabo (219-480 birds) and the race *goldmani* is known from San Ignacio (537-648 birds), Mulegé, Purísima (203-450 birds) and Comondú. It also occurs at San Pedro de la Presa, but it is unclear which subspecies is involved. It is common at most of these sites, but the area of suitable habitat is probably slightly less than 10 km². It is known to have been extirpated from three sites (Miraflores, Santiago and El Triunfo).
It occupies oases of reeds, cattails and tule, fringing permanent, lowland, freshwater marshes or rivers, and has been found occasionally in brackish coastal marshes. Birds are mostly located within 15 m of the water's edge, and never more than 50 m from water. The nest is up to 1.5 m above the ground, in cattails or tule, and eggs are laid between March and May. Birds have been recorded c. 200 km from the known breeding range suggesting it is capable of dispersing over reasonably large distances.

Threats
The oases of Baja California are under high human pressure, especially in the south. Accidental and induced fires, reed-cutting for tourism facilities and house construction, and drainage for agriculture and cattle-ranching have decreased suitable habitat. As its populations are isolated and disjunct, it is especially vulnerable to stochastic events, with hurricanes frequently eliminating portions of reedgrass vegetation in August-October.

Conservation actions to date
Surveys have improved knowledge of the species' distribution, but none of the known sites are protected. The IBA Estero de San José del Cabo, a 42 ha freshwater coastal lagoon at the southern tip of the peninsula of Baja California, México incorporates habitat for Belding's Yellowthroat. Angeles del Estero and Agrupación Ciudadana Ecologista - two small local NGOs in the adjacent town of San José del Cabo have a history of involvement in the conservation of this Important Bird Area (IBA).

Conservation actions required
- Monitor all populations and conduct formal surveys to ascertain the population size, trends and distribution.
- Prohibit burning and cutting the water-edge vegetation at all sites, especially Punta San Pedro and San Pedro de la Presa (as the only known localities for the nominate subspecies).
- Restore the lagoon at Santiago as a potential site for reintroducing the species. Marsh creation should be incorporated into development plans for areas within this species' range.
- Develop a species action plan.
- Initiate a public awareness programme.
- Promote bird tourism to generate income for protecting key sites.

BirdLife Species Guardian **Pronatura Noroeste, A. C.**

Baja California, 2006

Photo: © Steve Mlodinow

Montserrat Oriole
Icterus oberi
Population: 200-800 ↓

Photo: © James Morgan

Jersey Zoo

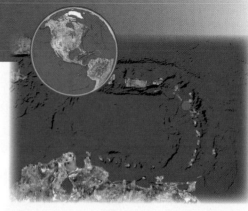

History
1880 – George Newbold Lawrence (1806-1895) describes the species and names it after American zoologist Fred Oberi.

1997 – the estimated population is c. 4,000 birds in December.

1999 – 8 birds are taken to Jersey Zoo for development of husbandry techniques.

Range & population
This species inhabits an extremely small area on Montserrat (to UK) in the Lesser Antilles. By the early 1990s, it occurred throughout the three main forested hill ranges on the island (the Centre, Soufière and South Soufière hills), but volcanic activity in 1995-1997 entirely destroyed two-thirds of remaining habitat. Initially, only the Centre Hills (c.14 km²) population was thought to have survived the pyroclastic flows (although even this area was heavily ashed), but a remnant population was later discovered in a 1-2 km² forest patch in the South Soufrière hills, just 1 km from the summit of the volcano. Intensive monitoring between 1997-2001 indicated that the Centre Hills population declined by 40-50%, despite reduced volcanic activity. In 2001, 2003 and 2006, further major volcanic eruptions caused heavy ash falls on large areas of the Centre Hills, destroying several nests and curtailing breeding. Recent evidence suggests that the downward fluctuation noted between 1997-2001 has reversed and the population is estimated at c.100-400 pairs and possibly increasing.

It occurs in most forest types between c. 150-900 m, but reaches highest densities in wetter, higher altitude forests, and is absent from areas of very dry forest. It is found in all successional stages, and sometimes at the edges of cultivated areas and banana plantations. Nesting occurs in March-August, but the exact timing probably depends on the rainy season. Nests are mainly suspended from the leaves of *Heliconia caribbaea*, although banana and other broad-leaved trees are also used. Clutch size is typically two or three. Unsuccessful pairs may attempt up to five clutches; successful pairs can rear two broods per year. It forages at all levels, but particularly in the understorey, feeding mainly on insects, but occasionally also on fruit and possibly nectar.

Threats
Volcanic eruptions in 1995-1997 all but extirpated the species from the Soufière and South Soufière hills. Although volcanic activity was reduced in 1998-2000, the population continued to decline. Potential causes are low insect availability and/or chronic ill-health of birds resulting from ash fall on remaining forest, and other unknown and indirect knock-on effects of volcanic activity. Research into reproductive success, using nest cameras, has also revealed high rates of nest predation by rats and native Pearly-eyed Thrashers *Margarops fuscatus*, both of which occur at high but fluctuating densities. In 2001 and 2003, drought appeared to cause reduced laying frequency and clutch size, and this may be an increasing problem now that this species is confined to lower, drier areas. Conversely, excessive rainfall can also have a negative impact.

Conservation actions to date
There is a comprehensive programme to monitor the population and breeding success, and in 2001 a new research programme into the causes of the continuing decline began. During 2003, preliminary tests of management interventions were made, aimed at boosting reproductive success. Birds have been taken to Jersey Zoo to enable the development of husbandry techniques and initial attempts at captive breeding have proven successful. The Centre Hills has been designated a protected area and development is not permitted within its marked boundaries.

Conservation actions required
- Continue the existing programme and research into the causes of the decline.
- Develop potential management interventions to boost reproductive success.
- Continue the close monitoring of the population.
- Investigate the reasons for the high densities of nest predators in the Centre Hills.

Centre Hills of Montserrat, 2001

Photo: © Chris Bowden / RSPB

Guadalupe Junco
Junco insularis
Population: 50-100 ↓

Guadalupe, February 2006

Photo: © Claudio Contreras

Guadalope Junco is retained as separate species contra the American Ornithologist's Union who include it as a subspecies of Dark-eyed Junco *J. hyemalis.*

Range & population
This junco is endemic to Guadalupe Island, 280 km west of Baja California, Mexico, where it was once common and among the island's most abundant birds. It is now patchily distributed in the north of the island where it is found mainly in remnant stands of cypress, but has also been observed feeding at the base of pines and oaks. The nest is constructed in a depression on the ground or in the low branches of a tree and the breeding season is in February-June

Threats
Intense grazing by goats is the major threat. Smaller forest patches presumably experience similar intense grazing, leading to a total lack of regeneration. Feral cats probably prey upon this species.

Conservation actions to date
Guadalupe is designated as a biosphere reserve, but there is little active management. There is apparently governmental interest in eradicating introduced predators and herbivores, and non-governmental organisations in the region are developing the capacity to undertake eradication programmes on such large islands.

Conservation actions required
- Eradicate goats and cats from the island.
- Survey to provide a more recent assessment of the population size and remaining habitat.

Hooded Seedeater
Sporophila melanops
Population: < 50, trend unknown

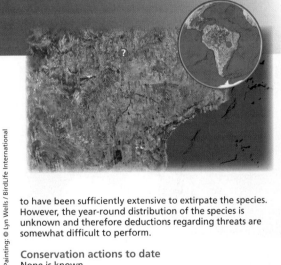

Painting: © Lyn Wells / BirdLife International

Range & population
This species is known from one adult male collected in October 1823. The specimen was taken at a lake 15 km north of Registro do Araguaia, on the east bank of the rio Araguaia in extreme west-central Goiás, Brazil. The type-specimen was obtained from a flock of other finches in presumably open habitat and was in heavy moult. It is not known whether the species is migratory or nomadic

Threats
None is known. Habitat destruction in the region is unlikely to have been sufficiently extensive to extirpate the species. However, the year-round distribution of the species is unknown and therefore deductions regarding threats are somewhat difficult to perform.

Conservation actions to date
None is known.

Conservation actions required
- Search *Sporophila spp.* flocks in Goiás and adjacent Mato Grosso.
- Revisit the type-locality to determine its current condition and target fieldwork at the nearest undisturbed lacustrine sites.
- Re-examine the type-specimen to help determine its validity.

Entre Rios Seedeater
Sporophila zelichi
Population: 50-249 ↓

Gualeguaychu, Puerto Boca, Argentina, January 2004

Photo: © Alec Earnshaw

Range & population
This seedeater is known from a small number of sites in north-east Argentina (Corrientes and Entre Ríos), southern Brazil (Rio Grande do Sul,) eastern Paraguay (Concepción and Itapúa) and south-east Uruguay (Rocha). Only tiny numbers have been found in the wild. It breeds in the austral summer in semi-open grasslands. Its movements are not known but it has been recorded in southern Brazil in November but not at the same site at other times of year, indicating passage. The wintering grounds are unknown but are probably in the Brazilian Cerrado or Pantanal.

Threats
Bird-trappers target this highly prized species. Rapid affore-station with eucalyptus and pinus is even affecting wet valley bottoms, regardless of their subsequent poor growth. Pesticides and other chemicals are widely used, and carried by drainage and run-off into marshes.

Conservation actions to date
It has been reported from El Palmar National Park (in May 1982), and near Iberá Provincial Park, Argentina, and from Bañados del Este Biosphere Reserve, Uruguay.

Conservation actions required
* Survey south Paraguay for breeding populations and Brazil for the wintering grounds.
* Monitor known populations.
* Develop an action plan for this and similar seedeaters.
* Remove incentives for afforesting grasslands.
* Protect Puerto Boca and Bañado Mora-cué, Entre Ríos.
* Establish a reserve network in southern Paraguay.
* Prohibit and penalise the trapping, trading and keeping of the species.
* Develop a CMS agreement for this and similar seedeaters.
* Elucidate its taxonomic status.

Carrizal Seedeater
Amaurospiza carrizalensis
Population: < 50, trend unknown

Isla Carrizal, Venezuela, 2001

Photo: © Miguel Lentino

Range & population
This species was described in 2003 following collection of the holotype on Isla Carrizal in the Río Caroni, Venezuela. Since then its habitat on the island has been destroyed in the development of Guri Dam. It has not been recorded elsewhere so is assumed to have an extremely small population and to be declining as other potentially suitable habitat continues to be destroyed. However, the low number of records may be partly due to the difficulty in surveying its habitat, which as a result has rarely been explored. It has only been found in stands of spiny bamboo forest. Its bill shows some degree of specialisation for feeding. From stomach content analysis of collected specimens it is known to feed on weevils which may be specific to its spiny forest habitat

Threats
Habitat at the only known locality was all destroyed during the development of the Guri Dam, which subsequently flooded this location. This development also destroyed other potentially suitable habitat in this area. Continuing forest clearance is likely to remain a threat to any other populations that exist.

Conservation actions to date
The species continues to be a focus for research by the Colección Ornitológica Phelps.

Conservation actions required
* Survey potentially suitable spiny bamboo forest along the Caroni and Orinoco rivers in Venezuela and Colombia.

Mangrove Finch
Camarhynchus heliobates
Population: 60-140, trend unknown

Isabela Island, Galapagos, July 2003

Photo: © Greg Laskey

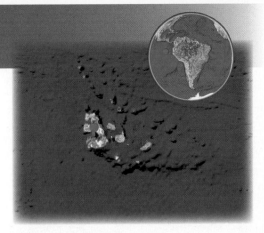

History

1898-99 – The Hopkins-Stanford Expedition collects 34 Mangrove Finches from Isabela and Fernandina.

1901 – Zoologists Robert Evans Snodgrass (1875-1962) and Edmund Heller (1875-1939) describe the species.

1905-06 – 26 birds are collected by the expedition of the California Academy of Science.

1962 – in a four-day census, Curio and Kramer estimate the population at Playa Tortuga Negra at 20 pairs at most.

1974 – three birds seen on Fernandina are the last ones from that island.

1997 – surveys on Isabela finds breeding populations in only two areas, estimated at 37 and 21 pairs respectively.

1999 – the populations are estimated at 36 and 16 pairs.

2007 – territory mapping reveals a maximum of 24 and 14 pairs respectively.

Range & population

This finch, which is one of the 'Darwin's finches', is restricted to the Galápagos Islands, Ecuador where it now breeds in only two sites; Playa Tortuga Negra and Caleta Black. Historically, it was known from at least six mangrove patches on east Fernandina and east, south and west Isabela. Recent surveys have failed to record the species on Fernandina, and it seems likely that it is now extinct as a breeding bird on the island. Surveys in the fairly extensive mangroves on the south-east coast of Isabela found three to five territories which probably contained breeding birds, but further areas of potentially suitable habitat remain unsurveyed.

It inhabits dense mangrove swamps, where it feeds on insects, larvae, spiders and some vegetable matter. Its breeding season coincides with the beginning of heavy rainfalls, normally in December to January, and lasts until the end of the rainy season, (May). Mangroves used by the species appear to be structurally different from areas where it is absent suggesting it has subtle habitat preferences and suffers from habitat degradation. It appears to favour mangroves with tall trees, relatively low canopy cover and abundant leaf litter and dead wood. A separation of the mangroves from the sea seems to be crucial, as this prevents the washing out of leaf litter which is the preferred feeding substrates.

Threats

It is not known why the species is declining but predation and competition with introduced animals seem to be the main threats. Rat abundance is high at both breeding sites and is believed to be the major reason for the high nesting failure due to predation (35% in 2007). Other possible introduced predators include feral cats (especially important during the post-fledging phase), Smooth-billed Ani *Crotophaga ani* and fire ants *Solenopsis spp*, though fire ants seemed to have been successfully exterminated in 1997. The blood sucking nest parasite *Philornis downi* is present in all nests and infestation is high (mean parasites per nest: 42). The first case of nesting mortality due to *Philornis* parasitizing was recorded in 2007. Research has shown that the species favours structurally distinct mangroves and hence, it may be susceptible to human modification of this habitat and, over time, geological impacts such as uplift which can radically alter the amount of available habitat.

Conservation actions to date

The habitat of this species is protected within the Galápagos National Park and, in 1979 the islands were declared a World Heritage Site though classified as threatened in 2007. Research is underway to determine if Black Rat is having an effect on its breeding success. Predator control is ongoing and a pilot study of control of *Philornis* will start with the breeding season 2007/08. A study of breeding biology commenced in 1999 and a follow up study started in 2006 as a three year Darwin Initiative Project co-ordinated by Durrell Wildlife Conservation Trust and Charles Darwin Foundation. Blood samples are being analysed to clarify whether hybridisation is occurring, but preliminary results for the latter are negative. The new Mangrove Finch project completed its first full year in 2007. This project aims to clarify the need and proceedings for a breeding or translocation project.

Conservation actions required

- Complete survey of distribution and numbers.
- Establish yearly monitoring at sites Playa Tortuga Negra and Caleta Black.
- Continue control measures for rats, wasps, anis, cats and fire ants at the sites Playa Tortuga Negra and Caleta Black, and monitor effects on the population.
- Study genetic differences between populations and assess hybridisation.
- Initiate captive breeding with view to establish new population in mangroves away from remaining sites.

Pale-headed Brush-finch
Atlapetes pallidiceps
Population: 134 ↑

Yunguilla, Ecuador, 2006

Photo: © Mery Juiña

History
1900 – Richard Bowdler Sharpe (1847-1909) describes the species.

1969 – the last record for some time is made.

1998 – Ana Agreda, Niels Krabbe, and Ofra Rodriguez find a population of 10-20 birds in the Yunguilla Valley in November.

1999 – a reserve is created by Fundación Jocotoco at Yunguilla to protect the species.

2002 – 27 territories are found.

2003 – estimated 33 pairs.

2004 – estimated 50 pairs.

Range & population
This species occurs in the Río Jubones drainage basin, in Azuay and Loja, south Ecuador. There were no records between 1969 and 1998. Despite repeated searches, it is unknown elsewhere within its presumed historical range. The population has increased in recent years thanks to intensive management, but further increases may be constrained by a lack of suitable habitat: in the Yungilla area there is only sufficient suitable habitat to support an estimated 50 pairs.
Its habitat is typical of regenerating landslides and fallow fields, with the species occurring in arid areas with dense low scrub at 1,650-1,800 m, which is mostly composite and herbaceous with a few Acacia and lauraceous trees lower down. Nests are placed within dense thickets of small bushes or bamboo. Birds have been observed feeding on fruit of a *Solanum sp.*, a *Morus sp.*, an introduced *Rubus sp.* and an unidentified *Polygonum sp.*, and gleaning insects on twigs. One stomach contained insect and seed remains. Historical records are all from oases in arid intermontane valleys, at 1,500-2,100 m. It is usually seen in pairs, mainly foraging around 2 m above the ground, but historically it was observed well above ground-level in Acacia. Immatures have been collected in June-July. Recent studies have investigated its breeding ecology and habitat usage. It coexists with Stripe-headed Brush-finch *Buarremon torquatus* but is subordinate to that species, and is replaced by Rufous-naped Brush-finch *A. latinuchus* at higher elevations.

Threats
Intensive grazing must be considered important in its decline, because the only apparent difference between occupied and unoccupied areas is the lack of access for cattle and goats to the former. However, in the absence of grazers habitat quickly re-grows into forest which is equally unsuitable for the species: open scrubby habitat is required which can be simulated by selectively thinning dense thickets. Widespread use of fire for clearing vegetation potentially threatens suitable habitat, particularly in the north of the reserve where there is no stream to act as a natural fire break. A large fire that threatened to destroy its habitat was extinguished by local people, who had been made aware of the bird and were interested in its preservation. Virtually no natural habitat remains in the Río León drainage, near Oña, where many specimens were taken. Brood parasitism by Shiny Cowbird *Molothrus bonariensis* has a significant impact on breeding success, with an overall parasitism rate of 42% in 2002 (with 61% of pairs breeding in the Yunguilla reserve parasitised). Recent study found that cowbird parasitism rates reached 50% in an ungrazed plot but just 14% in an adjacent grazed area.

Conservation actions to date
The remaining 27 ha of suitable habitat, including the area where it was observed in 1998, have been purchased by Fundación de Conservación Jocotoco and securely fenced off to remove grazing pressure. Cowbird removal in 2003 resulted in a strong increase in reproductive output, with 16 chicks fledged in Yunguilla reserve in 2003 compared to only five in 2002. A habitat management scheme was implemented by November 2002, in order to halt vegetation succession and convert unsuitable to suitable habitat by selective thinning of dense thickets. A habitat occupancy monitoring scheme was set up in 2004 to assess the success of this habitat management, and cowbird removal will also be implemented.

Conservation actions required
- Study the species and its habitat to facilitate successful land management.
- Maintain fences to exclude cattle and goats.
- Prevent fires.
- Protect the second known area and ravines between the sites.
- Establish a fire break at the northern reserve boundary.
- Fence currently degraded habitat on farmland in the area.
- Establish an environmental education programme in the surrounding area.
- Continue control of Shiny Cowbird *Molothrus bonariensis*.
- Continue to search in new areas for additional populations and apply a new strategy that allows population increase in other places where habitat exists.
- After further investigation, develop a management regime that prevents succession and minimises the level of cowbird parasitism through low intensity grazing.

Cone-billed Tanager
Conothraupis mesoleuca
Population: 50-249 ↓

Parque Nacional das Emas, Mineiros, Goiás, Brazil, 2004

Photo: © Dante Buzzetti

Range & population
Until recently, this species was known only from the type-specimen collected in 1938, c. 400 km north-west of Cuiabá, Mato Grosso, Brazil. An unconfirmed record of a female or juvenile was made in Noel Kempff Mercado National Park, in Bolivia in 1993. In 2003 the species was rediscovered in gallery woodlands in Emas National Park, Brazil. The type-specimen was taken amidst bushy vegetation in dry forest in the transitional zone between Amazonian rainforest and central Brazilian cerradão (closed-canopy cerrado). Evidence from Emas National Park suggests Cone-billed Tanager favours gallery forest and is strongly associated with water.

Threats
If it is dependent on cerradão or open cerrado and is likely to have suffered from extensive clearance and degradation through agricultural expansion and mechanisation in the region. The spread of soya cultivation in particular poses a serious threat outside Emas National Park.

Conservation actions to date
It is protected under Brazilian law. The species is only known from Emas National Park in the Center-West Region of Brazil. The park is reportedly well protected and does not face immediate threats from the surrounding human population. It is illegal to clear gallery forest in Brazil but this regulation is poorly enforced on many private lands.

Conservation actions required
* Research the status, distribution, ecology and habitat requirements of the species in the Emas National Park.
* Survey using tape-recordings of the song in remnant cerrado woodland and gallery forest in other areas.

Cherry-throated Tanager
Nemosia rourei
Population: 50-249 ↓

Vargem Alta, Espírito Santo State, August 2006

Photo: © Andre de Luca

Range & population
This species is currently known from Espírito Santo, Brazil, where it was rediscovered in 1998 (the last previous record was in 1941), and more recently from Mata do Caetés, Vargem Alta municipality. It occurs primarily in the canopy of humid montane forest at elevations of 900-1,100 m. The diet is reportedly arthropods. Nest-building has been observed in late November.

Threats
Extensive deforestation within its range must have had an impact on this species. However, the species has been recorded in eucalyptus and pinus plantations using this suboptimal habitat while moving between fragments.

Conservation actions to date
It is protected under Brazilian law. Mata do Caetés is a Reserva Particular do Patrimônio Natural (RPPN). The 1941 record site in Iterana is listed as an IBA owing to its importance for Atlantic forest endemics. Searches for the species have been conducted in other parts of Espírito Santo, Minas Gerais and Rio de Janeiro states.

Conservation actions required
* Survey the montane region of south Espírito Santo, and adjacent Minas Gerais and Rio de Janeiro, concentrating on elevations between 900 and 1,100 m and those sites which have previously been identified as potentially suitable for the species.
* Research ecology and seasonal abundance.
* Promote the creation of a Reserva Particular do Patrimônio Natural at Fazenda Pindobas IV.

Extinct Species

Since 1500, a total of 154 species have become extinct.

Snail-eating Coua
Coua delalandei
Extinct since 1834

Painting: © BirdLife International

16th century

1502 St Helena Rail
      Porzana astrictocarpus
1502 St Helena Crake
      Atlantisia podarces
1502 St Helena Dove
      Dysmoropelia dekarchiskos
1502 St Helena Hoopoe
      Upupa antaois
1502 Small St Helena Petrel
      Bulweria bifax
1502 Large St Helena Petrel
      Pterodroma rupinarum

17th century

1610 Réunion Owl
      Mascarenotus grucheti

1662 Dodo
      Raphus cucullatus
1672 Reunion Kestrel
      Falco buboisi
1675 Broad-billed Parrot
      Lophopsittacus mauritianus
1687 Réunion Night-Heron
      Nycticorax duboisi
1691 Réunion Island Sheldgoose
      Mascarenachen kervazoi
1693 Mascarene Coot
      Fulica newtoni
1695 Mauritian Shelduck
      Alopochen mauritianus
1696 Mauritian Duck
      Anas theodori
1696 Mauritius Night-Heron
      Nycticorax mauritianus

18th century

1700 Red Rail
Aphanapteryx bonasia
1705 Réunion Pigeon
Columba duboisi
1726 Rodrigues Pigeon
Alectroenas rodericana
1726 Rodrigues Owl
Mascarenotus murivorus
1726 Rodrigues Starling
Necropsar rodericanus
1730 Réunion Gallinule
Porphyrio coerulescens
1743 Rodrigues Night-Heron
Nycticorax megacephalus
1743 Rodrigues Rail
Aphanapteryx leguati
1750 St Helena Cuckoo
Nannococcyx psix
1759 Rodrigues Solitaire
Pezophaps solitaria
1760 Lesser Antillean Macaw
Ara guadeloupensis
1761 Rodrigues Parrot
Necropsittacus rodericanus
1761 Réunion Ibis
Threskiornis solitarius
1764 Mauritius Grey Parrot
Lophopsittacus bensoni
1773 Tahitian Sandpiper
Prosobonia leucoptera
1773 Raiatea Parakeet
Cyanoramphus ulietanus
1774 Tanna Ground-dove
Gallicolumba ferruginea
1775 Guadeloupe Parakeet
Aratinga labati
1779 Guadeloupe Parrot
Amazona violacea
1782 Jamaican Red Macaw
Ara gossei
1784 Miller's Rail
Porzana nigra
1788 White-winged Sandpiper
Prosobonia ellisi
1788 Tasman Booby
Sula tasmani
1789 Martinique Parrot
Amazona martinicana
1789 Mascarene Parrot
Mascarinus mascarinus
1793 Amsterdam Island Duck
Anas marecula

1800-1849

1800 Dominican Green-and-yellow Macaw
Ara atwoodi
1800 Norfolk Island Ground-dove
Gallicolumba norfolciensis
1802 King Island Emu
Dromaius ater
1810 Norfolk Island Kaka
Nestor productus

1812 Lord Howe Island Swamphen
Porphyrio albus
1815 Ascension Flightless Crake
Atlantisia elpenor
1823 Maupiti Monarch
Pomarea pomarea
1825 'Amaui
Myadestes oahensis
1825 Mysterious Starling
Aplonis mavornata
1827 Kangaroo Island Emu
Dromaius baudinianus
1828 Bonin Thrush
Zoothera terrestris
1828 Kosrae Starling
Aplonis corvina
1834 Snail-eating Coua
Coua delalandei
1835 Mauritius Blue-pigeon
Alectroenas nitidissima
1837 Mauritius Owl
Mascarenotus sauzieri
1837 O'ahu 'O'o
Moho apicalis
1840 Kosrae Crake
Porzana monasa
1840 Red-throated Wood-rail
Aramides gutturalis
1844 Black-fronted Parakeet
Cyanoramphus zealandicus
1847 Jamaican Green-and-yellow Macaw
Ara erythrocephala

1850-1859

1850 Pallas's Cormorant
Phalacrocorax perspicillatus
1852 Great Auk
Pinguinus impennis
1855 Réunion Starling
Fregilupus varius
1856 Dieffenbach's Rail
Gallirallus dieffenbachii
1859 Kioea
Chaetoptila angustipluma

1860-1869

1860 Gould's Emerald
Chlorostilbon elegans
1860 New Caledonia Gallinule
Porphyrio kukwiedei
1862 New Zealand Quail
Coturnix novaezelandiae

1870-1879

1871 Double-banded Argus
Argusianus bipunctatus
1875 Labrador Duck
Camptorhynchus labradorius
1875 Newton's Parakeet
Psittacula exsul
1877 Brace's Emerald
Chlorostilbon bracei

1880-1889

1881 Seychelles Parakeet
      Psittacula wardi
1884 Hawaiian Crake
      Porzana sandwichensis
1885 Cuban Macaw
      Ara tricolor
1886 Tristan Moorhen
      Gallinula nesiotis
1889 Bonin Wood-pigeon
      Columba versicolor

1890-1899

1890 Bonin Grosbeak
      Chaunoproctus ferreorostris
1891 Lesser Koa-finch
      Rhodacanthis flaviceps
1892 Maui Nui ' Akialoa
      Akialoa lanaiensis
1892 Ula-'ai-hawane
      Ciridops anna
1894 North Island Takahe
      Porphyrio mantelli
1894 Stephens Island Wren
      Traversia lyalli
1894 Kona Grosbeak
      Chloridops kona
1895 Hawkin's Rail
      Diaphorapteryx hawkinsi
1896 Greater Koa-finch
      Rhodacanthis palmeri
1898 Chatham Rail
      Cabalus modestus
1898 Hawai'i Mamo
      Drepanis pacifica

1900-1909

1900 Guadalupe Caracara
      Caracara lutosa
1900 Passenger Pigeon
      Ectopistes migratorius
1900 New Zealand Little Bittern
      Ixobrychus novaezelandiae
1900 Chatham Island Fernbird
      Bowdleria rufescens
1901 Greater 'Amakihi
      Hemignathus sagittirostris
1902 Auckland Island Merganser
      Mergus australis
1904 Carolina Parakeet
      Conuropsis carolinensis
1904 Choiseul Pigeon
      Microgoura meeki
1906 Chatham Island Bellbird
      Anthornis melanocephala
1907 Black Mamo
      Drepanis funereal
1907 Huia
      Heteralocha acutirostris

1910-1919

1910 Slender-billed Grackle
      Quiscalus palustris
1918 Lana'i Hookbill
      Dysmorodrepanis munroi

1920-1929

1922 Red-moustached Fruit-dove
      Ptilinopus mercierii
1923 Robust White-eye
      Zosterops strenuous

Atitlán Grebe
Podilymbus gigas
Extinct since 1986

Painting: © BirdLife International

1923 Norfolk Starling
Aplonis fusca
1927 Paradise Parrot
Psephotus pulcherrimus
1927 Lord Howe Gerygone
Gerygone insularis
1927 Thick-billed Ground-dove
Gallicolumba salamonis

1930-1939

1934 Hawai'i 'O'o
Moho nobilis
1935 Tahiti Rail
Gallirallus pacificus
1935 Nuku Hiva Monarch
Pomarea nukuhivae
1936 Ryukyu Pigeon
Columba jouyi
1938 Grand Cayman Thrush
Turdus ravidus

1940-1949

1940 Oahu 'Akialoa
Akialoa ellisiana
1940 'Akialoa
Hemignathus obscurus
1943 Wake Island Rail
Gallirallus wakensis
1944 Laysan Crake
Porzana palmeri
1945 Canarian Black Oystercatcher
Haematopus meadewaldoi

1950-1959

1955 North Island Piopio
Turnagra tanagra

1960-1969

1963 Kakawahie
Paroreomyza flammea
1963 South Island Piopio
Turnagra capensis
1965 Laughing Owl
Sceloglaux albifacies
1969 Kauai 'Akialoa
Akialoa stejnegeri

1970-1979

1972 Bush Wren
Xenicus longipes
1973 Bar-winged Rail
Nesoclopeus poecilopterus
1977 Colombian Grebe
Podiceps andinus
1977 Eiao Monarch
Pomarea fluxa

1980-1989

1981 Bishop's 'O'o
Moho bishopi
1983 Aldabra Warbler
Nesillas aldabrana
1983 Guam Flycatcher
Myiagra freycineti
1985 Ua Pou Monarch
Pomarea mira
1986 Atitlán Grebe
Podilymbus gigas
1987 Kaua'i 'O'o
Moho braccatus
1989 Kama'o
Myadestes myadestinus

1990-1999

None confirmed

2000-2007

None confirmed

Extinct in the Wild.
These species only occur in captivity.

	Year of extinction in the wild
Alagoas Curassow *Crax mitu*	1984
Socorro Dove *Zenaida graysoni*	1972
Guam Rail *Gallirallus owstoni*	1987
Spix's Macaw *Cyanopsitta spixii*	2000 not confirmed
Hawaiian Crow *Corvus hawaiiensis*	2002

Canarian Black Oystercatcher
Haematopus meadewaldoi
Extinct since 1945

Tour Operators
that will take you to Critically Endangered birds

NOW THAT YOU HAVE READ ABOUT THESE magnificent, rare birds, you may want to go and see them as well. Here is a listing of some tour operators which state that they see critically endangered birds on their trips. A listing here does not imply a stamp of quality by the Editor of this book nor that listed enterprises operate after strict ecotourism principles (see pp. 68-79). The listed continents refer to trips announced for 2008.

Access Uganda Tours (Uganda)
Website: www.accessugandatours.com
Email: accessug@utlonline.co.ug ,
mutebihassan@yahoo.com
Phone/fax: +256 (0)41 344 347
Africa

Albatross Encounter (New Zealand)
Website: www.encounterkaikoura.co.nz
Email: info@encounterkaikoura.co.nz
Phone: +64 3319 6777, 0800 733 365 (free phone)
New Zealand

Andean Birding (Ecuador)
Website: www.andeanbirding.com
Email: birding@andeanbirding.com
Phone: +593 2 224 4426
North America, South America

AVESTRAVEL (Ecuador)
Website: www.avestravel.com
E-mail: info@avestravel.com,
robertjonsson@avestravel.com
Phone +593 9 9206 628
South America

AviFauna (Sweden)
Website: www.avifauna.se
Email: avifauna@sofab.se
Phone: +46 (0)485 444 40
Africa, Asia, Asutralia, North America, South America

Bellavista Cloud Forest Reserve & Lodge (Ecuador)
Website: www.bellavistacloudforest.com
Email: info@bellavistacloudforest.com
Phone: +593 2 290 3166, 290 1536
South America

Bird Explorers (Australia)
Website: www.birdexplorers.com
Email: birdexplorers@surfbirder.com
Phone: +61 408933399

Africa (throughout), Asia (South Asia, Southeast Asia and Middle East), Europe (Eastern), Oceania (Australia and Pacific Islands), South Atlantic (New Georgia and Falklands).

Birdfinders (UK)
Website: www.birdfinders.co.uk
Email: birdfinders@aol.co.uk
Phone: +44 (0)1258 839066
Africa, Antarctica, Asia, Australasia, Europe, North America and South America

Birding in Paradise Safaris (Uganda)
Website: www.birdinginparadise.com
Email: enquiries@birdinginparadise.com
Phone: +256 (0)772 468521
Africa and Asia

Birdquest (UK)
Website: www.birdquest.co.uk
Email: birders@birdquest.co.uk
Phone: +44 (0)1254 826317
All continents

Birdseekers (UK)
Website: www.birdseekers.co.uk
Email: info@birdseekers.co.uk
Phone: +44 (0)1752 342001
All continents

Birdtour Asia (UK)
Website: www.birdtourasia.com
Email: info@birdtourasia.com
Phone: +44 (0)1332 516254
Asia

Bird Treks (USA)
Website: www.birdtreks.com
Email: info@birdtreks.com
Phone: +1 717 548 3303
North America, South America, Europe, Asia, and Africa

DOF Travel (Denmark)
Website: www.doftravel.dk
Email: travel@dof.dk
Phone: +45 3328 3800
Asia, Africa, South America

Eagle-Eye Tours (Canada)
Website: www.eagle-eye.com
Email: travel@eagle-eye.com
Phone: +1 250 342 8640 or 1-800 373 5678 toll free in
North America
North & South America, Africa, Asia, Europe, and
Australasia

EcoTours Colombia (Colombia)
Website: www.ecotours.com.co
Email: info@ecotours.org
Phone: +57 1 2876592 (London office +44 208 5432083)
South America

Fatbirder's Anytime Tours (UK)
Website: www.anytimetours.co.uk
Phone: +44 (0)1843 298488
Asia, South America, Africa, Australasia

Field Guides Incorporated (USA)
Website: www.fieldguides.com
Email: fieldguides@fieldguides.com
Phone: +1 512 263 7295 or 1-800 728 4953 toll free in
North America
North America, South America, Central America (and
Caribbean), Europe, Africa, Asia, Australasia.

Heliangelus Naturresor (Sweden)
Website: www.heliangelus.se
Email: heliangelus@telia.com
Phone: +46 (0)140 10744
South America

Heritage Expeditions (New Zealand)
Website: www.heritage-expeditions.com
Email: info@heritage-expeditions.com
Phone: +64 (0)3 365 3500
Asia, Western Pacific, Subantarctic Islands, Antarctic

Jenner Expeditions (UK)
Website: www.BirdingTours.info
Email: info@BirdingTours.info
Phone: +44 (0) 1342 713858 or +44 (0) 1494 721692
Africa, Asia.

Jetwing Eco Holidays (Sri Lanka)
Website: www.jetwingeco.com
Email: eco@jetwing.lk
Phone: + 94 11 234 5700 (Extensions 521 or 527).
India (Sri Lanka and Western Ghats in India)

Kalypso Adventures (India)
Website: www.birdskerala.com
Email: info@birdskerala.com
Phone: +91 484 2092280
Asia

KingBird Tours Inc. (USA)
Website: www.kingbirdtours.com
Email: kingbirdtours@earthlink.net
Phone: +1 (212) 866 7923
Asia

Kolibri Expeditions (Peru)
Website: www.kolibriexpeditions.com
Email: kolibriexp@gmail.com
Phone: +51 1 273 72 46
Specializes in Endemic and threatened birds all over
South America.

Limosa Holidays (UK)
Website: www.limosaholidays.co.uk
Email: info@limosaholidays.co.uk
Phone: +44 (0)1263 578143
All continents except Antarctica.

NOF-Travel (Norway)
Website: www.naturogfritid.no
Email: post@naturogfritid.no
Phone: +47 38 39 35 75
South America

Manu Expeditions (Peru)
Website: www.manuexpeditions.com,
www.birding-in-peru.com
Email: birding@manuexpeditions.com
Phone: +51 84 226671, 239974
South America

Seriema Nature Tours (Argentina)
Website: www.seriematours.com
Email: info@seriematours.com
Phone/Fax: +54 11 4312 6345
South America and Antarctica

Sunbird (UK)
Website: www.sunbirdtours.co.uk
Email: sunbird@sunbirdtours.co.uk
Phone: +44 (0)1767 262522
Europe, Asia, Australasia, Africa, South America, North
America, Antarctica,

Tropical Birding (USA)
Website: www.tropicalbirding.com
Email: info@tropicalbirding.com
Phone: +1 409 505 0514
North America, South America, Africa, Asia, Australasia

Ventures Birding and Nature Tours (USA)
Website: www.birdventures.com
Email: travel@birdventures.com
Phone: +1 866 253 427
All continents

Zambezi Safari and Travel Company (UK)
Website: www.zambezi.com, www.bushcamps.com
Email: info@zambezi.com
Phone: +44 (0)1548 830059
Africa

Threats to Critically Endangered species

IT IS NOT EASY TO PINPOINT THE EXACT REASONS for a species' decline, since many different factors often interact to cause it. In some cases so little information may be known about a species, its habits and the areas where it lives, that a certain amount of guesswork has to be used in analyzing the reasons for the decline. And for those species which have not been recorded for a certain number of years (see pp. 262-263), we just have to make assumptions as to why they have become so rare, based on the latest known information. The magnitude of the impact of a certain factor on a decline can of course be difficult to quantify, for the same reasons.

In the fact sheets that BirdLife International (www.birdlife.org/datazone/index.html) has carefully compiled, analyses of decline causes and a grading of their impact, timing, severity and scope can be found. The threats are ranked according to the IUCN Threats Classification Scheme, which can be viewed at www.iucnredlist.org/info/major_threats. In the following listing, I have chosen to list those threats that have been determined to have high or medium impacts, and those with unknown, past or low impacts have been excluded. Agricultural threats have been broken down to crop level where possible.

Residential and commercial development
Threats from human settlements or other non-agricultural land uses with a substantial footprint are included in this category. The threats posed from recreational activities of humans are found under "Human Intrusions & Disturbance".

Alagoas Antwren *Myrmotherula snowi*
Alagoas Foliage-gleaner *Philydor novaesi*
Araripe Manakin *Antilophia bokermanni*
Belding's Yellowthroat *Geothlypis beldingi*
Blue-billed Curassow *Crax alberti*
Cherry-throated Tanager *Nemosia rourei*
Dusky Starfrontlet *Coeligena orina*
Giant Ibis *Thaumatibis gigantea*
Kaempfer's Tody-tyrant *Hemitriccus kaempferi*
Northern Bald Ibis *Geronticus eremita*
Orange-bellied Parrot *Neophema chrysogaster*
Purple-winged Ground-dove *Claravis godefrida*
Restinga Antwren *Formicivora littoralis*
Rio de Janeiro Antwren *Myrmotherula fluminensis*

Siberian Crane *Grus leucogeranus*
White-shouldered Ibis *Pseudibis davisoni*

Agriculture & aquaculture
Both small-scale and large-scale activities are found in this category.

Annual & perennial non-timber crops
Examples which are relevant for the species in this book are coca, rice, coffee and sugar cane plantations. (See below for a more specific subdivision for some species)

Alagoas Antwren *Myrmotherula snowi*
Alagoas Foliage-gleaner *Philydor novaesi*
Anjouan Scops-owl *Otus capnodes*
Banggai Crow *Corvus unicolor*
Belding's Yellowthroat *Geothlypis beldingi*
Bengal Florican *Houbaropsis bengalensis*
Black-chinned Monarch *Monarcha boanensis*
Black-hooded Coucal *Centropus steerii*
Blue-billed Curassow *Crax alberti*
Blue-eyed Ground-dove *Columbina cyanopis*
Blue-fronted Lorikeet *Charmosyna toxopei*
Brazilian Merganser *Mergus octosetaceus*
Caerulean Paradise-flycatcher *Eutrichomyias rowleyi*
Cebu Flowerpecker *Dicaeum quadricolor*
Cherry-throated Tanager *Nemosia rourei*
Chestnut-bellied Hummingbird
  Amazilia castaneiventris
Cuban Kite *Chondrohierax wilsonii*
Djibouti Francolin *Francolinus ochropectus*
Faichuk White-eye *Rukia ruki*
Forest Owlet *Heteroglaux blewitti*
Giant Ibis *Thaumatibis gigantea*

Grand Comoro Scops-owl *Otus pauliani*
Grenada Dove *Leptotila wellsi*
Grey-breasted Parakeet *Pyrrhura griseipectus*
Gurney's Pitta *Pitta gurneyi*
Honduran Emerald *Amazilia luciae*
Iquitos Gnatcatcher *Polioptila clementsi*
Javan Lapwing *Vanellus macropterus*
Kaempfer's Woodpecker *Celeus obrieni*
Liberian Greenbul *Phyllastrephus leucolepis*
Madagascar Fish-eagle *Haliaeetus vociferoides*
Madagascar Pochard *Aythya innotata*
Minas Gerais Tyrannulet *Phylloscartes roquettei*
Moheli Scops-owl *Otus moheliensis*
Munchique Wood-wren *Henicorhina negreti*
Negros Bleeding-heart *Gallicolumba keayi*
Negros Fruit-dove *Ptilinopus arcanus*
Northern Bald Ibis *Geronticus eremita*
Orange-bellied Parrot *Neophema chrysogaster*
Pale-headed Brush-finch *Atlapetes pallidiceps*
Philippine Cockatoo *Cacatua haematuropygia*
Philippine Eagle *Pithecophaga jefferyi*
Pink-headed Duck *Rhodonessa caryophyllacea*
Polynesian Ground-dove *Gallicolumba erythroptera*
Purple-winged Ground-dove *Claravis godefrida*
Ridgway's Hawk *Buteo ridgwayi*
Rio de Janeiro Antwren *Myrmotherula fluminensis*
Rota Bridled White-eye *Zosterops rotensis*
Rueck's Blue-flycatcher *Cyornis ruckii*
Samoan Moorhen *Gallinula pacifica*
Sangihe Shrike-thrush *Colluricincla sanghirensis*
Sangihe White-eye *Zosterops nehrkorni*
Short-crested Coquette *Lophornis brachylophus*
Siberian Crane *Grus leucogeranus*
Sociable Lapwing *Vanellus gregarius*
Spix's Macaw *Cyanopsitta spixii*
Stresemann's Bristlefront *Merulaxis stresemanni*
Taita Apalis *Apalis fuscigularis*
Taita Thrush *Turdus helleri*
Trinidad Piping-guan *Pipile pipile*
White-bellied Heron *Ardea insignis*
White-collared Kite *Leptodon forbesi*
White-shouldered Ibis *Pseudibis davisoni*
White-winged Guan *Penelope albipennis*

Example of specific crops that can affect certain species:

Banana
Araripe Manakin *Antilophia bokermanni*

Cocoa
Dwarf Olive Ibis *Bostrychia bocagei*
Sao Tome Fiscal *Lanius newtoni*
Sao Tome Grosbeak *Neospiza concolor*

Coconut
Polynesian Ground-dove *Gallicolumba erythroptera*

Coffee
Blue-billed Curassow *Crax alberti*
Chestnut-bellied Hummingbird
 Amazilia castaneiventris
Gorgeted Wood-quail *Odontophorus strophium*

Grey-breasted Parakeet *Pyrrhura griseipectus*
Gurney's Pitta *Pitta gurneyi*
Kinglet Calyptura *Calyptura cristata*
Niceforo's Wren *Thryothorus nicefori*
Ridgway's Hawk *Buteo ridgwayi*
Sao Tome Fiscal *Lanius newtoni*
Short-crested Coquette *Lophornis brachylophus*

Illegal drugs (marijuana, coca)
Blue-billed Curassow *Crax alberti*
Chestnut-bellied Hummingbird
 Amazilia castaneiventris
Short-crested Coquette *Lophornis brachylophus*

Maize
Short-crested Coquette *Lophornis brachylophus*

Palm oil
Gurney's Pitta *Pitta gurneyi*
Sulu Bleeding-heart *Gallicolumba menagei*

Rice
Bengal Florican *Houbaropsis bengalensis*
Madagascar Fish-eagle *Haliaeetus vociferoides*
Madagascar Pochard *Aythya innotata*

Rubber
Gurney's Pitta *Pitta gurneyi*

Soy bean
Blue-eyed Ground-dove *Columbina cyanopis*
Brazilian Merganser *Mergus octosetaceus*
Caatinga Woodpecker *Celeus obrieni*
Cone-billed Tanage *Conothraupis mesoleuca*

Sugarcane
Alagoas Antwren *Myrmotherula snowi*
Alagoas Foliage-gleaner *Philydor novaesi*
Bachman's Warbler *Vermivora bachmanii*
Chestnut-bellied Hummingbird
 Amazilia castaneiventris
Gorgeted Wood-quail *Odontophorus strophium*
Niceforo's Wren *Thryothorus nicefori*
White-collared Kite *Leptodon forbesi*

Wood and pulp plantation
This includes stands of trees, often non-native species, that are planted for timber or fibre. Teak and Eucalyptus are examples.

Blue-eyed Ground-dove *Columbina cyanopis*
Cherry-throated Tanager *Nemosia rourei*
Entre Rios Seedeater *Sporophila zelichi*
Taita Apalis *Apalis fuscigularis*
Taita Thrush *Turdus helleri*

Livestock farming & ranching
In farming, animals are kept in enclosures, in ranching they roam in wild habitats.

Alagoas Antwren *Myrmotherula snowi*
Alagoas Foliage-gleaner *Philydor novaesi*
Bahia Tapaculo *Scytalopus psychopompus*

Belding's Yellowthroat *Geothlypis beldingi*
Bengal Florican *Houbaropsis bengalensis*
Black-chinned Monarch *Monarcha boanensis*
Blue-billed Curassow *Crax alberti*
Blue-eyed Ground-dove *Columbina cyanopis*
Entre Rios Seedeater *Sporophila zelichi*
Forest Owlet *Heteroglaux blewitti*
Galapagos Petrel *Pterodroma phaeopygia*
Honduran Emerald *Amazilia luciae*
Lear's Macaw *Anodorhynchus leari*
Minas Gerais Tyrannulet *Phylloscartes roquettei*
Orange-bellied Parrot *Neophema chrysogaster*
Pale-headed Brush-finch *Atlapetes pallidiceps*
Royal Cinclodes *Cinclodes aricomae*
Sociable Lapwing *Vanellus gregarius*
Somali Thrush *Turdus ludoviciae*
Stresemann's Bristlefront *Merulaxis stresemanni*
Yellow-eared Parrot *Ognorhynchus icterotis*

Energy production & mining
These threats are the results of production of non-biological resources, such as oil, windfarms and gold mining. The species listed here are all victims of quarrying and mining.

Blue-billed Curassow *Crax alberti*
Cebu Flowerpecker *Dicaeum quadricolor*
Chestnut-bellied Hummingbird
   Amazilia castaneiventris
Christmas Frigatebird *Fregata andrewsi*
Dusky Starfrontlet *Coeligena orina*
Junin Grebe *Podiceps taczanowskii*
White-bellied Heron *Ardea insignis*

Biological resource use
This means threats from use, intentional or unintentional, of "wild" resources for consumption. One example of intentional use would be the collecting of seabirds' eggs for consumption. An example of unintentional use could be by-catch of grebes when setting fish traps.

Hunting & collecting terrestrial animals
This relates to killing or trapping for, for example, commercial, recreation, subsistence or persecution reasons. Accidental mortality and bycatch are included here.

Alaotra Grebe *Tachybaptus rufolavatus*
Bali Starling *Leucopsar rothschildi*
Bengal Florican *Houbaropsis bengalensis*
Blue-billed Curassow *Crax alberti*
Blue-crowned Laughingthrush *Garrulax courtoisi*
Blue-throated Macaw *Ara glaucogularis*
Cuban Kite *Chondrohierax wilsonii*
Dwarf Olive Ibis *Bostrychia bocagei*
Entre Rios Seedeater *Sporophila zelichi*
Giant Ibis *Thaumatibis gigantea*
Gorgeted Wood-quail *Odontophorus strophium*
Grey-breasted Parakeet *Pyrrhura griseipectus*
Gurney's Pitta *Pitta gurneyi*
Himalayan Quail *Ophrysia superciliosa*
Javan Lapwing *Vanellus macropterus*
Lear's Macaw *Anodorhynchus leari*
Madagascar Pochard *Aythya innotata*

Marquesan Imperial-pigeon *Ducula galeata*
Mindoro Bleeding-heart *Gallicolumba platenae*
Negros Fruit-dove *Ptilinopus arcanus*
Northern Bald Ibis *Geronticus eremita*
Philippine Cockatoo *Cacatua haematuropygia*
Red-headed Vulture *Sarcogyps calvus*
Ridgway's Hawk *Buteo ridgwayi*
Rufous-headed Hornbill *Aceros waldeni*
Sociable Lapwing *Vanellus gregarius*
Spix's Macaw *Cyanopsitta spixii*
Sulu Hornbill *Anthracoceros montani*
Trinidad Piping-guan *Pipile pipile*
White-rumped Vulture *Gyps bengalensis*
White-shouldered Ibis *Pseudibis davisoni*
Yellow-crested Cockatoo *Cacatua sulphurea*

Gathering terrestrial plants
There is just one species which is affected to a high or medium degree by this, and in this case it relates to inappropriate cutting and burning regimes of its grassland habitat.

Bengal Florican *Houbaropsis bengalensis*

Logging/wood harvesting
Harvesting wood for timber, fuel or fibre is included in this threat. It can relate to either clear cutting, selective commercial logging or gathering of firewood.

Alagoas Antwren *Myrmotherula snowi*
Alagoas Foliage-gleaner *Philydor novaesi*
Black-breasted Puffleg *Eriocnemis nigrivestis*
Imperial Woodpecker *Campephilus imperialis*
Iquitos Gnatcatcher *Polioptila clementsi*
Liberian Greenbul *Phyllastrephus leucolepis*
Minas Gerais Tyrannulet *Phylloscartes roquettei*
Sulu Hornbill *Anthracoceros montani*
White-collared Kite *Leptodon forbesi*
Black-chinned Monarch *Monarcha boanensis*
Black-hooded Coucal *Centropus steerii*
Blue-billed Curassow *Crax alberti*
Blue-fronted Lorikeet *Charmosyna toxopei*
Brazilian Merganser *Mergus octosetaceus*
Caerulean Paradise-flycatcher *Eutrichomyias rowleyi*
Chestnut-bellied Hummingbird
   Amazilia castaneiventris
Colourful Puffleg *Eriocnemis mirabilis*
Cuban Kite *Chondrohierax wilsonii*
Djibouti Francolin *Francolinus ochropectus*
Forest Owlet *Heteroglaux blewitti*
Gorgeted Wood-quail *Odontophorus strophium*
Gurney's Pitta *Pitta gurneyi*
Isabela Oriole *Oriolus isabellae*
Kaempfer's Woodpecker *Celeus obrieni*
Long-billed Apalis *Apalis moreaui*
Madagascar Fish-eagle *Haliaeetus vociferoides*
Mindoro Bleeding-heart *Gallicolumba platenae*
Moheli Scops-owl *Otus moheliensis*
Munchique Wood-wren *Henicorhina negreti*
Negros Bleeding-heart *Gallicolumba keayi*
Pernambuco Pygmy-owl *Glaucidium mooreorum*
Philippine Cockatoo *Cacatua haematuropygia*
Philippine Eagle *Pithecophaga jefferyi*
Ridgway's Hawk *Buteo ridgwayi*

Rio de Janeiro Antwren *Myrmotherula fluminensis*
Rueck's Blue-flycatcher *Cyornis ruckii*
Sangihe White-eye *Zosterops nehrkorni*
Sulu Bleeding-heart *Gallicolumba menagei*
Sumatran Ground-cuckoo *Carpococcyx viridis*
Trinidad Piping-guan *Pipile pipile*
Uluguru Bush-shrike *Malaconotus alius*
White-bellied Heron *Ardea insignis*
White-shouldered Ibis *Pseudibis davisoni*
White-winged Guan *Penelope albipennis*
Yellow-crested Cockatoo *Cacatua sulphurea*

Fishing/harvesting aquatic resources
None of the species in this book are harvested directly as 'aquatic resources', but can be found as bycatch of such activities.

Amsterdam Albatross *Diomedea amsterdamensis*
Balearic Shearwater *Puffinus mauretanicus*
Chatham Albatross *Thalassarche eremita*
Chatham Islands Shag *Phalacrocorax onslowi*
Christmas Island Frigatebird *Fregata andrewsi*
Kittlitz's Murrelet *Brachyramphus brevirostris*
Madagascar Fish-eagle *Haliaeetus vociferoides*
Waved Albatross *Phoebastria irrorata*

Human intrusions & disturbance
These threats are caused by humans who, for example, exploit areas for recreational purposes such as building hotels and golf courses, or off-road driving. It also includes disturbance by illegal immigration, vandalism and even research.

Blue-crowned Laughingthrush *Garrulax courtoisi*
Brazilian Merganser *Mergus octosetaceus*
Djibouti Francolin *Francolinus ochropectus*
Giant Ibis *Thaumatibis gigantea*
Grenada Dove *Leptotila wellsi*
Javan Lapwing *Vanellus macropterus*
St. Helena Plover *Charadrius sanctaehelenae*
White-bellied Heron *Ardea insignis*
White-shouldered Ibis *Pseudibis davisoni*

Natural system modifications
With this, actions that convert or degrade habitat in service of "managing" natural systems to improve human welfare are included. Examples include flooding from dam construction, land reclamation projects, wetland filling for mosquito control, or levees and dikes.

Alagoas Antwren *Myrmotherula snowi*
Alagoas Foliage-gleaner *Philydor novaesi*
Carrizal Seedeater *Amaurospiza carrizalensis*
Junin Grebe *Podiceps taczanowskii*
Lear's Macaw *Anodorhynchus leari*
Nihoa Finch *Telespiza ultima*
Orange-bellied Parrot *Neophema chrysogaster*
Pale-headed Brush-finch *Atlapetes pallidiceps*
Pernambuco Pygmy-owl *Glaucidium mooreorum*
Royal Cinclodes *Cinclodes aricomae*
Siberian Crane *Grus leucogeranus*
Slender-billed Vulture *Gyps tenuirostris*

Invasive & other problematic species & genes
This is defined as threats from non-native and native plants, animals, pathogens/microbes, or genetic materials that have or are predicted to have harmful effects on biodiversity following their introduction, spread and/or increase in abundance. Island bird species are particularly vulnerable to such invasive aliens, which were often originally brought for food (pigs and cattle) or for predator control (cats) or simply introduced by accident (rats and ants). Pigs and cats in particular have become feral. Foreign bird species have been introduced by immigrants as a reminder of home, and have in many places become pests, affecting not just the farming sector but also competing with less hardy indigenous bird species occupying a similar niche. Another category of threat comes from native species which have got out of balance or been "released" as a result of human activities, leading to greater competition for resources and nest sites, or even hybridisation between closely related species. This is a major threat for many island-breeding species. Plants have also been introduced to many places, intentionally or by accident. They can compete with indigenous vegetation and alter habitats to the detriment of certain species of birds. Examples here are water plants such as water hyacinths that are introduced to lakes and reduce clear water areas, or introduced grasses which outcompete local grasses that are used for nesting material.

Invasive non-native alien species
These are species which have been introduced by humans, intentionally or unintentionally, in the last 10,000 years.

Alaotra Grebe *Tachybaptus rufolavatus*
Amsterdam Albatross *Diomedea amsterdamensis*
Azores Bullfinch *Pyrrhula murina*
Balearic Shearwater *Puffinus mauretanicus*
Beck's Petrel *Pseudobulweria becki*
Black Stilt *Himantopus novaezelandiae*
California Condor *Gymnogyps californianus*
Christmas Frigatebird *Fregata andrewsi*
Dwarf Olive Ibis *Bostrychia bocagei*
Faichuk White-eye *Rukia ruki*
Fatuhiva Monarch *Pomarea whitneyi*
Fiji Petrel *Pseudobulweria macgillivrayi*
Galapagos Petrel *Pterodroma phaeopygia*
Golden White-eye *Cleptornis marchei*
Grenada Dove *Leptotila wellsi*
Guadalupe Junco *Junco insularis*
Guadalupe Storm-petrel *Oceanodroma macrodactyla*
Jamaica Petrel *Pterodroma caribbaea*
Jamaican Pauraque *Siphonorhis americana*
Juan Fernandez Firecrown *Sephanoides fernandensis*
Laysan Duck *Anas laysanensis*
Madagascar Pochard *Aythya innotata*
Magenta Petrel *Pterodroma magentae*
Makira Moorhen *Gallinula silvestris*
Malherbe's Parakeet *Cyanoramphus malherbi*
Mascarene Petrel *Pseudobulweria aterrima*
Maui Parrotbill *Pseudonestor xanthophrys*
Mauritius Fody *Foudia rubra*
Mauritius Olive White-eye *Zosterops chloronothus*
Millerbird *Acrocephalus familiaris*
Montserrat Oriole *Icterus oberi*
New Caledonian Rail *Gallirallus lafresnayanus*
New Zealand Storm-petrel *Oceanites maorianus*
Nihoa Finch *Telespiza ultima*
Nukupuu *Hemignathus lucidus*
Olomao *Myadestes lanaiensis*
Orange-bellied Parrot *Neophema chrysogaster*
Ou *Psittirostra psittacea*
Polynesian Ground-dove *Gallicolumba erythroptera*
Poo-uli *Melamprosops phaeosoma*
Puerto Rican Amazon *Amazona vittata*
Raso Lark *Alauda razae*
Red-headed Vulture *Sarcogyps calvus*
Red-throated Lorikeet *Charmosyna amabilis*
Rota Bridled White-eye *Zosterops rotensis*
Samoan Moorhen *Gallinula pacifica*
Seychelles Paradise-flycatcher *Terpsiphone corvina*
Socorro Mockingbird *Mimus graysoni*
Spix's Macaw *Cyanopsitta spixii*
Tahiti Monarch *Pomarea nigra*
Townsend's Shearwater *Puffinus auricularis*

Problematic native species
These are defined as harmful plants, animals, or
pathogens and other microbes that originate within
the ecosystem(s) in question, but have become "out-
of-balance" or "released" directly or indirectly due to
human activity. An example here is the hybridization
of Black and Pied Stilts in New Zealand.

Alaotra Grebe *Tachybaptus rufolavatus*
Black Stilt *Himantopus novaezelandiae*
Chatham Petrel *Pterodroma axillaris*
Cuban Kite *Chondrohierax wilsonii*
Forest Owlet *Heteroglaux blewitti*

Galapagos Petrel *Pterodroma phaeopygia*
Montserrat Oriole *Icterus oberi*
Puerto Rican Amazon *Amazona vittata*

Pollution
This is defined as threats from the introduction
of exotic and/or excess materials or energy from
point and nonpoint sources. Example of this include
the decline of three Asian vulture species through
ingesting the veterinary drug diclofenac from
carcasses, agricultural pollutants which build up in
species high up in the food chain and oil spills.

Alaotra Grebe *Tachybaptus rufolavatus*
Balearic Shearwater *Puffinus mauretanicus*
Djibouti Francolin *Francolinus ochropectus*
Indian Vulture *Gyps indicus*
Kittlitz's Murrelet *Brachyramphus brevirostris*
Madagascar Pochard *Aythya innotata*
Northern Bald Ibis *Geronticus eremita*
Philippine Eagle *Pithecophaga jefferyi*
Red-headed Vulture *Sarcogyps calvus*
Rota Bridled White-eye *Zosterops rotensis*
Siberian Crane *Grus leucogeranus*
Slender-billed Vulture *Gyps tenuirostris*
White-bellied Heron *Ardea insignis*
White-rumped Vulture *Gyps bengalensis*
Yellow-crested Cockatoo *Cacatua sulphurea*

Geological events
Volcanoes are included in this threat category.
Although a natural phenomenon, an eruption
may weaken an already diminished population
considerably.

Black-breasted Puffleg *Eriocnemis nigrivestis*
Montserrat Oriole *Icterus oberi*

Climate change & severe weather
Anthropogenic (human-derived) climate change (see
pp. 42-51) is already having severe effect on birds. It
alters habitats and raises sea levels which in the long
run can be disadvantageous to birds with restricted
ranges and small populations. Increased temperatures also affect food supplies directly, and can help
other species to colonise new areas and outcompete
indigenous species.

Akikiki *Oreomystis bairdi*
Chatham Albatross *Thalassarche eremita*
Cozumel Thrasher *Toxostoma guttatum*
Faichuk White-eye *Rukia ruki*
Laysan Duck *Anas laysanensis*
Millerbird *Acrocephalus familiaris*
Montserrat Oriole *Icterus oberi*
Nihoa Finch *Telespiza ultima*
Nukupuu *Hemignathus lucidus*
Orange-bellied Parrot *Neophema chrysogaster*
Puaiohi *Myadestes palmeri*
Puerto Rican Amazon *Amazona vittata*
Raso Lark *Alauda razae*
Rota Bridled White-eye *Zosterops rotensis*
Tahiti Monarch *Pomarea nigra*

Which countries hold which species?

THE CRITICALLY ENDANGERED SPECIES FOUND in the different countries of the world are listed here. This list is based on a list produced by BirdLife International, but only those species with a somewhat regular, current or historical, occurrence are mentioned. Vagrants, such as Slender-billed Curlew in the United Kingdom, are not included. Furthermore, seabirds often range over vast expanses of international, oceanic territory and they are only included here for countries where they nest or regularly occur offshore from.

Afghanistan
Indian Vulture *Gyps indicus*
Siberian Crane *Grus leucogeranus*
Sociable Lapwing *Vanellus gregarius*
Slender-billed Curlew *Numenius tenuirostris*

Albania
Slender-billed Curlew *Numenius tenuirostris*

Algeria
Balearic Shearwater *Puffinus mauretanicus*
Northern Bald Ibis *Geronticus eremita*
Slender-billed Curlew *Numenius tenuirostris*

Argentina
Brazilian Merganser *Mergus octosetaceus*
Eskimo Curlew *Numenius borealis*
Purple-winged Ground-dove *Claravis godefrida*
Glaucous Macaw *Anodorhynchus glaucus*
Entre Rios Seedeater *Sporophila zelichi*

Armenia
Sociable Lapwing *Vanellus gregarius*

Australia
Chatham Albatross *Thalassarche eremita*
Orange-bellied Parrot *Neophema chrysogaster*
Night Parrot *Pezoporus occidentalis*

Christmas Island (to Australia)
Christmas Frigatebird *Fregata andrewsi*

Norfolk Island (to Australia)
Chatham Albatross *Thalassarche eremita*
White-chested White-eye *Zosterops albogularis*

Azerbaijan
Siberian Crane *Grus leucogeranus*
Sociable Lapwing *Vanellus gregarius*
Slender-billed Curlew *Numenius tenuirostris*

Bangladesh
Pink-headed Duck *Rhodonessa caryophyllacea*
White-bellied Heron *Ardea insignis*
Slender-billed Vulture *Gyps tenuirostris*
Red-headed Vulture *Sarcogyps calvus*
Bengal Florican *Houbaropsis bengalensis*

Bhutan
White-bellied Heron *Ardea insignis*
White-rumped Vulture *Gyps bengalensis*
Red-headed Vulture *Sarcogyps calvus*

Bolivia
Blue-throated Macaw *Ara glaucogularis*
Royal Cinclodes *Cinclodes aricomae*

Brazil
Brazilian Merganser *Mergus octosetaceus*
White-collared Kite *Leptodon forbesi*
Eskimo Curlew *Numenius borealis*
Blue-eyed Ground-dove *Columbina cyanopis*
Purple-winged Ground-dove *Claravis godefrida*
Lear's Macaw *Anodorhynchus leari*
Glaucous Macaw *Anodorhynchus glaucus*
Spix's Macaw *Cyanopsitta spixii*
Grey-breasted Parakeet *Pyrrhura griseipectus*
Pernambuco Pygmy-owl *Glaucidium mooreorum*
Kaempfer's Woodpecker *Celeus obrieni*
Araripe Manakin *Antilophia bokermanni*

Kinglet Calyptura *Calyptura cristata*
Minas Gerais Tyrannulet *Phylloscartes roquettei*
Kaempfer's Tody-tyrant *Hemitriccus kaempferi*
Rondonia Bushbird *Clytoctantes atrogularis*
Rio de Janeiro Antwren *Myrmotherula fluminensis*
Alagoas Antwren *Myrmotherula snowi*
Restinga Antwren *Formicivora littoralis*
Stresemann's Bristlefront *Merulaxis stresemanni*
Bahia Tapaculo *Scytalopus psychopompus*
Alagoas Foliage-gleaner *Philydor novaesi*
Hooded Seedeater *Sporophila melanops*
Cone-billed Tanager *Conothraupis mesoleuca*
Cherry-throated Tanager *Nemosia rourei*

Brunei
Christmas Frigatebird *Fregata andrewsi*

Bulgaria
Slender-billed Curlew *Numenius tenuirostris*

Cambodia
White-shouldered Ibis *Pseudibis davisoni*
Giant Ibis *Thaumatibis gigantea*
Christmas Frigatebird *Fregata andrewsi*
White-rumped Vulture *Gyps bengalensis*
Slender-billed Vulture *Gyps tenuirostris*
Red-headed Vulture *Sarcogyps calvus*
Bengal Florican *Houbaropsis bengalensis*

Canada
Eskimo Curlew *Numenius borealis*
Kittlitz's Murrelet *Brachyramphus brevirostris*

Chile
Chatham Albatross *Thalassarche eremita*
Eskimo Curlew *Numenius borealis*
Juan Fernandez Firecrown *Sephanoides fernandensis*
Masafuera Rayadito *Aphrastura masafuerae*

China
Crested Shelduck *Tadorna cristata*
White-shouldered Ibis *Pseudibis davisoni*
Christmas Frigatebird *Fregata andrewsi*
Red-headed Vulture *Sarcogyps calvus*
Siberian Crane *Grus leucogeranus*
Chinese Crested Tern *Sterna bernsteini*
Blue-crowned Laughingthrush *Garrulax courtoisi*

Colombia
Blue-billed Curassow *Crax alberti*
Gorgeted Wood-quail *Odontophorus strophium*
Waved Albatross *Phoebastria irrorata*
Galapagos Petrel *Pterodroma phaeopygia*
Yellow-eared Parrot *Ognorhynchus icterotis*
Indigo-winged Parrot *Hapalopsittaca fuertesi*
Sapphire-bellied Hummingbird *Lepidopyga lilliae*
Chestnut-b. Hummingbird *Amazilia castaneiventris*
Dusky Starfrontlet *Coeligena orina*
Turquoise-throated Puffleg *Eriocnemis godini*
Colourful Puffleg *Eriocnemis mirabilis*
Niceforo's Wren *Thryothorus nicefori*
Munchique Wood-wren *Henicorhina negreti*

Comoros
Anjouan Scops-owl *Otus capnodes*
Moheli Scops-owl *Otus moheliensis*
Grand Comoro Scops-owl *Otus pauliani*

Cook Islands
Chatham Albatross *Thalassarche eremita*

Costa Rica
Galapagos Petrel *Pterodroma phaeopygia*

Croatia
Slender-billed Curlew *Numenius tenuirostris*

Cuba
Cuban Kite *Chondrohierax wilsonii*
Ivory-billed Woodpecker *Campephilus principalis*
Bachman's Warbler *Vermivora bachmanii*

Djibouti
Djibouti Francolin *Francolinus ochropectus*

Dominican Republic
Ridgway's Hawk *Buteo ridgwayi*

Ecuador
Waved Albatross *Phoebastria irrorata*
Galapagos Petrel *Pterodroma phaeopygia*
Yellow-eared Parrot *Ognorhynchus icterotis*
Black-breasted Puffleg *Eriocnemis nigrivestis*
Turquoise-throated Puffleg *Eriocnemis godini*
Mangrove Finch *Camarhynchus heliobates*
Pale-headed Brush-finch *Atlapetes pallidiceps*

El Salvador
Galapagos Petrel *Pterodroma phaeopygia*

Eritrea
Northern Bald Ibis *Geronticus eremita*
Sociable Lapwing *Vanellus gregarius*

Ethiopia
Northern Bald Ibis *Geronticus eremita*

Fiji
Fiji Petrel *Pseudobulweria macgillivrayi*
Red-throated Lorikeet *Charmosyna amabilis*

France
Balearic Shearwater *Puffinus mauretanicus*
French Southern Territories
Amsterdam Albatross *Diomedea amsterdamensis*
French Polynesia
Chatham Albatross *Thalassarche eremita*
Polynesian Ground-dove *Gallicolumba erythroptera*
Marquesan Imperial-pigeon *Ducula galeata*
Tuamotu Kingfisher *Todiramphus gambieri*
Tahiti Monarch *Pomarea nigra*
Fatuhiva Monarch *Pomarea whitneyi*

New Caledonia (to France)
Chatham Albatross *Thalassarche eremita*
New Caledonian Rail *Gallirallus lafresnayanus*
New Caledonian Lorikeet *Charmosyna diadema*
New Caledonian Owlet-nightjar *Aegotheles savesi*

Réunion (to France)
Mascarene Petrel *Pseudobulweria aterrima*

Wallis and Futuna Islands (to France)
Chatham Albatross *Thalassarche eremita*

Greece
Slender-billed Curlew *Numenius tenuirostris*

Grenada
Grenada Dove *Leptotila wellsi*

Guatemala
Galapagos Petrel *Pterodroma phaeopygia*

Haiti
Ridgway's Hawk *Buteo ridgwayi*

Honduras
Honduran Emerald *Amazilia luciae*

Hong Kong
Christmas Frigatebird *Fregata andrewsi*

Hungary
Slender-billed Curlew *Numenius tenuirostris*

India
Himalayan Quail *Ophrysia superciliosa*
Pink-headed Duck *Rhodonessa caryophyllacea*
White-bellied Heron *Ardea insignis*
White-rumped Vulture *Gyps bengalensis*
Indian Vulture *Gyps indicus*
Slender-billed Vulture *Gyps tenuirostris*
Red-headed Vulture *Sarcogyps calvus*
Bengal Florican *Houbaropsis bengalensis*
Siberian Crane *Grus leucogeranus*
Sociable Lapwing *Vanellus gregarius*
Jerdon's Courser *Rhinoptilus bitorquatus*
Forest Owlet *Heteroglaux blewitti*

Indonesia
White-shouldered Ibis *Pseudibis davisoni*
Christmas Frigatebird *Fregata andrewsi*
Javan Lapwing *Vanellus macropterus*
Chinese Crested Tern *Sterna bernsteini*
Silvery Wood-pigeon *Columba argentina*
Yellow-crested Cockatoo *Cacatua sulphurea*
Blue-fronted Lorikeet *Charmosyna toxopei*
Sumatran Ground-cuckoo *Carpococcyx viridis*
Siau Scops-owl *Otus siaoensis*
Sangihe Shrike-thrush *Colluricincla sanghirensis*
Caerulean Paradise-flycatcher *Eutrichomyias rowleyi*
Black-chinned Monarch *Monarcha boanensis*
Banggai Crow *Corvus unicolor*
Sangihe White-eye *Zosterops nehrkorni*
Bali Starling *Leucopsar rotschildi*
Rueck's Blue-flycatcher *Cyornis ruckii*

Islamic Republic of Iran
White-rumped Vulture *Gyps bengalensis*
Siberian Crane *Grus leucogeranus*
Sociable Lapwing *Vanellus gregarius*
Slender-billed Curlew *Numenius tenuirostris*

Iraq
Northern Bald Ibis *Geronticus eremita*
Sociable Lapwing *Vanellus gregarius*
Slender-billed Curlew *Numenius tenuirostris*

Ireland
Balearic Shearwater *Puffinus mauretanicus*

Jamaica
Jamaica Petrel *Pterodroma caribbaea*
Jamaican Pauraque *Siphonorhis americana*

Japan
Kittlitz's Murrelet *Brachyramphus brevirostris*
Okinawa Woodpecker *Dendrocopos noguchii*

Kazakhstan
Siberian Crane *Grus leucogeranus*
Sociable Lapwing *Vanellus gregarius*
Slender-billed Curlew *Numenius tenuirostris*

Kenya
Taita Apalis *Apalis fuscigularis*
Taita Thrush *Turdus helleri*

Kyrgyzstan
Sociable Lapwing *Vanellus gregarius*
Slender-billed Curlew *Numenius tenuirostris*

Laos
White-shouldered Ibis *Pseudibis davisoni*
Giant Ibis *Thaumatibis gigantea*
White-rumped Vulture *Gyps bengalensis*
Slender-billed Vulture *Gyps tenuirostris*
Red-headed Vulture *Sarcogyps calvus*

Liberia
Liberian Greenbul *Phyllastrephus leucolepis*

Libya
Slender-billed Curlew *Numenius tenuirostris*

The Former Yugoslav Republic of Macedonia
Slender-billed Curlew *Numenius tenuirostris*

Madagascar
Madagascar Pochard *Aythya innotata*
Alaotra Grebe *Tachybaptus rufolavatus*
Madagascar Fish-eagle *Haliaeetus vociferoides*

Malaysia
Christmas Frigatebird *Fregata andrewsi*
Red-headed Vulture *Sarcogyps calvus*
Chinese Crested Tern *Sterna bernsteini*
Silvery Wood-pigeon *Columba argentina*

Mauritania
Northern Bald Ibis *Geronticus eremita*

Mauritius
Mauritius Olive White-eye *Zosterops chloronothus*
Mauritius Fody *Foudia rubra*

Mexico
Galapagos Petrel *Pterodroma phaeopygia*
Townsend's Shearwater *Puffinus auricularis*
Guadalupe Storm-petrel *Oceanodroma macrodactyla*
Short-crested Coquette *Lophornis brachylophus*
Imperial Woodpecker *Campephilus imperialis*
Socorro Mockingbird *Mimus graysoni*
Cozumel Thrasher *Toxostoma guttatum*
Belding's Yellowthroat *Geothlypis beldingi*
Guadalupe Junco *Junco insularis*

Federated States of Micronesia
Faichuk White-eye *Rukia ruki*
Pohnpei Starling *Aplonis pelzelni*

Mongolia
Siberian Crane *Grus leucogeranus*

Morocco
Balearic Shearwater *Puffinus mauretanicus*
Northern Bald Ibis *Geronticus eremita*
Slender-billed Curlew *Numenius tenuirostris*

Mozambique
Long-billed Apalis *Apalis moreaui*

Myanmar
Pink-headed Duck *Rhodonessa caryophyllacea*
White-shouldered Ibis *Pseudibis davisoni*
White-bellied Heron *Ardea insignis*
White-rumped Vulture *Gyps bengalensis*
Slender-billed Vulture *Gyps tenuirostris*
Red-headed Vulture *Sarcogyps calvus*
Gurney's Pitta *Pitta gurneyi*

Nepal
White-rumped Vulture *Gyps bengalensis*
Slender-billed Vulture *Gyps tenuirostris*
Red-headed Vulture *Sarcogyps calvus*
Bengal Florican *Houbaropsis bengalensis*

New Zealand
Campbell Islands Teal *Anas nesiotis*
Chatham Albatross *Thalassarche eremita*
Magenta Petrel *Pterodroma magentae*
Chatham Petrel *Pterodroma axillaris*
New Zealand Storm-petrel *Oceanites maorianus*
Chatham Islands Shag *Phalacrocorax onslowi*
Black Stilt *Himantopus novaezelandiae*
Kakapo *Strigops habroptila*
Malherbe's Parakeet *Cyanoramphus malherbi*

Niue (to New Zealand)
Chatham Albatross *Thalassarche eremita*

Nicaragua
Galapagos Petrel *Pterodroma phaeopygia*

Northeast Atlantic
Balearic Shearwater *Puffinus mauretanicus*

Oman
Sociable Lapwing *Vanellus gregarius*
Slender-billed Curlew *Numenius tenuirostris*

Pakistan
White-rumped Vulture *Gyps bengalensis*
Indian Vulture *Gyps indicus*
Siberian Crane *Grus leucogeranus*
Sociable Lapwing *Vanellus gregarius*

Panama
Galapagos Petrel *Pterodroma phaeopygia*

Papua New Guinea
Beck's Petrel *Pseudobulweria becki*

Paraguay
Brazilian Merganser *Mergus octosetaceus*
Purple-winged Ground-dove *Claravis godefrida*
Glaucous Macaw *Anodorhynchus glaucus*
Entre Rios Seedeater *Sporophila zelichi*

Peru
White-winged Guan *Penelope albipennis*
Waved Albatross *Phoebastria irrorata*
Chatham Albatross *Thalassarche eremita*
Galapagos Petrel *Pterodroma phaeopygia*
Junin Grebe *Podiceps taczanowskii*
Purple-backed Sunbeam *Aglaeactis aliciae*
Royal Cinclodes *Cinclodes aricomae*
Iquitos Gnatcatcher *Polioptila clementsi*

Philippines
Philippine Eagle *Pithecophaga jefferyi*
Chinese Crested Tern *Sterna bernsteini*
Mindoro Bleeding-heart *Gallicolumba platenae*
Negros Bleeding-heart *Gallicolumba keayi*
Sulu Bleeding-heart *Gallicolumba menagei*
Negros Fruit-dove *Ptilinopus arcanus*
Philippine Cockatoo *Cacatua haematuropygia*
Black-hooded Coucal *Centropus steerii*
Sulu Hornbill *Anthracoceros montani*
Rufous-headed Hornbill *Aceros waldeni*
Isabela Oriole *Oriolus isabellae*
Cebu Flowerpecker *Dicaeum quadricolor*

Portugal
Balearic Shearwater *Puffinus mauretanicus*
Azores Bullfinch *Pyrrhula murina*

Cape Verde
Raso Lark *Alauda razae*

Romania
Slender-billed Curlew *Numenius tenuirostris*

Russia
Crested Shelduck *Tadorna cristata*
Siberian Crane *Grus leucogeranus*
Kittlitz's Murrelet *Brachyramphus brevirostris*
Sociable Lapwing *Vanellus gregarius*
Slender-billed Curlew *Numenius tenuirostris*

Samoa
Samoan Moorhen *Gallinula pacifica*

Sâo Tomé e Principe
Dwarf Olive Ibis *Bostrychia bocagei*
Sao Tome Fiscal *Lanius newtoni*
Sao Tome Grosbeak *Neospiza concolor*

Saudi Arabia
Northern Bald Ibis *Geronticus eremita*
Sociable Lapwing *Vanellus gregarius*
Slender-billed Curlew *Numenius tenuirostris*

Serbia and Montenegro
Slender-billed Curlew *Numenius tenuirostris*

Seychelles
Seychelles Paradise-flycatcher *Terpsiphone corvina*

Singapore
Christmas Frigatebird *Fregata andrewsi*

Solomon Islands
Beck's Petrel *Pseudobulweria becki*
Makira Moorhen *Gallinula silvestris*

Somalia
Bulo Burti Boubou *Laniarius liberatus*
Archer's Lark *Heteromirafra archeri*
Somali Thrush *Turdus ludoviciae*

South Korea
Crested Shelduck *Tadorna cristata*
Siberian Crane *Grus leucogeranus*

Spain
Balearic Shearwater *Puffinus mauretanicus*

Sri Lanka
Christmas Frigatebird *Fregata andrewsi*

St Lucia
Semper's Warbler *Leucopeza semperi*

Sudan
Sociable Lapwing *Vanellus gregarius*

Syria
Northern Bald Ibis *Geronticus eremita*
Sociable Lapwing *Vanellus gregarius*

Taiwan
Chinese Crested Tern *Sterna bernsteini*

Tajikistan
Sociable Lapwing *Vanellus gregarius*

Tanzania
Uluguru Bush-shrike *Malaconotus alius*
Long-billed Apalis *Apalis moreaui*

Thailand
Christmas Frigatebird *Fregata andrewsi*
White-rumped Vulture *Gyps bengalensis*
Red-headed Vulture *Sarcogyps calvus*
Chinese Crested Tern *Sterna bernsteini*
Gurney's Pitta *Pitta gurneyi*
White-eyed River-martin *Eurochelidon sirintarae*

Timor-Leste
Christmas Frigatebird *Fregata andrewsi*
Yellow-crested Cockatoo *Cacatua sulphurea*

Trinidad and Tobago
Trinidad Piping-guan *Pipile pipile*

Tunisia
Slender-billed Curlew *Numenius tenuirostris*

Turkey
Northern Bald Ibis *Geronticus eremita*
Sociable Lapwing *Vanellus gregarius*
Slender-billed Curlew *Numenius tenuirostris*

Turkmenistan
Siberian Crane *Grus leucogeranus*
Sociable Lapwing *Vanellus gregarius*
Slender-billed Curlew *Numenius tenuirostris*

Ukraine
Slender-billed Curlew *Numenius tenuirostris*

United Kingdom
Balearic Shearwater *Puffinus mauretanicus*

Gibraltar (to UK)
Balearic Shearwater *Puffinus mauretanicus*

Montserrat (to UK)
Montserrat Oriole *Icterus oberi*

Pitcairn Islands (to UK)
Chatham Albatross *Thalassarche eremita*

St Helena (to UK)
St Helena Plover *Charadrius sanctaehelenae*

Urugay
Glaucous Macaw *Anodorhynchus glaucus*
Entre Rios Seedeater *Sporophila zelichi*

USA
Laysan Duck *Anas laysanensis*
California Condor *Gymnogyps californianus*
Eskimo Curlew *Numenius borealis*
Kittlitz's Murrelet *Brachyramphus brevirostris*
Ivory-billed Woodpecker *Campephilus principalis*
Millerbird *Acrocephalus familiaris*
Olomao *Myadestes lanaiensis*
Puaiohi *Myadestes palmeri*
Nihoa Finch *Telespiza ultima*
Ou *Psittirostra psittacea*
Maui Parrotbill *Pseudonestor xanthophrys*
Nukupuu *Hemignathus lucidus*
Akikiki *Oreomystis bairdi*

Oahu Alauahio *Paroreomyza maculata*
Akohekohe *Palmeria dolei*
Poo-uli *Melamprosops phaeosoma*
Bachman's Warbler *Vermivora bachmanii*

American Samoa
Chatham Albatross *Thalassarche eremita*

Guam (to USA)
Townsend's Shearwater *Puffinus auricularis*

Northern Mariana Islands (to USA)
Townsend's Shearwater *Puffinus auricularis*
Rota Bridled White-eye *Zosterops rotensis*
Golden White-eye *Cleptornis marchei*

Puerto Rico (to USA)
Puerto Rican Amazon *Amazona vittata*
Puerto Rican Nightjar *Caprimulgus noctitherus*

United States Minor Outlying Islands (to USA)
Townsend's Shearwater *Puffinus auricularis*

Uzbekistan
Sociable Lapwing *Vanellus gregarius*
Slender-billed Curlew *Numenius tenuirostris*

Venezuela
Carrizal Seedeater *Amaurospiza carrizalensis*

Vietnam
White-shouldered Ibis *Pseudibis davisoni*
White-rumped Vulture Gyps bengalensis
Red-headed Vulture *Sarcogyps calvus*
Bengal Florican *Houbaropsis bengalensis*

Yemen
Northern Bald Ibis *Geronticus eremita*
Slender-billed Curlew *Numenius tenuirostris*

Last Record

A NUMBER OF THE CRITICALLY ENDANGERED SPECIES in this book have not been recorded reliably for many years but are still not treated as Extinct on the Red List ; Archer's Lark occurs in Somalia, in areas where large numbers of refugees have settled owing to unrest in that country. No ornithologists have surveyed the area in recent times, so it could still be extant there. Hooded Seedeater is known from only a single specimen trapped in Brazil, in an area which is poorly known to ornithologists. The individual could have been on migration and have a very small total population, contributing to the difficulty of rediscovering it. Guadalupe Storm-petrel is difficult to distinguish from Leach's Storm-petrel which also breeds on Guadalupe island. It is nocturnal at the breeding sites which makes locating the species without intensive surveys difficult.

Years within brackets are unconfirmed records.

1823	Hooded Seedeater	*Sporophila melanops*
1850 (1976)	Turquoise-throated Puffleg	*Eriocnemis godini*
1860	Jamaican Pauraque	*Siphonorhis americana*
1866	Siau Scops Owl	*Otus siaoensis*
1873 (2003)	Samoan Moorhen	*Gallinula pacifica*
1876 (2003)	Himalayan Quail	*Ophrysia superciliosa*
1879	Jamaica Petrel	*Pterodroma caribbaea*
1890 (1984)	New Caledonian Rail	*Gallirallus lafresnayanus*
1891 (1995)	Sulu Bleeding-heart	*Gallicolumba menagei*
1912	Guadalupe Storm Petrel	*Oceanodroma macrodactyla*
1918	Rueck's Blue flycatcher	*Cyornis ruckii*
1940	Javan Lapwing	*Vanellus macropterus*
1944 (2007)	Ivory-billed Woodpecker	*Campephilus principalis*
1949 (2004)	Pink-headed Duck	*Rhodonessa caryophyllacea*
1953	Negros Fruit-dove	*Ptilinopus arcanus*
1953 (2004)	Makira Moorhen	*Gallinula silvestris*
1955 (2004)	Archer's Lark	*Heteromirafra archeri*
1956 (2005)	Imperial Woodpecker	*Campephilus imperialis*
1960 (1998)	New Caledonian Owlet-nightjar	*Aegotheles savesi*
1961 (2003)	Semper's Warbler	*Leucopeza semperi*
1964	Crested Shelduck	*Tadorna cristata*
1968 (2004)	White-eyed River Martin	*Eurochelidon sirintarae*
1976	New Caledonian Lorikeet	*Charmosyna diadema*
1980	Olomao	*Myadestes lanaiensis*
1980 (2005)	White-chested White-eye	*Zosterops albogularis*
1981 (2006)	Blue-fronted Lorikeet	*Charmosyna toxopei*
1981 (2006)	Eskimo Curlew	*Numenius borealis*
1985	O'ahu 'alauahio	*Paroreomyza maculata*
1988	Alaotra Grebe	*Tachybaptus rufolavatus*
1988 (2002)	Bachman's Warbler	*Vermivora bachmanii*
1989 (1995)	O'u	*Psittirostra psittacea*
1992	Cuban Kite	*Chondrohierax wilsonii*
1996	Kinglet Calyptura	*Calyptura cristata*
1996	Nukupu'u	*Hemignathus lucidus*
1999	Sangihe White-eye	*Zosterops nehrkorni*
2000	Spix's Macaw	*Cyanopsitta spixii*
2001	Red-throated Lorikeet	*Charmosyna amabilis*
2004	Po`ouli	*Melamprosops phaeosoma*
2004 (2006)	Cozumel Thrasher	*Toxostoma guttatum*

INDEX

Laysan Duck. Photo: © Mark Alexander MacDonald

Checklist

- [ ] White-winged Guan *Penelope albipennis*
- [ ] Trinidad Piping-guan *Pipile pipile*
- [ ] Blue-billed Curassow *Crax alberti*
- [ ] Gorgeted Wood-quail *Odontophorus strophium*
- [ ] Djibouti Francolin *Francolinus ochropectus*
- [ ] Himalayan Quail *Ophrysia superciliosa*
- [ ] Crested Shelduck *Tadorna cristata*
- [ ] Laysan Duck *Anas laysanensis*
- [ ] Campbell Islands Teal *Anas nesiotis*
- [ ] Pink-headed Duck *Rhodonessa caryophyllacea*
- [ ] Madagascar Pochard *Aythya innotata*
- [ ] Brazilian Merganser *Mergus octosetaceus*
- [ ] Amsterdam Albatross *Diomedea amsterdamensis*
- [ ] Waved Albatross *Phoebastria irrorata*
- [ ] Chatham Albatross *Thalassarche eremita*
- [ ] Galapagos Petrel *Pterodroma phaeopygia*
- [ ] Jamaica Petrel *Pterodroma caribbaea*
- [ ] Magenta Petrel *Pterodroma magentae*
- [ ] Chatham Petrel *Pterodroma axillaris*
- [ ] Fiji Petrel *Pseudobulweria macgillivrayi*
- [ ] Beck's Petrel *Pseudobulweria becki*
- [ ] Mascarene Petrel *Pseudobulweria aterrima*
- [ ] Balearic Shearwater *Puffinus mauretanicus*
- [ ] Townsend's Shearwater *Puffinus auricularis*
- [ ] New Zealand Storm-petrel *Oceanites maorianus*
- [ ] Guadalupe Storm-petrel *Oceanodroma macrodactyla*
- [ ] Alaotra Grebe *Tachybaptus rufolavatus*
- [ ] Junin Grebe *Podiceps taczanowskii*
- [ ] White-bellied Heron *Ardea insignis*
- [ ] White-shouldered Ibis *Pseudibis davisoni*
- [ ] Giant Ibis *Thaumatibis gigantea*
- [ ] Northern Bald Ibis *Geronticus eremita*
- [ ] Dwarf Olive Ibis *Bostrychia bocagei*
- [ ] Christmas Island Frigatebird *Fregata andrewsi*
- [ ] Chatham Islands Shag *Phalacrocorax onslowi*
- [ ] California Condor *Gymnogyps californianus*
- [ ] White-collared Kite *Leptodon forbesi*
- [ ] Cuban Kite *Chondrohierax wilsonii*
- [ ] Madagascar Fish-eagle *Haliaeetus vociferoides*
- [ ] White-rumped Vulture *Gyps bengalensis*
- [ ] Indian Vulture *Gyps indicus*
- [ ] Slender-billed Vulture *Gyps tenuirostris*
- [ ] Red-headed Vulture *Sarcogyps calvus*
- [ ] Ridgway's Hawk *Buteo ridgwayi*
- [ ] Philippine Eagle *Pithecophaga jefferyi*

- [ ] Bengal Florican *Houbaropsis bengalensis*
- [ ] New Caledonian Rail *Gallirallus lafresnayanus*
- [ ] Samoan Moorhen *Gallinula pacifica*
- [ ] Makira Moorhen *Gallinula silvestris*
- [ ] Siberian Crane *Grus leucogeranus*
- [ ] Black Stilt *Himantopus novaezelandiae*
- [ ] Javan Lapwing *Vanellus macropterus*
- [ ] Sociable Lapwing *Vanellus gregarius*
- [ ] St Helena Plover *Charadrius sanctaehelenae*
- [ ] Eskimo Curlew *Numenius borealis*
- [ ] Slender-billed Curlew *Numenius tenuirostris*
- [ ] Jerdon's Courser *Rhinoptilus bitorquatus*
- [ ] Chinese Crested Tern *Sterna bernsteini*
- [ ] Kittlitz's Murrelet *Brachyramphus brevirostris*
- [ ] Silvery Wood-pigeon *Columba argentina*
- [ ] Blue-eyed Ground-dove *Columbina cyanopis*
- [ ] Purple-winged Ground-dove *Claravis godefrida*
- [ ] Grenada Dove *Leptotila wellsi*
- [ ] Mindoro Bleeding-heart *Gallicolumba platenae*
- [ ] Negros Bleeding-heart *Gallicolumba keayi*
- [ ] Sulu Bleeding-heart *Gallicolumba menagei*
- [ ] Polynesian Ground-dove *Gallicolumba erythroptera*
- [ ] Negros Fruit-dove *Ptilinopus arcanus*
- [ ] Marquesan Imperial-pigeon *Ducula galeata*
- [ ] Kakapo *Strigops habroptila*
- [ ] Yellow-crested Cockatoo *Cacatua sulphurea*
- [ ] Philippine Cockatoo *Cacatua haematuropygia*
- [ ] Blue-fronted Lorikeet *Charmosyna toxopei*
- [ ] New Caledonian Lorikeet *Charmosyna diadema*
- [ ] Red-throated Lorikeet *Charmosyna amabilis*
- [ ] Malherbe's Parakeet *Cyanoramphus malherbi*
- [ ] Orange-bellied Parrot *Neophema chrysogaster*
- [ ] Night Parrot *Pezoporus occidentalis*
- [ ] Lear's Macaw *Anodorhynchus leari*
- [ ] Glaucous Macaw *Anodorhynchus glaucus*
- [ ] Spix's Macaw *Cyanopsitta spixii*
- [ ] Blue-throated Macaw *Ara glaucogularis*
- [ ] Yellow-eared Parrot *Ognorhynchus icterotis*
- [ ] Grey-breasted Parakeet *Pyrrhura griseipectus*
- [ ] Indigo-winged Parrot *Hapalopsittaca fuertesi*
- [ ] Puerto Rican Amazon *Amazona vittata*
- [ ] Sumatran Ground-cuckoo *Carpococcyx viridis*
- [ ] Black-hooded Coucal *Centropus steerii*
- [ ] Siau Scops-owl *Otus siaoensis*
- [ ] Anjouan Scops-owl *Otus capnodes*